608-ㄥㄥㄣ-ㄥㄖ

21
28
26
7 7
17
14 DE

Success Studybooks

Success in

OR GANIC
CH EMISTRY

Malcolm D. Hawkins, M.A., M.Sc., Ph.D., C.Chem., F.R.S.C.

Head of Chemistry and Physical Sciences,
Bedford College of Higher Education.

John Murray

First published 1981 by
John Murray (Publishers) Ltd
50 Albemarle Street, London, w1x 4bd

Filmset by The Universities Press (Belfast) Ltd
Printed in Hong Kong by Wing King Tong Ltd

British Library Cataloguing in Publication Data
Hawkins, Malcolm David
  Success in organic chemistry.—(Success
  studybooks).
  1. Chemistry, Organic
  I. Title   II. Series
  547   QD253
  ISBN 0-7195-3795-9

Preface

This book covers the organic chemistry content of the GCE Advanced-level syllabuses and of the certificate and diploma courses of the Technician Education Council (TEC, Levels II and III). It should also be useful to first-year degree students and to anyone working in industry, or studying applied science, biology, biochemistry or the medical sciences, where a basic understanding of the subject is needed.

Readers following the text should have a knowledge of chemistry to about O level, or equivalent, but it is not expected that they will have any previous knowledge of organic chemistry. The course is comprehensive and self-contained, offering the maximum help to independent students and to those who have only limited study periods with a teacher, or are working through it for revision purposes.

Many students do not have free access to well-equipped laboratories so the practical work given consists of basic experiments which use only the simplest of apparatus. However, all topics are presented in a clear, logical style that concentrates on essentials and is backed up by illustrations which explain and reinforce the text. There are self-testing questions at the end of each Unit of study (with answers at the back of the book) so that students are able to assess their own progress as they work through the course. For those who wish to take their studies beyond the scope of this book, the list of further reading offers guidance on other, more specialized, areas of study.

SI units have been used throughout and the nomenclature is based on the recommendations of the Association for Science Education (ASE) and the International Union of Pure and Applied Chemistry (IUPAC).

Students working for examinations should obtain copies of relevant syllabuses and selections of past examination questions as different boards vary in their coverage of topics. Students should, therefore, concentrate on those areas of study which they are certain to need.

Organic chemistry is a logical discipline and learning names, structures, formulae and reactions of the functional groups of the various classes of organic compounds is a necessary stage in building the patterns and framework which lead to a good mastery of the subject. An effective way of studying is first to read through a Unit quickly, noting the section headings and main points for discussion; then to study the whole Unit, slowly and carefully, one section at a time, making notes, summaries and drawings of structures and reaction schemes. In this way, students will arrive at a thorough understanding of each concept and thus be able to commit it to memory and assimilate it before proceeding with the next.

M.D.H.

Acknowledgments

In writing this book I have been conscious of the inspiration, help and encouragement that I have received from innumerable colleagues and students, present and past, and from my own teachers; this I gratefully acknowledge. I am indebted, too, to the following who read and gave constructive criticism to the text during its various stages of preparation: Karl Singer, Jim Hutton, John Phillips, John Peet and Tim Healey.

Particular thanks are also due to Irene Slade, the editor of the Success Studybooks series, and Anne Webster of John Murray; to Jean Macqueen who so meticulously edited the text, to R. F. Harburn who supplied photographs, and to June Jessop who typed the manuscript.

M.D.H.

Contents

x Contents

Foreword

Nomenclature and Units

The use of systematic units and nomenclature in chemistry has been recommended for a century and more. SI (*Système International*, or the International System of Units) is now widely adopted, but the traditional and frequently unsystematic names of many common organic compounds will probably remain in use for many years to come. The nomenclature used in this book is based on the recommendations of the IUPAC and the ASE (*Chemical Nomenclature, Symbols and Terminology*, Association for Science Education, 1979). The system is both logical and simple. It is explained in general terms in Unit 1.4 and for each class of compound in the relevant Unit. Where two fundamentally different names are in use the common (trivial) or traditional name is usually given in brackets after the recommended form.

Practical Work

The importance of practical work in organic chemistry cannot be over-emphasized. As an organic chemist, you should be able to prepare, separate and purify a variety of liquid, solid and gaseous compounds in satisfactory yield. You should also be able to determine such physical constants as melting-point and boiling-point and carry out tests to characterize and identify an organic compound. You should always write up an account of your experimental work *at the time* in your practical book.

Many of the experiments described in this book require only simple apparatus. The use of equipment with interchangeable standard ground-glass joints such as that manufactured by Quartz-Quickfit is recommended; the units can be used to build systems for a whole range of different purposes. It is not necessary to grease the joints unless the apparatus is to be used at high temperatures or with concentrated alkalis. The equipment should always be dismantled and washed thoroughly immediately after use (and especially after reactions involving caustic alkalis) to prevent seizure of the ground-glass joints.

To avoid interference from dissolved ions, distilled water should be used whenever water is mentioned as a solvent or reactant in the experiments described in this book.

Calculation of Percentage Yields

Side-reactions with the formation of unwanted by-products frequently occur in the course of the preparation of an organic compound, and thereby reduce the yield. You can minimize further losses via evaporation, the wetting of flasks, soaking into filter-papers and so on by choosing apparatus and containers of the smallest size (consistent with safety) required for the quantity of material and by keeping flasks firmly stoppered. The amount of purified product obtained from a given weight or volume of the starting material in a preparation should always be noted. The following example illustrates how the *percentage yield* is calculated.

Example. 6.2 g of N-phenylethanamide, $C_6H_5NHCOCH_3$, was obtained by treating 5 cm^3 of phenylamine, $C_6H_5NH_2$, with an excess of ethanoic anhydride. Calculate the percentage yield of N-phenylethanamide.

$$C_6H_5NH_2 + (CH_3CO)_2O \longrightarrow C_6H_5NHCOCH_3 + CH_3CO_2H$$

phenylamine	ethanoic anhydride	N-phenylethanamide
RMM = 93	(present in excess)	RMM = 135

If the reaction proceeded to completion and none of the product was lost during separation and purification, 135 g of N-phenylethanamide would be obtained from 93 g of phenylamine.

5 cm^3 of phenylamine ($d = 1.022$ g cm^{-3}) weighs $5 \times 1.022 = 5.11$ g.

Theoretical yield of N-phenylethanamide from 5.11 g of phenylamine = $\dfrac{135}{93} \times 5.11 = 7.42$ g.

$$\text{Percentage yield} = \frac{\text{Actual yield}}{\text{Theoretical yield}} \times 100$$

$$= \frac{6.2}{7.42} \times 100 = \underline{\underline{84 \text{ per cent}}}$$

Safety

The dangers associated with concentrated sulphuric acid, caustic alkalis, strong acids and other inorganic substances are well known. Practical organic chemistry presents other potential hazards as well, arising particularly from the high flammability of many organic solvents and from the toxicity—both by skin absorption and by the inhalation of the vapour—of some organic compounds. It is important that you follow to the letter the instructions given for the experiments in this book.

The possibility of fires or explosions can be minimized by using only small quantities of flammable solvents, rather than the 2.5-litre Winchester stock bottles, and ensuring that there are no naked flames in the vicinity when such liquids are transferred. Avoid direct heating by flames; reaction mixtures containing flammable solvents should be heated in a bath of boiling water and preferably in a fume-cupboard. *Always* use safety screens to reduce the effects of implosion or explosion when carrying out reactions *in vacuo* or under reduced pressure. **Wear spectacles or goggles at all times**.

Treat all organic compounds with respect. *Never* taste them; avoid touching them or allowing them to come into contact with the skin. Clean up any spilled chemicals at once. Any harmful substance accidentally spilled on the skin should be washed off immediately with plenty of water, preferably under a running tap. Splashes of chemicals in the eyes are particularly dangerous as they can result in permanent eye damage or blindness. The immediate first-aid treatment before seeking a doctor's advice is to wash out the eye thoroughly for several minutes with water. Experiments involving hazardous volatile substances, such as benzene, phenylamine and hydrazine, should always be carried out in a fume-cupboard. If only small amounts of material (three or four drops if possible—at most a few cm^3) are used, the hazards associated with toxic, corrosive and other harmful organic substances will be negligible. As a general rule, the use of asbestos is unnecessary; if it is unavoidable, the substance should be transferred with care and stored under water when it is not in use.

Cuts from broken glassware and burns caused by touching hot apparatus are the commonest injuries in chemistry laboratories, though such accidents are almost invariably the result of carelessness and are therefore avoidable. A simple first-aid kit should be kept in the laboratory in an accessible place.

Unit One

Introduction

1.1 What is Organic Chemistry?

The short answer to this question is that organic chemistry is the branch of chemistry that is concerned with the study of the compounds of carbon. The oxides, carbonates and metal carbonyls are excluded; the preparation, properties, structure and reactions of these substances and of the compounds of the other hundred or so elements in the Periodic Table are the province of inorganic chemistry. A vast range of organic compounds is known, and the properties of these compounds vary enormously—think of just a few familiar instances, such as natural gas, penicillin, sugar and candle-wax—yet they nevertheless can be seen as having more in common with each other than with inorganic compounds like salt, water and quartz; and the special, indeed unique, properties of organic compounds are the justification for regarding their chemistry as a separate field of study.

The first important organic substances to be recognized were the sugars, alcohol, oils, vegetable dyes and other materials of animal or plant origin. At first it was thought that organic compounds could be synthesized only in the tissues of living organisms and that the influence of a 'vital force' was necessary for their preparation. In 1828, however, the German chemist Friedrich Wöhler synthesized the organic compound carbamide (urea) by the evaporation of an aqueous solution of ammonium cyanate which he had prepared from purely inorganic sources:

$$NH_4{}^+CNO^- \longrightarrow O{=}C\begin{smallmatrix} NH_2 \\ \\ NH_2 \end{smallmatrix}$$

carbamide

The vital force theory was therefore discounted and since that time over a million different organic compounds have been prepared and tens of thousands of new ones are synthesized every year. Organic compounds play an increasingly important part in our lives, in the form of plastics, drugs, paints, polymers, fuels, man-made fibres, soaps, synthetic dyes and so forth. The study of organic chemistry therefore forms an essential part of the training, not only of chemists, but of doctors, pharmacists, veterinary surgeons, materials scientists, biologists, plastics technologists and a host of others.

What then is so special about the element carbon to make its compounds more numerous than those of all the other elements in the Periodic Table combined?

1.2 The Carbon Atom

Carbon has four electrons in its outer energy level and, as the first element in Group IV, it occupies a central position in the Periodic Table. It has a covalency of four and forms stable bonds with hydrogen, oxygen, nitrogen, sulphur, phosphorus and the halogens. For example, the molecule of methane, the major constituent of natural gas, consists of one carbon atom joined to four hydrogen atoms:

$$
\begin{array}{c}
\text{H} \\
| \\
\text{H}-\text{C}-\text{H} \\
| \\
\text{H}
\end{array}
$$

Similarly tetrachloromethane (an important solvent in dry-cleaning) contains a carbon atom linked to four chlorine atoms: CCl_4. Other examples include methanol and methylamine:

$$
\begin{array}{c}
\text{H} \\
| \\
\text{H}-\text{C}-\text{O}-\text{H} \\
| \\
\text{H}
\end{array}
\qquad \text{and} \qquad
\begin{array}{c}
\text{H} \quad\; \text{H} \\
| \quad\; / \\
\text{H}-\text{C}-\text{N} \\
| \quad\; \backslash \\
\text{H} \quad\; \text{H}
\end{array}
$$

methanol   methylamine

The carbon atom has two exceptional properties:

(a) It can form multiple bonds with other carbon atoms or with the atoms of other elements, such as oxygen and nitrogen:

$$
\text{C}=\text{C} \qquad -\text{C}\equiv\text{C}- \qquad \text{C}=\text{O} \qquad \text{C}=\text{N}- \qquad -\text{C}\equiv\text{N}
$$

(b) It can form stable chains or rings; for instance:

$$
\begin{array}{c}
\text{H} \;\; \text{H} \;\; \text{H} \;\; \text{H} \;\; \text{H} \;\; \text{H} \;\; \text{H} \;\; \text{H} \\
| \;\; | \;\; | \;\; | \;\; | \;\; | \;\; | \;\; | \\
\text{H}-\text{C}-\text{C}-\text{C}-\text{C}-\text{C}-\text{C}-\text{C}-\text{C}-\text{H} \\
| \;\; | \;\; | \;\; | \;\; | \;\; | \;\; | \;\; | \\
\text{H} \;\; \text{H} \;\; \text{H} \;\; \text{H} \;\; \text{H} \;\; \text{H} \;\; \text{H} \;\; \text{H}
\end{array}
\qquad
\begin{array}{c}
\text{CH}_2 \\
\text{CH}_2 \qquad \text{CH}_2 \\
\text{CH}_2 \qquad \text{CH}_2 \\
\text{CH}_2
\end{array}
$$

octane   cyclohexane

This property is known as *catenation* and is demonstrated to an extraordinary extent by carbon. The molecules of some plastics and natural and synthetic rubber, for example, consist of chains composed of thousands of carbon atoms linked to each other by covalent bonds.

1.3 General Properties of Organic Compounds

(a) Bonding

Virtually all organic compounds are covalent. They do not conduct electricity, and, as there is little attraction between the uncharged molecules of a covalent compound, they tend to be gases, volatile liquids or low-melting solids.

Most organic compounds decompose on strong heating and burn in air to yield carbon dioxide and water. Many of their reactions are slow compared with those of inorganic compounds, as they involve the fission of covalent bonds rather than the rapid reaction of free ions. Prolonged heating, sometimes in the presence of a catalyst, is often necessary, and even then the reaction rarely goes to completion. Occasionally numerous by-products are formed which can make the isolation and purification of the desired product difficult.

(b) Solubility

Organic compounds are usually soluble in organic non-polar solvents such as benzene, petrol, tetrachloromethane, ethanol and ethoxyethane (ether), but tend to be insoluble in water unless they contain hydroxyl (—OH), amino-(—NH$_2$), carboxy-(—CO$_2$H), sulphonic acid (—SO$_3$H) or other polar groups.

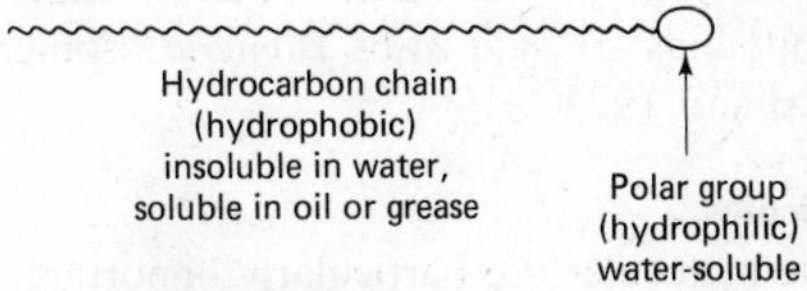

Hydrocarbon chain
(hydrophobic)
insoluble in water,
soluble in oil or grease

Polar group
(hydrophilic)
water-soluble

Fig. 1.1   A soap molecule

This difference in solubility between covalent and ionic portions of a molecule accounts for the way in which soaps and detergents remove soiling by grease or oils. These compounds contain long hydrocarbon chains attached to a polar carboxylate (—CO$_2^-$Na$^+$ or —CO$_2^-$K$^+$) or sulphonate (—SO$_3^-$Na$^+$) group. For example, CH$_3$(CH$_2$)$_{15}$CO$_2^-$Na$^+$ and CH$_3$(CH$_2$)$_{17}$CO$_2^-$Na$^+$ are both soaps. The hydrocarbon chain dissolves readily in oil, fats or grease which are insoluble in water. The surface tension at the oil–water interface is lowered and the oil is dispersed into the water as fine droplets which are stabilized by the presence of the polar water-soluble groups at their surface (Fig. 1.2).

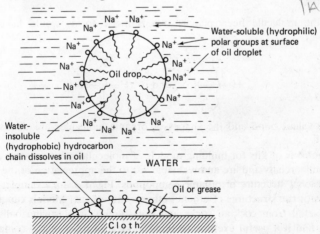

Fig. 1.2   The action of soaps and detergents

(c) Isomerism

It is common to find that a given molecular formula applies to several quite different organic compounds. For example, the three compounds

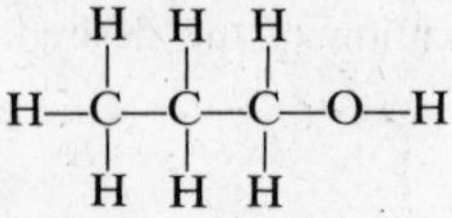

$$
\begin{array}{ccc}
\underset{\text{propan-1-ol}}{\overset{\displaystyle \text{H}\;\;\text{H}\;\;\text{H}}{\underset{\displaystyle \text{H}\;\;\text{H}\;\;\text{H}}{\text{H}-\text{C}-\text{C}-\text{C}-\text{O}-\text{H}}}}
&
\underset{\text{propan-2-ol}}{\overset{\displaystyle \text{H}\;\;\text{H}\;\;\text{H}}{\text{H}-\text{C}-\text{C}-\text{C}-\text{H}}}
&
\text{and}
\end{array}
$$

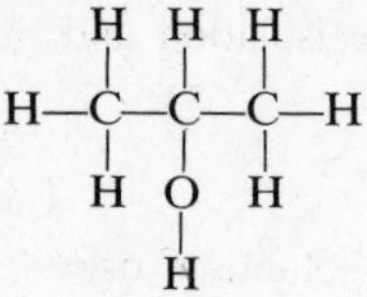

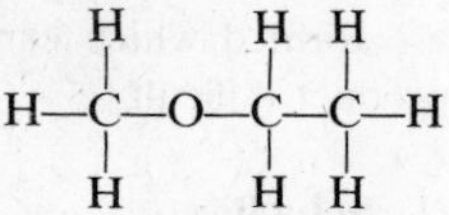

all have the molecular formula C_3H_8O, but differ in the arrangement of the atoms in their molecules: they also have different chemical and physical properties. The compounds are said to be *isomeric*; isomerism is discussed in detail in Units 1.6 and 19.

(d) Shapes of Molecules

The shape of organic molecules are particularly important: they frequently determine the course of a reaction and the rate at which it will occur. In *saturated* compounds (compounds in which the carbon atoms are linked by single bonds only) the four groups attached to each carbon atom are arranged tetrahedrally around it. Thus there is only one form of disubstituted methane, CH_2X_2:

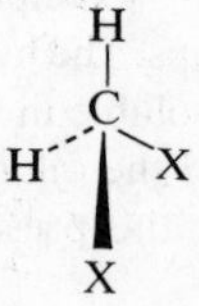

Had the molecule been planar, two isomeric forms would have been possible:

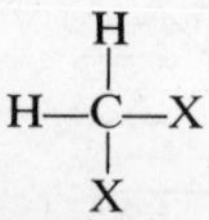

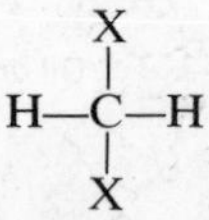

The covalent bond and the shapes of organic molecules are discussed in Unit 4.

A number of kits for building models of molecular structures are available commercially and are an invaluable aid to the appreciation of the three-dimensional structure of organic compounds. Fig. 1.3, for example, shows models of the structures of ethane, ethene and ethyne. Models can also be constructed from cocktail sticks and polystyrene or plasticine balls. You would find it a useful exercise to build models of most of the compounds referred to in the early Units of this book.

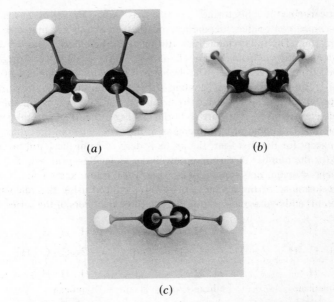

Fig. 1.3   *Molecular models: (a) ethane, (b) ethene, (c) ethyne*

1.4 Classes of Organic Compounds

(a) The Hydrocarbons

The hydrocarbons are the simplest class of organic compounds and, as their name indicates, consist of carbon and hydrogen only. Like other organic compounds, they are classified as either *saturated* or *unsaturated*, depending respectively on whether the carbon atoms are linked solely by single bonds, as in

butane   2-methylbutane

or whether the molecule contains a multiple bond, for example:

propene   ethyne (acetylene)

Hydrocarbons may be further classified as either *cyclic* or *acyclic* (or *open-chain*) compounds, depending on whether or not the molecule contains a ring. The open-chain hydrocarbons and their derivatives are often called *aliphatic compounds* (Greek *aliphos* = fat), as they were originally derived from the fatty acids. The *aromatic compounds* (see Units 1.4(*a*)(iv) and 9.1), on the other hand, contain stable, unsaturated ring structures.

(i) **The alkanes.** The saturated hydrocarbons are known as the *alkanes* (discussed in Unit 5). They are the principal constituents of natural gas and petroleum. The name of each member of the series ends in the suffix -*ane*, and, except for the first four, the prefix is derived from the Latin or Greek word for the number of carbon atoms in the molecule—*pent*- = five, *hex*- = six, *hept*- = seven, *oct*- = eight, *non*- = nine, *dec*- = ten, and so on.

The formulae of the alkanes are readily deduced using the valencies of carbon (4) and hydrogen (1); thus the first three members of the series are:

$$
\begin{array}{ccc}
\begin{array}{c}
\mathrm{H} \\
| \\
\mathrm{H-C-H} \\
| \\
\mathrm{H}
\end{array}
&
\begin{array}{c}
\mathrm{H\ \ H} \\
|\ \ \ | \\
\mathrm{H-C-C-H} \\
|\ \ \ | \\
\mathrm{H\ \ H}
\end{array}
\quad \text{and} \quad
&
\begin{array}{c}
\mathrm{H\ \ H\ \ H} \\
|\ \ \ |\ \ \ | \\
\mathrm{H-C-C-C-H} \\
|\ \ \ |\ \ \ | \\
\mathrm{H\ \ H\ \ H}
\end{array}
\end{array}
$$

methane   ethane   propane
CH_4 C_2H_6 C_3H_8

and the general formula for all alkanes in the series is C_nH_{2n+2}.

Isomerism is possible with alkanes having four or more carbon atoms; thus there are two compounds with the formula C_4H_{10} (the butanes):

$$
\begin{array}{cc}
\begin{array}{c}
\mathrm{H\ \ H\ \ H\ \ H} \\
|\ \ \ |\ \ \ |\ \ \ | \\
\mathrm{H-C-C-C-C-H} \\
|\ \ \ |\ \ \ |\ \ \ | \\
\mathrm{H\ \ H\ \ H\ \ H}
\end{array}
\quad \text{and} \quad
&
\begin{array}{c}
\mathrm{H}\mathrm{H}\mathrm{H} \\
||| \\
\mathrm{H-CCC-H} \\
||| \\
\mathrm{H\ \ H-C-H\ \ H} \\
|\ \\
\mathrm{H}
\end{array}
\end{array}
$$

The theoretical number of possible isomers grows sharply as the number of carbon atoms in the molecule increases. For example, there are five isomeric hexanes, 75 decanes and over a third of a million possible alkanes of formula $C_{20}H_{22}$. $C_{25}H_{52}$ has nearly 37 million possible isomers and $C_{30}H_{62}$ has 4.1×10^9. Very few of this enormous number have been isolated or prepared, however. The names, formulae and the number of possible isomers of the first ten alkanes are listed in Table 1.1.

The names of the alkanes are important, as they form the basis of the nomenclature of all the other aliphatic compounds. You should therefore learn carefully the names and formulae of the first half-dozen or so members of the series before you proceed to the other classes of organic compounds.

(ii) **The alkenes.** The alkenes (see Unit 7) contain a carbon–carbon double bond, and each therefore has two fewer hydrogen atoms in its molecule

Table 1.1 The alkanes

Name	Formula	Number of possible isomers
Methane	CH_4	1
Ethane	C_2H_6	1
Propane	C_3H_8	1
Butane	C_4H_{10}	2
Pentane	C_5H_{12}	3
Hexane	C_6H_{14}	5
Heptane	C_7H_{16}	9
Octane	C_8H_{18}	18
Nonane	C_9H_{20}	35
Decane	$C_{10}H_{22}$	75

than has the corresponding alkane. For example, compare

$$CH_3CH{=}CH_2 \quad \text{and} \quad CH_3CH_2CH_3$$

propene   propane
C_3H_6 C_3H_8

The general formula for the alkenes that contain one double bond is thus C_nH_{2n}. The first member is ethene, C_2H_4,

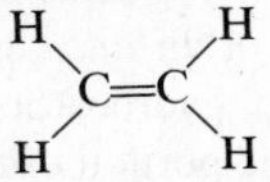

and the compounds are named by changing the suffix of the alkane with the same number of carbon atoms from -ane to -ene (Table 1.2).

Table 1.2 The alkenes

Number of carbon atoms	Formula	Name
2	C_2H_4	ethene
3	C_3H_6	propene
4	C_4H_8	butene
5	C_5H_{10}	pentene
6	C_6H_{12}	hexene

(iii) **The alkynes.** The alkynes (or acetylenes) contain a carbon–carbon triple bond (see Unit 8). The general formula of those containing only one multiple bond is therefore C_nH_{2n-2} and the compounds are named by changing the suffix of the corresponding alkane -ane to -yne: $CH_3C{\equiv}C{-}H$, for example is called *propyne*. The first member of the series, $H{-}C{\equiv}C{-}H$, is *ethyne*, also known as *acetylene*; it is the gas that is used commercially in oxy-acetylene welding.

(iv) **The aromatic hydrocarbons.** These are stable, but highly unsaturated, cyclic compounds. Their ring structures may be written as though the carbon atoms in the ring were joined by alternate double and single bonds, but this is an over-simplification. Benzene, for example, has the formula C_6H_6 and the structure may be shown as

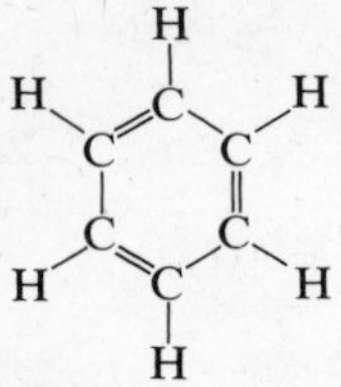

or, better, as

since all the carbon–carbon bonds are identical. The structures of aromatic compounds and the reasons for their great stability are discussed in Unit 9.5.

(*b*) **The Main Classes of Organic Compounds**
The other classes of simple organic compounds are formed by the replacement of a hydrogen atom in an alkane or aromatic hydrocarbon by an atom of another element, such as a halogen, or by a group of atoms such as —OH, —NH_2, —CO_2H or —CHO. Thus saturated aliphatic compounds may be regarded as derivatives of an *alkyl group*, which contains one less hydrogen atom than the parent hydrocarbon molecule, and a *functional group*, a term used to describe the portion of the molecule that determines a compound's properties. (This is frequently the substituent or non-hydrocarbon part of the molecule, but in alkenes and alkynes the functional group is the multiple bond itself.) Alkyl groups are represented by the symbol R— and their general formula is C_nH_{2n+1}—.

Alkane	Alkyl group	Name
CH_4 (methane)	CH_3—	methyl
C_2H_6 (ethane)	C_2H_5—	ethyl
C_3H_8 (propane)	C_3H_7—	propyl
C_4H_{10} (butane)	C_4H_9—	butyl

The principal classes of organic compounds, their functional groups, their formulae and their recommended nomenclature are summarized in Table 1.3.

For example, the alcohols and ethers with general formulae R—OH and R—O—R', can be regarded as compounds formed by the replacement of one or both of the hydrogen atoms in water respectively by alkyl groups:

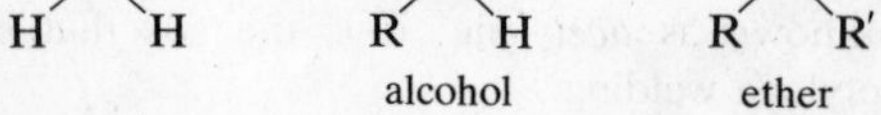

alcohol   ether

Table 1.3 Principal classes of aliphatic compounds

General formula	Functional group	Suffix or prefix	Class of compound	Name
C_nH_{2n+2} or R—H	—H	-ane	alkanes	alkanes
C_nH_{2n}	$\diagdown C{=}C\diagdown$	-ene	alkenes	alkenes
C_nH_{2n-2}	—C≡C—	-yne	alkynes	alkynes
R—Hal	—halogen	halogeno-	halogenoalkanes	
R—OH	—OH	-ol	alcohols	alkanols
R—O—R'	—OR'	alkoxy-	ethers	alkoxyalkanes
R—NH$_2$	—NH$_2$	-amine	amines	alkylamines
R—C⟨H,O (aldehyde)	—C⟨H,O	-al	aldehydes	alkanals
R—COR'	$\diagdown C{=}O$ (the carbonyl group)	-one	ketones	alkanones
R—C⟨OH,O	—CO$_2$H	-oic acid	carboxylic acids	alkanoic acids
R—C⟨OR',O	—CO$_2$R'	-oate	esters	alkyl alkanoates
R—C⟨O⁻,O	—CO$_2^-$	-oate	carboxylate anion (salts of carboxylic acids)	alkanoates
R—COOCOR'	—C⟨O,OCOR'	-oic anhydride	acid anhydrides	alkanoic anhydrides
R—C⟨O,NH$_2$	—CONH$_2$	-amide	amides	alkanamides
R—C⟨O,Hal	—CO Hal	-oyl halide	acyl halides	alkanoyl halides
R—CN	—CN	-onitrile	nitriles	alkanonitriles
R—N⟨O,O (nitro)	—NO$_2$	nitro-	nitro- compounds	nitroalkanes

(handwritten annotations: "fruity odour" next to alkyl alkanoates; "usually yellow" next to nitroalkanes)

The two alkyl groups in an ether may be the same $(R = R')$, as in $C_2H_5OC_2H_5$, ethoxyethane (diethyl ether), or different, as in $CH_3OC_2H_5$, methoxyethane (ethyl methyl ether).

The alcohols are named systematically by adding the suffix -ol to the name of the corresponding alkane, preceded if necessary by a number to indicate the position of the hydroxy-group in the molecule. The carbon atoms in a chain are numbered so as to keep the figures as small as possible. Thus CH_3OH is known as *methanol* (methyl alcohol), $CH_3CH_2CH_2OH$ is *propan-1-ol* (n-propyl alcohol) and $CH_3CH(OH)CH_3$ is *propan-2-ol* (isopropyl alcohol), while $CH_3CH_2CH_2CH_2OH$ is *butan-1-ol*, rather than butan-4-ol. (In the trivial names for these compounds, n- stands for *normal*, and was used to describe compounds having an unbranched carbon chain in the molecule, such as n-hexane, or the derivatives of such a compound in which the substituent is attached to the carbon atom at the end of the chain, such as $CH_3CH_2CH_2CH_2OH$, once called n-butyl alcohol. The prefix *iso*- was applied to compounds containing the $CH_3{-}CH{-}$ grouping.)

$$\underset{\displaystyle CH_3}{|}$$

The aliphatic amines may be regarded as alkyl-substituted ammonia, NH_3. They are classified as *primary*, *secondary* and *tertiary* amines, having the general formulae RNH_2, $RR'NH$ and $RR'R''N$ respectively, depending on the number of hydrogen atoms substituted. Thus *methylamine*, CH_3NH_2, and *isopropylamine*, $(CH_3)_2CHNH_2$, are both primary amines, while *ethyl-methylamine*, $CH_3NHC_2H_5$, and *trimethylamine*, $(CH_3)_3N$, are secondary and tertiary amines respectively.

Although a fuller account of the nomenclature of the different classes of organic compounds is given in the relevant Units, the information in Table 1.3 is sufficient to assign an organic compound of known structural formula to its class and often to give it a systematic name.

Examples

CH_2O. The structural formula is $\begin{matrix} H \\ {} \\ H \end{matrix}\!\!\!\diagdown C{=}O$ and the compound is an *aldehyde* as it contains the $-C{\diagup}^{H}_{\diagdown O}$ group. It is the first member of the series RCHO or $C_nH_{2n+1}CHO$; when $n = 0$, $R = H$. The compound is called *methanal*.

$C_2H_5COCH_3$ is a *ketone* as it has the general formula $\begin{matrix} R \\ {} \\ R' \end{matrix}\!\!\!\diagdown C{=}O$. It is called ethyl methyl ketone or, more systematically, *butanone* as the molecule contains four carbon atoms and is therefore a derivative of butane.

Aromatic compounds may similarly be regarded as derivatives of *aryl* (or

Ar—) groups which each contain one hydrogen atom less than the parent aromatic hydrocarbon. For example, the phenyl group (C_6H_5—)

is derived from benzene.

The classification of aromatic compounds follows a similar pattern to that of aliphatic compounds; for example:

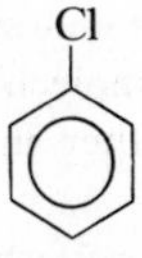

Cl

(C_6H_5Cl)

chlorobenzene

CH_3

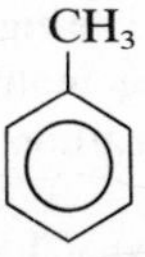

($C_6H_5CH_3$)

methylbenzene
(toluene)

NH_2

($C_6H_5NH_2$)

phenylamine

CH_2OH

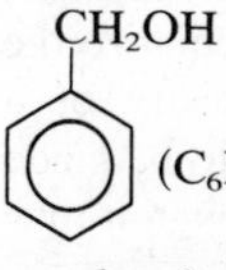

($C_6H_5CH_2OH$)

phenylmethanol
(benzyl alcohol)

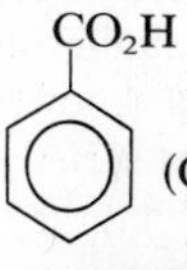

CO_2H

($C_6H_5CO_2H$)

benzenecarboxylic
acid
(benzoic acid)

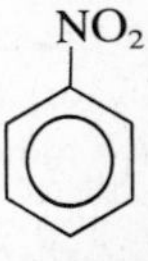

NO_2

($C_6H_5NO_2$)

nitrobenzene

Aromatic compounds in which an —OH group is attached directly to a carbon atom in the ring (general formula ArOH) are, however, classified as *phenols* rather than as alcohols (ROH).

1.5 Homologous Series

If the compounds belonging to any of the classes summarized in Table 1.3 are arranged in order of increasing number of carbon atoms, the list so obtained is known as a *homologous series*. For example, the general formula of the carboxylic acids is RCO_2H or $C_nH_{2n+1}CO_2H$; thus the first members of the carboxylic acid homologous series are:

n	R	Formula
0	H—	HCO_2H
1	CH_3—	CH_3CO_2H
2	C_2H_5—	$C_2H_5CO_2H$
3	C_3H_7—	$C_3H_7CO_2H$
4	C_4H_9—	$C_4H_9CO_2H$

The general characteristics of any homologous series are:

(*a*) all the compounds in the series have the same functional group and the same general formula;

(b) each compound differs from the next in the series by a —CH₂— group or (as the relative atomic masses of carbon and hydrogen are 12 and 1 respectively) by 14 relative molecular mass units;

(c) all the compounds in the series have similar chemical properties and may be prepared by similar methods; and

(d) the physical properties of the compounds in the series show a progressive change with increasing relative molecular mass. Examples of physical properties which to some extent are dependent on the number of carbon atoms present in the molecule include boiling-point, melting-point, solubility and density. This is well illustrated by the boiling-points and melting-points of the alkanes (Fig. 1.4). The zig-zag pattern of the melting-point curve is a result of the difference in the way in which molecules containing odd and even numbers of carbon atoms pack together in a crystal as the liquid alkane solidifies.

Occasionally there are irregularities in the chemical or physical properties of members of a homologous series. This is especially true of the first member of a series, which is therefore generally regarded as atypical. Nevertheless the general trends and similarities do help to systematize the chemistry of organic compounds: a knowledge of the chemistry of a representative member of the relevant series allows predictions to be made about the properties and reactions of another member, even though it may contain more than one functional group.

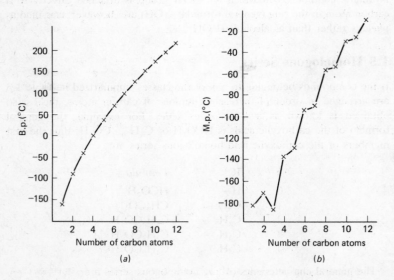

Fig. 1.4 (a) The boiling-points and (b) the melting-points of the unbranched-chain alkanes

1.6 Isomerism

The two main classes of isomerism (see Unit 1.3(c)) are *structural isomerism* and *stereoisomerism*. In structural isomerism the isomers have the same molecular formula but differ in structure, that is, in the order in which the different atoms are linked together in the molecule. In stereoisomerism the isomers have the same molecular formula and the same structure, but differ in the spatial arrangement of the groups.

(a) Stereoisomerism

Stereoisomerism is of two kinds: *geometrical* and *optical isomerism*.

(i) **Geometrical isomerism.** Geometrical isomers are a result of a hindrance to rotation of a covalent bond, for example, by the presence of a double bond. There are, for instance, two isomeric butenedioic acids:

cis-butenedioic acid   *trans*-butenedioic acid
m.p. 130°   m.p. 286°

Both compounds have the same structure; both consist of two carbon atoms, each linked to a hydrogen atom and a carboxy-group, joined together by a double bond. However, they have different chemical and physical properties as a result of the different spatial arrangements of their groups. The prefix *cis*- refers to the positioning of the two carboxy-groups on the same side of the plane of the double bond; in the *trans*-isomer the two carboxy-groups lie on opposite sides.

(ii) **Optical isomerism.** Optical isomers have identical structural formulae and for the most part identical chemical properties but, as a result of the different spatial arrangements of the atoms in their molecules, they differ in their optical properties.

Optical and geometrical isomerism are discussed in detail in Unit 21.

(b) Structural Isomerism

(i) **Chain (or nuclear) isomerism.** Here the isomers differ in the arrangement of the carbon atoms, for example:

$$CH_3-CH_2-CH_2-CH_3 \quad and \quad CH_3-CH-CH_3$$
$$\underset{\text{butane}}{} \qquad\qquad \underset{CH_3}{|}$$

butane   2-methylpropane

(ii) **Position isomerism.** Positional isomers have the same carbon skeleton and belong to the same homologous series, but differ in the position of the substituent group, and hence usually in their chemical properties; for example:

$$CH_3-CH_2-CH_2-Cl \quad \text{and} \quad CH_3-\underset{\underset{Cl}{|}}{CH}-CH_3$$

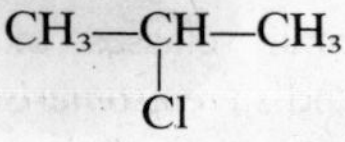

1-chloropropane   2-chloropropane

Position isomerism is important in cyclic compounds; for example, there are three different isomers of disubstituted benzene, $C_6H_4X_2$. The carbon atoms are numbered to indicate the positions of the substituents:

The three isomers of dibromobenzene are:

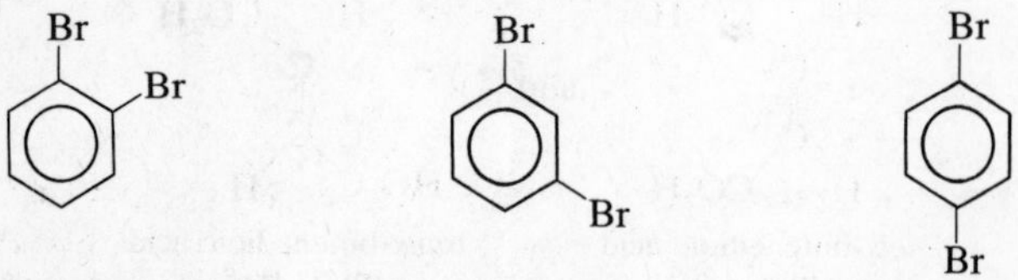

1,2-dibromobenzene   1,3-dibromobenzene   1,4-dibromobenzene

(iii) **Functional-group isomerism.** Functional-group isomers have the same molecular formula but belong to different homologous series, that is, they differ in the nature of the functional group. This type of isomerism is exhibited by many classes of organic compounds; for instance:

1. Alcohols and ethers, e.g. CH_3CH_2OH and CH_3OCH_3
                               ethanol   methoxymethane

2. Aldehydes and ketones, e.g. $CH_3CH_2C\overset{\textstyle H}{\underset{\textstyle O}{\big\langle}}$ and $CH_3-\underset{\underset{O}{\|}}{C}-CH_3$

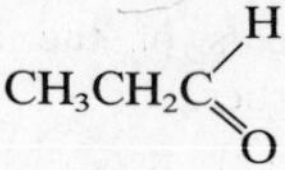

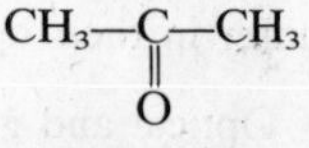

                                 propanal   propanone

3. Carboxylic acids and esters, e.g.

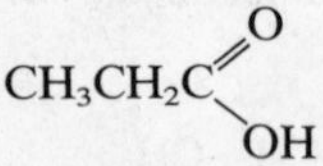

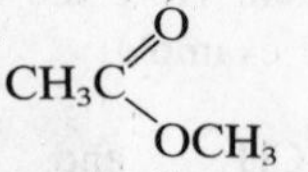

$$CH_3CH_2C\overset{\textstyle O}{\underset{\textstyle OH}{\big\langle}} \qquad CH_3C\overset{\textstyle O}{\underset{\textstyle OCH_3}{\big\langle}} \quad \text{and} \quad H-C\overset{\textstyle O}{\underset{\textstyle OC_2H_5}{\big\langle}}$$

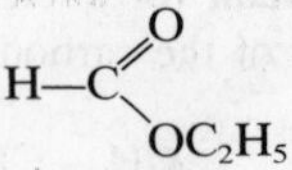

  propanoic acid   methyl ethanoate   ethyl methanoate

(iv) **Metamerism.** Isomers belonging to the same homologous series are known as *metamers*. For example:

1. Ethers, e.g. $C_2H_5OC_2H_5$, $CH_3OCH_2CH_2CH_3$
                  ethoxyethane   methoxypropane

and

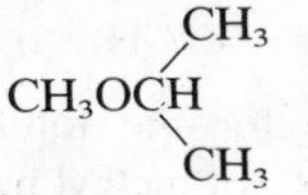

$$CH_3OCH \begin{matrix} CH_3 \\ \\ CH_3 \end{matrix}$$

1,1-dimethylmethoxymethane

2. Esters, e.g. $HCO_2C_2H_5$ and $CH_3CO_2CH_3$
ethyl methanoate   methyl ethanoate

(v) **Tautomerism** is essentially a special type of functional-group isomerism in which the isomers are in dynamic equilibrium with each other. For example, ethyl 3-oxobutanoate is an equilibrium mixture of two forms:

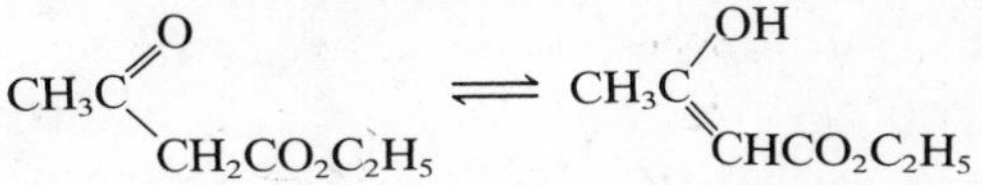

$$CH_3C \underset{CH_2CO_2C_2H_5}{\overset{O}{\Big\langle}} \quad \rightleftharpoons \quad CH_3C \underset{CHCO_2C_2H_5}{\overset{OH}{\Big\langle}}$$

keto-form   enol form

At room temperature the mixture contains approximately 93 per cent of the keto- and 7 per cent of the enol forms. The compound shows characteristic reactions of both the carbonyl ($>C=O$) and the hydroxy-groups.

Test Yourself on Unit 1

1. Indicate whether the following statements are true or false:
   (a) The reactions of organic compounds are generally slower than those of inorganic compounds because they involve ions of opposite charge which tend to repel one another.
   (b) The action of soaps is governed by the low solubility of the hydrocarbon chain in oil or grease.
   (c) The carbonyl group $>C=O$ is present in both aldehydes and ketones.
   (d) There are two isomeric propenes: $CH_3CH=CH_2$ and $CH_2=CHCH_3$.
   (e) Hydrophilic groups are insoluble in water, but hydrophobic groups dissolve readily in aqueous solutions.
   (f) Organic compounds are usually more volatile and have lower melting-points than inorganic compounds because there is less force of attraction between uncharged molecules than between oppositely charged ions.

2. What are the molecular formulae of (a) the alkyne, (b) the alkene, (c) the carboxylic acid and (d) the alcohol containing eight carbon atoms? The structural formula and names of isomers are not required.

3. Name the following compounds: (a) HCO_2Na, (b) $HCONH_2$, (c) $CH_3COOCOCH_3$, (d) CCl_3CHO, (e) $(CH_3)_2CO$, (f) $CH_3CH_2NH_2$, (g) C_2H_5CN, (h) $CH_3CH_2CH_2CH{=}CHCH_3$, (i) CHI_3, (j) $CH_2{=}CHCl$.

4. Draw structural formulae for the following compounds: (a) 1,1,1-trichloropropane, (b) propanal, (c) methyl methanoate, (d) buta-1,3-diene, (e) ammonium benzoate, (f) ethylbenzene, (g) 2-methylphenol, (h) 1,3,5-trimethylbenzene.

The Separation and Purification of Organic Compounds

The method chosen for the purification of an organic compound is largely determined by the physical and chemical properties of the substance concerned. The principal techniques are: distillation, recrystallization, sublimation, solvent extraction and chromatography.

2.1 Distillation

This method applies to substances in the liquid phase. When an impure liquid or a liquid mixture is boiled the vapour first evolved contains a higher proportion of the more volatile (or lower-boiling) component than the original mixture. The vapour is condensed and the collected distillate may be redistilled if necessary to yield the pure liquid. Frequently a simple distillation apparatus, consisting of a flask with a side-arm fitted with a condenser, is used. Some small pieces of unglazed porcelain or a few 'anti-bumping' granules are always added to the distillation flask before the liquid is boiled, to prevent superheating. The particles provide nuclei for the formation of vapour bubbles and thus ensure gentle boiling. Flammable liquids of low boiling-point are always heated in a hot-water bath for additional safety.

If the boiling-points of the liquid components are close together, an efficient *fractionating column* is required, and the condensation–vaporization process takes place repeatedly in the course of a single distillation. The column is packed with small glass rings or metal coils to increase the surface area in contact with both the vapour passing up the column and the condensed liquid returning to the flask. The fractionating column is surrounded by a heat-retaining jacket and the products are distilled over slowly in order to maintain the vapour–liquid equilibrium. The temperature decreases progressively up the column, and the component with the lowest boiling-point is condensed first. The receiver is then changed, and on further heating the temperature rises and the component with the next highest boiling-point distils over, and so on.

A suitable apparatus for fractional distillation is shown in Fig. 2.1.

(a) Reduced-pressure Distillation

Liquids boil when their vapour pressure is equal to the external (or atmospheric) pressure. If the pressure is lowered by attaching the distillation apparatus to a vacuum pump liquids with very high boiling-points at atmospheric pressure may be distilled at considerably lower temperatures.

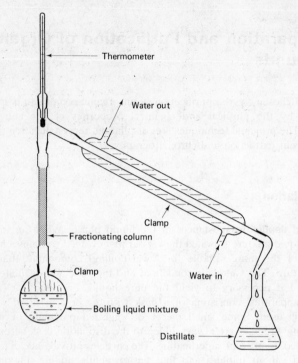

Thermometer

Water out

Clamp

Fractionating column

Clamp

Water in

Boiling liquid mixture

Distillate

Fig. 2.1 Fractional distillation apparatus

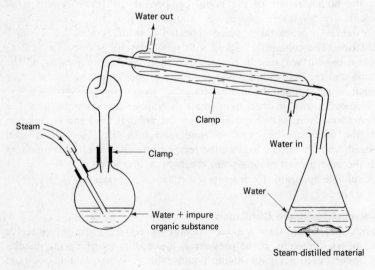

Water out

Steam

Clamp

Clamp

Water in

Water

Water + impure organic substance

Steam-distilled material

Fig. 2.2 Steam-distillation apparatus

(b) Steam-distillation

Some organic compounds are *steam-volatile*, that is, when such a compound is boiled with water the vapour evolved contains both steam and the vapour of the organic substance, even though the boiling-point of the compound may be much higher than that of water. The compound can thus be distilled at a far lower temperature than by normal distillation methods.

The apparatus used is shown in Fig. 2.2. Steam is passed into a flask containing the impure substance. The temperature increases and soon steam mixed with the vapour of the purified compound passes into the condenser and the distillate is collected in the receiver. The organic compound is subsequently separated from the water. The uses of steam-distillation include the isolation of fragrant oils or perfumes from flowers, fruits or herbs.

2.2 Recrystallization

Recrystallization is probably the most frequently used method of purifying organic solids. A solvent is found in which the substance will dissolve readily on warming, but in which it is sparingly soluble when cold. The hot solution is filtered, preferably through a Buchner funnel (Fig. 2.3), to remove any insoluble impurities and the filtrate is allowed to cool slowly. Pure crystals of the compound separate out and are filtered off, again using a Buchner funnel. The compound may be purified further by repeating the process.

The collected solid is washed on the filter-paper with a little of the pure *cold* solvent, and is dried by first sucking off as much liquid as possible through the Buchner funnel and then allowing to stand in air. A vacuum desiccator (Fig. 2.4) may be used; a stable, high-melting compound may be dried in an oven at an appropriate temperature. A little animal charcoal is frequently added to the boiling solution when recrystallizing; the charcoal adsorbs any coloured impurities and is removed when the hot solution is filtered.

2.3 Sublimation

Some solids do not melt on heating, but *sublime*, that is, they pass directly into the vapour state and will resolidify on cooling. The process may be used to purify certain organic compounds.

2.4 Solvent Extraction

The greater solubility of organic compounds in non-aqueous solvents such as 'ether' (ethoxyethane, or diethyl ether) may be used to separate them from solutions in water. The aqueous solution is shaken with a small amount of ether in a separating funnel (Fig. 2.5). Most of the organic compound dissolves in the ether which, as it is less dense than water and is

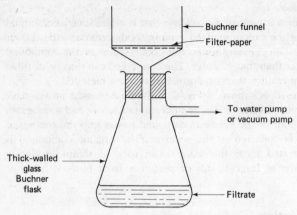

Fig. 2.3   A Buchner funnel and flask

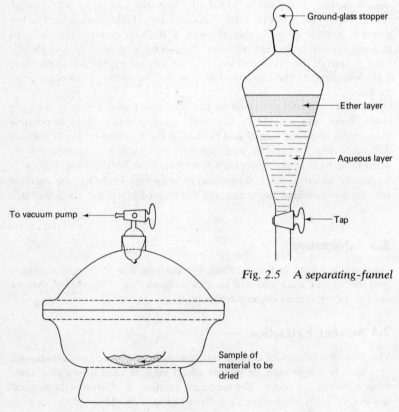

Fig. 2.5   A separating-funnel

Fig. 2.4   A vacuum desiccator

insoluble in it, forms a layer on the top of the solution. The tap is opened and the aqueous layer is run off into a beaker and the ether layer is transferred to a separate container. By repeating the process with one or two further samples of ether, virtually all the organic compound is removed from the aqueous solution.

The ethereal extracts are combined and the ether is removed by careful distillation from a hot-water bath. **Extreme care must be taken** as ethoxyethane is very volatile (b.p. 35°) and highly flammable.

More efficient extraction is obtained if the ether is used in several small portions in successive extractions rather than all at once.

2.5 Chromatography

Separation by chromatography depends on the differences in the rates at which the components of a mixture are moved along an inert *stationary phase* (such as paper or alumina) by a liquid or gas (the *moving phase*). The method may be used for the separation and, in some cases, the identification of the different components in extremely small samples of a mixture.

(a) Paper Chromatography

Paper chromatography has been used to separate a wide range of compounds including plant pigments, amino-acids and sugars.

A pencil line is ruled across the bottom of the paper chosen as the stationary phase, and a drop of the solution of the mixture is applied on the line at point X (see Fig. 2.6), using a capillary tube or fine pipette. A series

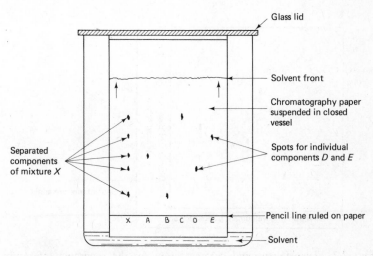

Fig. 2.6   *Separation of the components of a mixture by paper chromatography*

of spots of solutions of the various pure components (*A* to *E*) believed to be present in the mixture are placed beside it. When the paper has dried it is suspended in a glass tank with its lower edge just dipping into a suitable solvent. As the liquid (the *moving phase* or *eluting solvent*) gradually moves up the paper by capillary action the components of the mixture are separated into a number of spots according to their relative solubilities in the solvent and in the water molecules adsorbed on the cellulose fibres of the filter paper.

The components may be identified by comparing the positions of the spots with those of the known compounds or by measuring the distance the solute has travelled along the paper relative to the solvent front and comparing this with the results obtained with known substances under identical conditions.

The *relative band speed* or R_F value of a particular compound is defined as:

$$R_F = \frac{\text{Distance component moves}}{\text{Distance travelled by solvent front}}$$

R_F values are constant for compounds under the conditions of the experiment and may be used to identify the substances in a mixture.

Chromatographic separation is obvious with mixtures of inks, dyes, plant pigments or other coloured materials. With colourless substances the spots are often detected under ultra-violet light (which causes many organic compounds to fluoresce) or by chemical methods—amino-acids, for example,

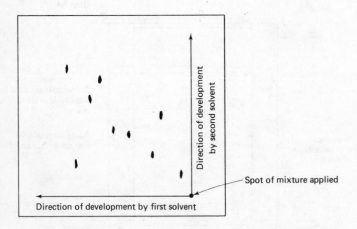

Fig. 2.7   Two-dimensional chromatogram for the separation of a nine-component mixture

show up as blue or purple spots after the paper is sprayed with ninhydrin, while sugars give red or brown colorations after treatment with phenylamine and benzene-1,2-dicarboxylic acid.

Complex mixtures are frequently separated by two-dimensional chromatography. A sample of the mixture is placed near one corner of the paper and is partly separated using the first solvent. The paper is then turned through 90° and the separation is repeated using a different solvent or solvent mixture (Fig. 2.7).

(b) Column Chromatography

In this technique, the stationary phase consists of a powdered solid such as alumina or Celite contained in a glass column plugged at the bottom with loosely packed glass wool (Fig. 2.8). The column is prepared by pouring a slurry of the powder in the eluting solvent into the tube; the solid sinks and forms an evenly packed layer which is kept immersed in the solvent until

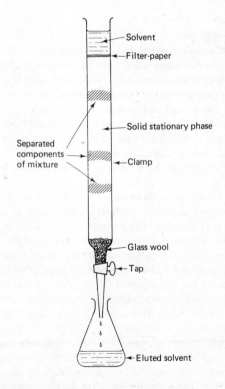

Fig. 2.8   Column (liquid) chromatography

required. The column must not be allowed to dry out, or cracks will form in the stationary phase.

A solution of the mixture is then poured on to the top of the column and passed slowly down the tube by adding further samples of the eluting solvent. The components in the mixture are separated as they move down the column, according to their relative strengths of adsorption by the stationary phase. The solutions of the separated components may be collected as they are eluted from the column.

(c) Thin-layer Chromatography

This method is similar in principle to column chromatography, but the stationary phase (a solid such as alumina, silica gel or Celite) is spread as a uniform layer up to about 1 mm thick on a glass plate. The sample is 'spotted' on the plate, and the components are separated and R_F values calculated in the same way as in paper chromatography.

The process is quicker than column chromatography and, as it is on a much smaller scale, it is used principally for identifying the components of a mixture rather than as a method of purification.

(d) Gas Chromatography

In gas–liquid chromatography (GLC) the stationary phase is an involatile liquid supported on an inert solid, such as powdered alumina or Celite, whereas in gas–solid chromatography (GSC) the inert solid itself (usually alumina or silica gel) acts as the stationary phase. Nitrogen, argon or some other unreactive gas is used as the *carrier gas* (or moving phase). A sample of the mixture is introduced into the end of the column from a gas cell or (in the case of liquids) by injecting a small sample through a self-sealing septum cap with a hypodermic syringe. The mixture is carried by the stream of gas into the column which may be heated in a temperature-controlled oven if required (Fig. 2.9).

As the separated components emerge from the column they pass through a suitable detector system which records their passage as a series of peaks on a moving chart (Fig. 2.10). The area under each peak is proportional to the amount of the relevant component in the mixture. Gas chromatography thus also provides a quick, convenient method of quantitative analysis for extremely small samples (of the order of 0.01 g) of complex materials.

The time required for a compound to pass through the column is known as its *retention time*, and is characteristic for a particular substance under the conditions used for the separation—flow rate, column temperature, nature and concentration of the stationary phase, length of column and so forth. Thus by comparing retention times with those of known compounds under the same conditions it is often possible to identify a component. Alternatively a pure sample of a suspected compound may be introduced with the mixture to see if the corresponding peak on the chromatogram is enlarged. Sometimes two compounds do have the same retention time on a particular

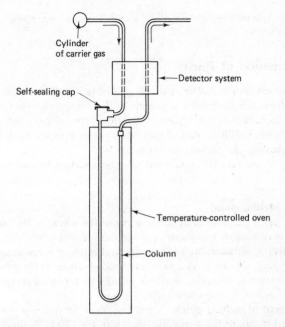

Fig. 2.9   *Diagrammatic representation of a gas chromatograph*

column but by changing to other columns with different stationary phases reasonably certain identifications can be made.

Gas chromatography may be used for the separation of mixtures on a preparative scale by injecting 1–3 g samples into wider columns than are used for analytical purposes and collecting the separated components in separate U-tubes immersed in a freezing mixture as they emerge from the

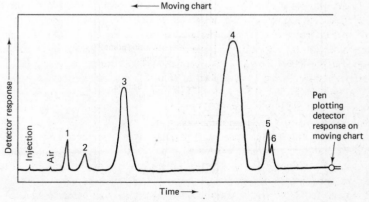

Fig. 2.10   *Gas chromatogram of a six-component mixture*

column. The receiver is changed as each peak is registered on the chromatograph.

2.6 Confirmation of Purity

Frequently information concerning the degree of purity of a substance may be inferred from the material's appearance. If a compound—glucose, for example—is expected to be a clear, colourless, crystalline solid, even a non-chemist would deduce that a grey amorphous powder or a yellow-brown evil-smelling tarry solid was impure.

The purity of an organic compound may be checked by the following criteria:

(a) A Sharp Melting-point

A pure solid has a sharp, definite melting-point: the whole of the solid will melt over a very narrow temperature range (less than 1–2°C). An impure solid melts over a considerably wider range and often at a lower temperature than the pure substance. A solid compound obtained as the product of an organic reaction is therefore purified, usually by repeated recrystallization, until it has a constant sharp melting-point.

(i) **Measurement of melting-point.** A melting-point (or freezing-point) can be determined by using the apparatus shown in Fig. 2.11. A short length

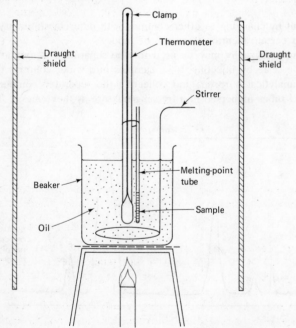

Fig. 2.11   Apparatus for the determination of melting-points

(about 6 cm) of thin-walled capillary tubing is sealed at one end by heating it in a Bunsen burner flame. A sample of the powdered organic compound is placed in this melting-point tube by dipping the open end into the sample and then forcing the material down to the bottom with a length of fine wire or by scraping the side of the tube with the milled edge of a coin. The tube is attached to a thermometer by a piece of wire or cotton so that the sample is level with the thermometer bulb. The thermometer is then suspended in a small beaker of liquid paraffin and the oil is stirred as it is heated slowly (1 or 2° per minute as the melting-point is approached). The melting-point and temperature range over which the substance melts are noted.

Alternatively, an electrical melting-point apparatus may be used. The melting-point tube containing the sample is placed close to the thermometer bulb in a small hole drilled into a metal block which is heated by an electric current. The sample is observed through a lens as the temperature is progressively increased by adjusting the current input to the coils surrounding the heating block.

It is often more convenient to find an approximate melting-point first (to within about 5°C) by rapid heating. The oil or heating block is then allowed to cool until it is a few degrees below this point before increasing the temperature very slowly to determine the accurate value with a second sample of the compound.

(ii) **Mixed melting-points.** The fact that a pure substance has a sharp and definite melting-point may be used to identify an organic compound. Suppose, for example, that an unidentified substance X melting close to 133° was thought to be one of the following three compounds:

A (3-phenylpropenoic acid) m.p. 133°;

B (carbamide) m.p. 132°; or

C (propanedioic acid) m.p. 134°.

The melting-points of mixtures of X with each of the pure substances would be determined, and the result might appear thus:

Mixture	m.p.
$X + A$	114–129°
$X + B$	131.5–132°
$X + C$	86–99°

X is the compound which does not alter the melting-point when mixed with the unknown substance. In this example, X is carbamide (compound B).

(b) A Sharp Boiling-point

A pure liquid boils at a sharp and definite temperature and all the liquid distils over within a very small temperature range (about 1°C). The converse is not always true, however, and a material which distils at a constant temperature is not necessarily a single pure compound. Many organic liquids form *constant-boiling-point mixtures* (or *azeotropes*) of definite composition, and two or more components will distil over together at the same temperature. Liquids that form a constant-boiling mixture cannot therefore be separated by distillation. Ethanol (b.p. 78.5°), for example, forms a constant-boiling mixture with water that contains about 96 per cent of ethanol and boils at 78.1°; thus, in spite of the wide difference in boiling-points, pure ethanol cannot be obtained by distillation of an aqueous solution containing less than 96 per cent ethanol.

Owing to the possibility of the formation of a constant-boiling mixture the purity of a liquid is frequently checked by measuring its *refractive index*, which is strongly dependent on its purity and which may be quickly determined with a refractometer. Alternatively, a sample of the liquid may be injected into a gas chromatograph: the appearance of a single peak using columns with different stationary phases indicates the presence of a single pure substance.

Test Yourself on Unit 2

1. An organic compound S was prepared and found to have a melting-point of 222°. After the first, second and third recrystallizations, the melting-point was 224°, 226° and 226° respectively. The melting-points of mixtures of S with pure samples of the organic compounds P, Q and R were 221–4°, 220–3° and 226° respectively. Comment on the significance of these melting-point values.

Indicate whether the statements in Questions 2 to 12 are true or false.

2. Paper chromatography is used only for the separation of coloured compounds.

3. A larger amount of an organic compound is extracted by shaking its aqueous solution with 75 cm³ of ether than by using three separate portions of 25 cm³.

4. Sublimation is used for the separation and purification of compounds with low melting-points.

5. Pure ethanol (b.p. 78°) cannot be obtained by the fractional distillation of a mixture containing equal volumes of ethanol and water.

6. The retention time of a compound in gas chromatography is constant under all conditions.

7. The temperature at the top of a fractionating column is generally lower than that of the boiling liquid in the distillation flask.

8. The boiling-point of a liquid increases as the pressure is reduced.

9. Pieces of unglazed porcelain promote even boiling when added to a liquid in a distillation flask.

10. An azeotrope is a liquid mixture of definite composition which boils at a constant temperature at atmospheric pressure.

11. Animal charcoal is added to a solution during recrystallization to ensure even boiling.

12. A recrystallized solid is washed well with an excess of the hot solvent before being dried.

Unit Three

The Determination of the Structure of Organic Compounds

3.1 Introduction

The procedure adopted for a particular structure determination depends largely on the nature and complexity of the compound concerned. While different methods are used for such widely diverse compounds as a simple hydrocarbon and a complex protein, the first two stages are always the isolation of the material, and confirmation that it is a pure substance (as described in Unit 2). In this Unit, we examine the general procedure adopted for the assignment and confirmation of the structural formula of a pure organic compound.

3.2 Qualitative Analysis

The first step is to identify the constituent elements of the compound.

(a) Carbon and Hydrogen

The presence of carbon and hydrogen in a compound is shown by powdering a sample (c. 0.5 g) of the material with an equal volume of *dry* copper(II) oxide and heating the mixture in a clean, dry test-tube. Any carbon and hydrogen is converted into carbon dioxide and water respectively by this treatment:

$$3CuO + \begin{cases} C- \\ 2H- \end{cases} \xrightarrow{\text{heat}} 3Cu + CO_2 + H_2O$$

in organic
compound

The carbon dioxide is identified by its reaction with lime-water. The water condenses as droplets of colourless liquid on the cooler parts of the test-tube where it may be identified by the blue colour it produces with white anhydrous copper(II) sulphate or by the pink colour observed when it is treated with blue anhydrous cobalt(II) chloride paper.

Experiment 3.1 *To test for the presence of carbon and hydrogen*
Place 2 or 3 g of powdered copper(II) oxide in a crucible and heat strongly to remove any moisture which may be present in the hygroscopic solid. Transfer the hot crucible to a desiccator and allow to cool.

Carry out the tests for the presence of carbon and hydrogen on samples (c. 0.5 g) of readily available organic compounds, such as sucrose, carbamide (urea) or benzoic acid.

(b) **Halogen, Nitrogen and Sulphur**

The presence of these elements is demonstrated by fusing the organic compound with sodium. The fusion converts halogen and sulphur in the compound into sodium halide and sodium sulphide respectively:

$$3Na + \begin{cases} -Cl \\ -S \end{cases} \xrightarrow{\text{fuse}} NaCl + Na_2S$$

in organic
compound

and nitrogen in the presence of carbon from the organic compound yields sodium cyanide:

$$Na + (C, N) \xrightarrow{\text{fuse}} NaCN$$

Experiment 3.2 *To test for the presence of halogen, nitrogen and sulphur: the Lassaigne sodium fusion*

(Care: this experiment can be dangerous and must only be carried out under competent supervision.) Add a small piece of metallic sodium (a 3 mm cube is sufficient) to a sample (*c.* 0.1 g) of the organic compound in a small soda-glass or Pyrex test-tube (about 6 cm × 8–10 mm i.d.) held in a pair of tongs. Heat the mixture gently over a Bunsen burner flame until the sodium melts and begins to react with the compound; remove the tube from the flame if the reaction become vigorous.

When the initial reaction is complete, heat the tube strongly until it is red-hot and no further fumes are evolved. Then, holding a square of metal gauze over it in case any pieces of glass fly out, plunge the hot tube into a mortar containing about 25 cm^3 of distilled water. Grind up the broken tube and the products of the Lassaigne fusion with a pestle and transfer the contents of the mortar to a boiling-tube. Boil the mixture, and filter it. Divide the filtrate into four portions.

Portion 1: *Halogen test.* Acidify the solution with dilute nitric acid and boil it gently in an evaporating basin until the volume has been reduced to half its original bulk. (This treatment is necessary in order to destroy any sodium cyanide, which would be present if the original organic compound contained nitrogen, as on treatment with aqueous silver nitrate it forms a white precipitate of silver cyanide which can be confused with silver chloride.) Then add about 1 cm^3 of silver nitrate solution:

$$\left. \begin{array}{l} NaCl \\ \\ NaBr \\ \\ NaI \end{array} \right\} \xrightarrow{AgNO_3/HNO_3} \left\{ \begin{array}{l} AgCl \text{ — white precipitate, soluble in} \\ \qquad \text{an excess of aqueous ammonia} \\ AgBr \text{ — off-white precipitate,} \\ \qquad \text{sparingly soluble in an excess} \\ \qquad \text{of aqueous ammonia} \\ AgI \text{ — yellow precipitate, insoluble} \\ \qquad \text{in aqueous ammonia} \end{array} \right.$$

Portion 2: *Sulphur test.* Add about 1 cm³ of lead ethanoate (acetate) solution to the second portion of the filtrate. An immediate black precipitate of lead sulphide indicates the presence of sulphur:

$$Pb^{2+}_{(aq)} + S^{2-}_{(aq)} \rightarrow PbS_{(s)}$$

Portion 3: *An extremely sensitive test for sulphur.* Add 1 or 2 cm³ of a *dilute*, freshly prepared aqueous solution of sodium pentacyanonitrosyl-ferrate(II) (sodium nitroprusside, $Na_2[Fe(CN)_5NO].2H_2O$) to the filtrate. An immediate pink or purple coloration (similar to manganate(VII)) which slowly fades on standing confirms the presence of sulphur.

Portion 4: *Nitrogen test.* Add 0.3–0.5 g of crystalline iron(II) sulphate to the filtrate and boil the mixture gently for a minute or so to form hexacyanoferrate(II):

$$Fe^{2+} + 6CN^- \rightarrow [Fe(CN)_6]^{4-}$$

A few drops of iron(III) chloride solution are now added, followed by an excess of dilute sulphuric acid, and the solution is filtered. The presence of intensely coloured specks of Prussian Blue on the filter-paper or of a green-blue coloration of the solution indicates the presence of nitrogen in the organic compound:

$$[Fe(CN)_6]^{4-} \xrightarrow{Fe^{3+}(aq)} \text{Prussian Blue}$$

3.3 Quantitative Analysis

The next stage is to determine the amounts or relative proportions of the elements present in the compound.

(a) Carbon and Hydrogen

These elements are estimated by heating a known mass (*c.* 25 mg) of the compound in a stream of dry oxygen in a stainless steel combustion tube at about 900°. The hydrogen and carbon present in the organic compound burn to form water and carbon dioxide, which are absorbed in previously weighed tubes containing magnesium chlorate(VII) and soda-lime respectively. The tubes are then re-weighed to give the masses of water and carbon dioxide absorbed.

The relative atomic masses of carbon, hydrogen and oxygen are 12, 1 and 16 respectively; thus the percentages of carbon and hydrogen present in the original organic compound may be calculated from:

$$\text{Mass of carbon} = \frac{12}{44} \times \text{Mass of } CO_2 \text{ obtained}$$

$$\text{Mass of hydrogen} = \frac{2}{18} \times \text{Mass of } H_2O \text{ obtained}$$

Example

0.071 86 g of an organic compound, A, yielded 0.102 0 g of carbon dioxide and 0.062 59 g of water on combustion. What is the percentage of (a) carbon and (b) hydrogen in A?

(a) Percentage of carbon in $A = \dfrac{\text{Mass of carbon}}{\text{Mass of compound}} \times 100$

$$= \frac{12}{44} \times \frac{\text{Mass of CO}_2 \text{ obtained}}{\text{Mass of compound}} \times 100$$

$$= \frac{12}{44} \times \frac{0.102\,0}{0.071\,86} \times 100 = \underline{\underline{38.71 \text{ per cent}}}$$

(b) Percentage of hydrogen in $A = \dfrac{\text{Mass of hydrogen}}{\text{Mass of compound}} \times 100$

$$= \frac{2}{18} \times \frac{\text{Mass of H}_2\text{O obtained}}{\text{Mass of compound}} \times 100$$

$$= \frac{2}{18} \times \frac{0.062\,59}{0.071\,86} \times 100 = \underline{\underline{9.68 \text{ per cent}}}$$

(b) Halogen (Carius's Method)

A weighed sample of the material (sufficient to yield 0.2–0.5 g of silver halide) is heated with a mixture of fuming nitric acid and an excess of silver nitrate in a sealed tube. After several hours at about 270° any halogen present in the compound is converted to the corresponding silver halide:

$$\sim\text{Cl (or } \sim\text{Br or } \sim\text{I)} + \text{AgNO}_{3(aq)} \xrightarrow{\text{fuming HNO}_3/270°}$$

$$\text{AgCl}_{(s)} \text{ (or AgBr or AgI)} + \text{NO}^-_{3(aq)}$$

The tube is allowed to cool and is then opened. The precipitated silver halide is filtered off, washed, dried and weighed. The percentage of halogen ($X \stackrel{\sim}{=} \text{Cl}$, Br or I) present in the compound may be calculated from:

$$\text{Mass of halogen present} = \frac{\text{RAM of X}}{\text{RMM of Ag X}} \times \text{Mass of AgX obtained}$$

(c) Sulphur (Carius's Method)

A sample (0.2–0.3 g) of the compound is heated in a sealed Carius tube with fuming nitric acid for several hours at 270°. This treatment oxidizes any carbon, hydrogen and sulphur in the material to carbon dioxide, water and sulphate ions respectively. After cooling to room temperature the tube is opened and the contents are treated with an excess of barium chloride solution to precipitate the sulphate ions as barium sulphate:

$$\text{Ba}^{2+}_{(aq)} + \text{SO}_4{}^{2-}{}_{(aq)} \rightarrow \text{BaSO}_{4(aq)}$$

The precipitate is filtered off, washed, dried and weighed.

$$\text{Mass of sulphur in compound} = \frac{\text{RAM of S}}{\text{RMM of BaSO}_4} \times \text{Mass of BaSO}_4 \text{ obtained}$$

(d) Nitrogen

Two methods are in common use for the estimation of nitrogen. In *Dumas'* *method* the nitrogen in a weighed sample of the organic compound is converted into gaseous nitrogen by heating the substance with an excess of copper(II) oxide in the absence of air. Any oxides of nitrogen which may be formed are reduced by passing the gases over heated copper. The nitrogen is then collected and measured in a graduated tube (known as a *nitrometer*) over 50 per cent aqueous potassium hydroxide which absorbs all the carbon dioxide and sulphur dioxide from the gaseous products. The percentage of nitrogen in the organic compound may be calculated, using the fact that 1 mole of nitrogen molecules (or 28 g of nitrogen) occupies $22\,400\,\text{cm}^3$ at s.t.p.

In *Kjeldahl's method*, the nitrogen in a weighed sample of the compound is converted into ammonium sulphate by the action of boiling concentrated sulphuric acid and potassium sulphate. The reaction mixture is then diluted and boiled with an excess of sodium hydroxide solution, and the ammonia which is evolved is absorbed in a known volume of standard acid and estimated by back-titration.

(e) Oxygen

The amount of oxygen in an organic compound is usually found by difference, that is, by adding up the percentages of the other elements present and subtracting the total from 100.

3.4 The Empirical Formula

The *empirical formula* of a compound indicates the *simplest ratio* of the number of atoms of each element present in the molecule. For example, glucose, $C_6H_{12}O_6$, and ethanoic acid, $C_2H_4O_2$, have the same empirical formula (CH_2O), since the *ratio* of the numbers of carbon, hydrogen and oxygen atoms is the same in both compounds.

The method of calculating the empirical formula of an organic compound is explained in Unit 3.5.

3.5 Calculation of the Molecular Formula

The *molecular formula* of a compound shows the *actual* number of the atoms of each element present in the molecule.

The relationship between the empirical formula and the molecular formula of a compound is given by:

$$\text{Molecular formula} = (\text{Empirical formula})_n$$

where n is a whole number that may be calculated if the relative molecular mass of the compound is known.

$$n = \frac{\text{RMM}}{\text{Empirical formula weight}}$$

Example

An organic compound, E, approximate RMM $= 59$, contains C, 40.1 per cent and H, 6.67 per cent. Calculate (a) the empirical formula and (b) the molecular formula of E, assuming that the compound contains only carbon, hydrogen and oxygen.

Percentage of oxygen $= 100 - (40.1 + 6.67) = 53.23$

	Carbon		Hydrogen		Oxygen
Ratio of weights (per cent):	40.1	:	6.67	:	53.23
Divide by RAM of the relevant elements:	$\dfrac{40.1}{12}$	:	$\dfrac{6.67}{1}$	:	$\dfrac{53.23}{16}$
	3.34	:	6.67	:	3.33
Divide by the smallest quotient:	$\dfrac{3.34}{3.33}$	:	$\dfrac{6.67}{3.33}$	:	$\dfrac{3.33}{3.33}$
to give					
Ratio of weights (per cent):	1.003	:	2.003	:	1
or, to nearest whole number:	1	:	2	:	1

Empirical formula of $E = \underline{CH_2O}$

Molecular formula of E (RMM $= 59$ approx.) $= (CH_2O)_n$
Empirical formula weight of $CH_2O = 12 + (2 \times 1) + 16 = 30$

$$n = \frac{\text{RMM}}{\text{Empirical formula weight}} = \frac{59}{30} = 2 \text{ (to the nearest whole number)}$$

$\therefore$ Molecular formula of $E = \underline{C_2H_4O_2}$.

A possible structural formula for E is:

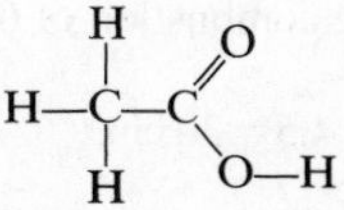

(ethanoic acid)

Eudiometry. The molecular formula of a gaseous hydrocarbon may be determined directly by measuring the volume changes that occur when a known volume is burnt in an excess of oxygen. The general equation for the combustion of a gaseous hydrocarbon of formula C_xH_y to carbon dioxide and water is:

$$C_xH_{y(g)} + \left(x + \frac{y}{4}\right)O_{2(g)} \rightarrow xCO_{2(g)} + \frac{y}{2}H_2O_{(l)}$$

thus   1 volume of C_xH_y requires $\left(x+\dfrac{y}{4}\right)$ volumes of oxygen and yields x volumes of carbon dioxide,

or, V cm^3 C_xH_y requires $V\left(x+\dfrac{y}{4}\right)$ cm^3 O_2 and yields Vx cm^3 CO_2

After cooling the reaction products to room temperature, any water present will be in the liquid phase and its volume may be neglected. (At room temperature, 1 mole of any gas occupies about 22 400 cm^3, and 1 mole of $H_2O_{(1)}$—RMM $= 18$—just 18 cm^3.) The gaseous products thus consist of carbon dioxide and unreacted oxygen. The amount of carbon dioxide is found by measuring the contraction in volume which occurs when aqueous potassium hydroxide is introduced into the eudiometer tube.

It follows from the equation that:

$$x = \frac{\text{Volume of carbon dioxide formed}}{\text{Volume of } C_xH_y}$$

Volume of oxygen required for the combustion of V cm^3 of C_xH_y

$$= V\left(x+\frac{y}{4}\right)$$

Example

6.0 cm^3 of a gaseous hydrocarbon were exploded with 34.5 cm^3 of oxygen in a eudiometer tube. The volume of the gaseous products after cooling to room temperature was 22.5 cm^3, which contracted to 4.5 cm^3 on treatment with potassium hydroxide. What is the molecular formula of the hydrocarbon?

$$\text{Volume of } CO_2 = 22.5 - 4.5 = 18.0 \text{ cm}^3$$

$$x = \frac{\text{Volume of } CO_2}{\text{Volume of } C_xH_y} = \frac{18.0}{6.0} = 3$$

The 4.5 cm^3 of gas remaining in the eudiometer after absorbing the carbon dioxide in potassium hydroxide was unreacted oxygen.

$\therefore$ Volume of oxygen required for the combustion of 6.0 cm^3 of C_xH_y

$$= 6\left(x+\frac{y}{4}\right) = 34.5 - 4.5 = 30 \text{ cm}^3.$$

Substituting for x:

$$6\left(3+\frac{y}{4}\right) = 30$$

$$\left(3+\frac{y}{4}\right) = 5$$

and hence $$y = 8$$

The molecular formula of the gaseous hydrocarbon is $\underline{C_3H_8}$ (propane).

3.6 Assignment of Structural Formula

The *structural formula* of a compound shows how the atoms are arranged or linked together in the molecule.

For simple compounds, where the number of isomers is small, a series of possible structural formulae may be deduced from the molecular formula, using the known valencies of the elements. For example, a compound with the molecular formula C_2H_6O has two possible structures:

$$
\begin{array}{cc}
\begin{array}{c}
\text{H}\ \ \text{H} \\
|\ \ \ | \\
\text{H—C—C—O—H} \\
|\ \ \ | \\
\text{H}\ \ \text{H} \\
A
\end{array}
&
\begin{array}{c}
\text{H}\ \ \ \ \ \text{H} \\
|\ \ \ \ \ | \\
\text{H—C—O—C—H} \\
|\ \ \ \ \ | \\
\text{H}\ \ \ \ \ \text{H} \\
B
\end{array}
\end{array}
$$

or

that is, it is either ethanol (structure A) or methoxymethane (structure B). This is all that can be inferred from the analysis results and molecular formula. Additional information is required before the *actual* structural formula can be assigned to this compound, such as a knowledge of:

(a) its chemical reactions;

(b) its physical properties;

(c) the results of physical studies by, for example, infra-red, nuclear magnetic resonance and mass spectroscopy; and

(d) if possible, unambiguous synthesis.

(a) The Reactions of the Compound

Chemical tests are carried out on the compound to confirm the presence or absence of specific functional groups such as hydroxyl, carboxyl or amino-groups. This may eliminate a number of possible isomers and thus simplify the choice of a probable structural formula for the compound.

Information concerning the structure of more complex substances may be obtained by using heat (*pyrolysis*), hydrolysis, oxidation, reduction or some other degradation method to break down the compound into smaller molecules that can be relatively easily identified.

(b) Physical Properties

Occasionally physical properties, such as boiling-point or melting-point, help to assign a particular structural formula to a compound. The criteria used are based on a knowledge of the general properties of different homologous series. For example, alcohols have considerably higher boiling-points than the isomeric ethers (*cf.* Table 3.1). Similarly, carboxylic acids and other hydroxy-compounds in which hydrogen bonding is possible also boil at unexpectedly high temperatures (see Unit 12.2).

Sometimes colour or smell can be of use in assigning an organic compound to a particular homologous series. Aromatic nitro-compounds, for example, are usually yellow, and almost all esters have a pleasant 'fruity' odour which helps to distinguish them from the carboxylic acids with

Table 3.1 Boiling-points of isomeric alcohols and ethers

Alcohol	b.p. (°C)	Ether	b.p. (°C)
CH_3CH_2OH	78.5	CH_3OCH_3	-25
$CH_3CH_2CH_2OH$	97	$CH_3OC_2H_5$	7

which they are isomeric. Similarly the foul-smelling isonitriles (general formula RNC or ArNC) are readily distinguished from their isomers RCN or ArCN which have relatively pleasant odours.

Other examples of physical and chemical properties which help to characterize particular structures or functional groups are described in later units.

(c) Physical Methods
A wide range of physical methods is available for the study of the structures of organic compounds, but only a few can be discussed here.

Absorption spectroscopy. Visible light, infra-red and ultra-violet radiation, X-rays and radio waves are all forms of *electromagnetic radiation*, having the same velocity $(3 \times 10^8 \, \text{m s}^{-1})$ but differing in their wavelengths. The wavelength of radiation is related to its frequency:

$$\text{Frequency} = \frac{\text{Velocity}}{\text{Wavelength}}$$

and also to its *wave number* (that is, the number of waves per centimetre):

$$\text{Wave number} = \frac{1}{\text{Wavelength (cm)}}$$

Frequencies, wavelengths and wave numbers are all used to measure positions in the electromagnetic spectrum, shown in Fig. 3.1.

When electromagnetic radiation passes through matter, radiation of certain wavelengths is absorbed by the substance, and the spectrum of the emergent radiation thus shows a characteristic pattern of *absorption bands*. The energy of the radiation is absorbed in small 'packets' or *quanta*, and the energy change ΔE due to the absorption of a single quantum of energy is

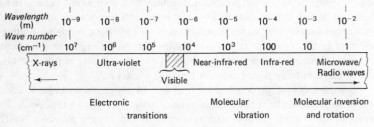

Fig. 3.1　The electromagnetic spectrum

given by

$$\Delta E = E_2 - E_1 = h\nu$$

where E_1 and E_2 are the energy levels of the initial and final states respectively, h is Planck's constant $(6.63 \times 10^{-34}\,\mathrm{J\,s})$ and ν is the frequency of the radiation.

Ultra-violet and visible-region spectroscopy. The energy absorbed in this portion of the electromagnetic spectrum—radiation of wavelength 185–800 nm or of wave number 50 000–12 500 cm^{-1}—promotes electrons from the ground state to higher energy levels, known as *excited states.* The frequency or wavelength of the radiation absorbed depends on the nature of the absorbing group or *chromophore*, and the intensity of the absorption is determined by how tightly the electrons are coupled within the molecule. Ultra-violet (and occasionally visible-region) spectroscopy can be used to detect nitro-groups and other multiple bonds, especially in *conjugated systems* where double and single bonds alternate as in —C≡C—C≡C— chains and in benzene and other aromatic rings. The spectrum of phenylethanone, for example, is shown in Fig. 3.2.

The substance is usually dissolved in a solvent which does not absorb radiation in the region under investigation, such as water, ethanol or hexane. A tungsten lamp is employed as the light source in the visible region, but for measurements in the ultra-violet a hydrogen or deuterium lamp is required and silica cells must be used, as glass does not transmit light of these wavelengths. Visible-region spectroscopy may, of course, only be used with coloured substances. Spectra in the visible and ultra-violet regions are used principally for quantitative analysis of solutions, since the intensity of absorption is related to the concentration of the solution.

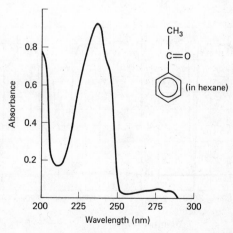

Fig. 3.2   The ultra-violet absorption spectrum of phenylethanone

Infra-red spectroscopy. Infra-red spectra, which are recorded over the wave number range $4\,000\text{–}650\ \mathrm{cm}^{-1}$ (wavelengths $2\,500\text{–}15\,000$ nm) show far more absorption peaks and yield more structural information than the comparatively simple ultra-violet and visible-region spectra. The identification of functional groups, of geometrical isomers and of the position of substitution in aromatic nuclei, the demonstration of hydrogen bonding and the detection of impurities are just a few of the many applications of infra-red spectroscopy.

Radiation absorbed in the infra-red region produces changes in the vibrational energy levels of the bonds in the molecule. The wave number range from $1\,500$ to $650\ \mathrm{cm}^{-1}$ is known as the *fingerprint region* as this is where the absorption peaks associated with the vibrational changes of specific bonds and functional groups occur, and the spectrum in this region is thus characteristic of the particular compound.

As both quartz and glass are opaque to infra-red light, the optical components, cells and plates for infra-red spectroscopy are frequently made from rock salt (NaCl). Liquids and low-melting solids are examined as thin films between polished sodium chloride plates, while gases are studied in cells fitted with sodium chloride windows. Solids are usually ground into a fine paste or *mull* using a few drops of Nujol or hexachlorobutadiene. A typical infra-red spectrum is shown in Fig. 3.3.

Mass spectroscopy. If the molecules of an organic compound are bombarded with electrons at a low pressure ($10^{-5}\text{–}10^{-6}$ mm Hg) in the gas phase, *molecular* (or *parent*) *ions* are usually formed:

$$M + e \rightarrow M^+ + 2e$$

Most of these parent ions break down to yield a number of positively charged and neutral fragments:

$$M^+ \rightarrow X^+ + Y + Z$$

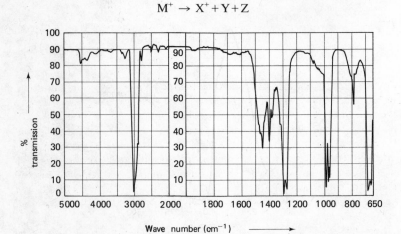

Fig. 3.3   The infra-red absorption spectrum of chloroethane (C_2H_5Cl)

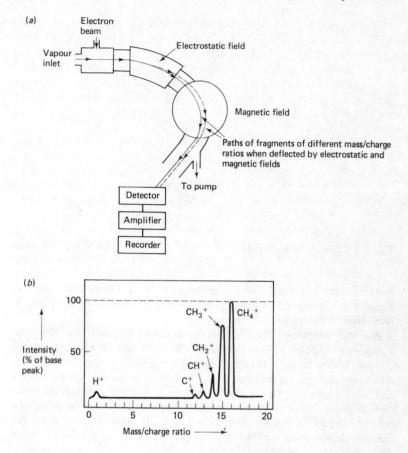

Fig. 3.4   (a) *Simplified diagram of a mass spectrometer*; (b) *the mass spectrum of methane*

By accelerating the ions in an electric field and then deflecting them by a magnetic field, the various charged particles may be separated according to their masses (Fig. 3.4) and the relative abundance of the different masses is recorded as a *mass spectrum* or *fragmentation pattern*.

Fragmentation patterns are dependent on the structure of the compound involved. Specific patterns are frequently associated with particular groupings, thus enabling an unknown compound to be identified. Masses are readily measured with extreme accuracy, so if the parent or molecular ion appears on the mass spectrum the relative molecular mass of the compound is also obtained.

Sometimes a single ion gives more than one peak. This is especially apparent with chlorine compounds and is a result of the existence of two or

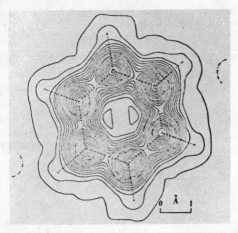

Fig. 3.5   The electron-density map of benzene, obtained by X-ray diffraction studies

more isotopes ($^{35}_{17}Cl$ and $^{37}_{17}Cl$ for instance) in the naturally occurring element. The relative abundance of the isotopes is reflected in the different intensities of the peaks.

X-ray diffractometry. This technique depends on the fact that the wavelengths of X-rays are of the same order of magnitude as the lengths of covalent bonds. When X-rays pass through crystalline substances, therefore, diffraction patterns are obtained from which accurate values of bond lengths and bond angles may be calculated, even for extremely complex molecules such as proteins and enzymes. Powerful computers are required to analyse the data and to plot the resulting electron-density maps. Fig. 3.5 shows the electron-density map for benzene, calculated from the results of X-ray diffraction studies of a single crystal.

(d) Synthesis

Synthesis involves building up a compound step by step from simpler substances of known structure. At one time unambiguous synthesis was the final step in confirming the structure of any organic compound, but nowadays, with the availability of physical methods and the complexity and very high molecular masses of some substances of current interest, this method is no longer of general application.

Test Yourself on Unit 3

(RAM: H = 1; C = 12; N = 14; O = 16; Cl = 35.5; Ag = 108; I = 127)

1. How would you show that an organic compound contained the following elements: carbon, hydrogen, nitrogen, chlorine and sulphur?

2. Distinguish between the empirical and molecular formulae of an organic compound.

3. Write an account summarizing the application of instrumental methods in the determination of the structural formula of an organic compound.

4. 0.025 92 g of pure aspirin—a compound containing carbon, hydrogen and oxygen only—yielded 0.057 02 g carbon dioxide and 0.010 37 g water on combustion. What is (a) the percentage composition and (b) the empirical formula?

5. 0.032 16 g of an organic compound, F, yielded 0.036 08 g of carbon dioxide and 0.011 07 g of water on combustion. 0.030 59 g of F yielded 0.055 91 g of silver chloride in a Carius determination. What is (a) the percentage composition and (b) the empirical formula of F?

6. The ammonia obtained from 0.304 4 g of a protein in a Kjeldahl determination was absorbed in 50.0 cm³ of hydrochloric acid (concentration, 0.100 0 mol HCl litre⁻¹). The unreacted acid required 22.2 cm³ of sodium hydroxide solution (concentration, 0.100 0 mol NaOH litre⁻¹) for neutralization. What is the percentage by weight of nitrogen in the protein?

7. 0.161 4 g of an iodomethane, G, yielded 0.288 9 g of silver iodide in a Carius determination. What is the percentage of iodine by weight in G?

8. 0.024 54 g of H (RMM = approximately 40) yielded 0.052 80 g of carbon dioxide and 0.016 20 g of water on combustion. 0.032 39 g of H in a Dumas determination yielded 8.85 cm³ of nitrogen (corrected to s.t.p.). Deduce the molecular formula of H and suggest possible structural formulae.

9. A carboxylic acid (RMM = 70) contains C, 51.44 per cent; H, 2.86 per cent. What is its structural formula?

10. A compound, I, contains C, 40.6 per cent; H, 8.47 per cent; N, 23.7 per cent. If the RMM of I is 59, calculate its molecular formula and suggest three possible structural formulae.

11. 0.021 24 g of J (RMM = approximately 60) yielded 0.047 52 g of carbon dioxide and 0.029 16 g of water on combustion. In a Dumas determination 0.036 45 g of J yielded 6.92 cm³ of nitrogen (corrected to s.t.p.). Deduce the molecular formula of J and suggest possible structural formulae.

12. Write balanced equations for the combustion of the following gaseous hydrocarbons: (a) ethane, (b) methane, (c) propene, (d) ethyne, (e) propyne, (f) butane, (g) ethene, (h) butene, (i) propane, (j) butyne.
    In each case calculate (i) the volume of oxygen required and (ii) the volume of carbon dioxide obtained from 12 cm³ of the hydrocarbon, assuming no change in temperature or pressure.

13. 7.2 cm³ of a gaseous hydrocarbon, K, were exploded with 50.2 cm³ of oxygen. After cooling to room temperature the volume of the gaseous products was 32.2 cm³, which contracted to 3.4 cm³ on treatment with potassium hydroxide. What is the molecular formula of K?

14. 8.0 cm³ of a gaseous hydrocarbon, L, were exploded with 54.0 cm³ of oxygen. The volume of the gaseous products after cooling to room temperature was 38.0 cm³, of which 6.0 cm³ remained after treatment with aqueous potassium hydroxide. What is the molecular formula of L? Suggest (and name) possible structural formulae.

15. 12 cm³ of a mixture of ethane and propane yielded 29.0 cm³ of carbon dioxide on combustion. What is the composition of the mixture?

16. 20 cm³ of a mixture of methane and propene yielded 36 cm³ of carbon dioxide on combustion. What is the composition of the mixture? What volume of oxygen is required for this combustion?

electrons pair in the orbitals. The electronic configurations of the elements boron to neon are thus:

Boron: $1s^2\,2s^2\,2p_x^1$
Carbon: $1s^2\,2s^2\,2p_x^1\,2p_y^1$
Nitrogen: $1s^2\,2s^2\,2p_x^1\,2p_y^1\,2p_z^1$
Oxygen: $1s^2\,2s^2\,2p_x^2\,2p_y^1\,2p_z^1$
Fluorine: $1s^2\,2s^2\,2p_x^2\,2p_y^2\,2p_z^1$
Neon: $1s^2\,2s^2\,2p_x^2\,2p_y^2\,2p_z^2$

When atoms react electrons are either transferred or shared to give electronic configurations in which each orbital is occupied by two electrons of opposite spin.

4.3 Molecular Orbitals

A *molecular orbital* is obtained when atomic orbitals containing unpaired electrons overlap to form a covalent bond. The two singly occupied atomic orbitals thus form one molecular orbital containing two electrons of opposite spins which extends over the nuclei of both atoms. The formation of the hydrogen molecule, for example, is represented diagrammatically in Fig. 4.3. Other examples of molecular orbitals are described in Unit 4.4.

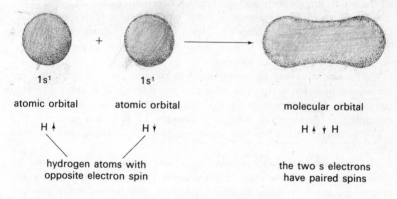

$1s^1$ $1s^1$

atomic orbital   atomic orbital   molecular orbital

H ↑   H ↓   H ↑ ↓ H

hydrogen atoms with
opposite electron spin   the two s electrons
                             have paired spins

Fig. 4.3 The hydrogen molecule

4.4 Hybridization and the Shapes of Organic Molecules

(a) The Carbon Atom

In virtually all its compounds carbon is tetravalent. The carbon atom (electronic configuration $1s^2 2s^2 2p_x^1 2p_y^1$) has only two unpaired electrons, the $2p_x^1$ and $2p_y^1$. When the carbon atom reacts, the paired 2s electrons in the ground-state or lowest-energy configuration become uncoupled, and one is *promoted* to the unfilled $2p_z$ orbital, thus giving four unpaired electrons:

2s	2p$_x$	2p$_y$	2p$_z$
↑↓	↑	↑	

Ground-state configura-
tion of carbon

2s	2p$_x$	2p$_y$	2p$_z$
↑	↑	↑	↑

Bonding configuration
of carbon

The energy required to promote this electron to a 2p orbital is small ($+405 \text{ kJ mol}^{-1}$) compared with that released in the formation of four covalent bonds (for example, $4 \times -435 = -1\,740 \text{ kJ mol}^{-1}$ for the formation of the four carbon–hydrogen bonds in methane).

(b) Saturated Carbon Compounds: sp³ Hybridization

In saturated compounds the unpaired $2s^1\ 2p_x^1\ 2p_y^1\ 2p_z^1$ electrons have *hybridized* to form four identical orbitals which are arranged tetrahedrally about the nucleus (Fig. 4.4). These orbitals can overlap with the 1s orbitals of four hydrogen atoms to form methane (Fig. 4.5).

The electronic charge in the molecular orbitals in the methane molecule is concentrated between the nuclei of the carbon and hydrogen atoms. Bonds of this type are known as σ (Greek letter, sigma) bonds. In methane all the bonds are identical and the four hydrogen atoms are arranged at the corners of a regular tetrahedron. Each bond angle is therefore 109°28′. Other saturated carbon compounds have a similar structure, although the bond angles may deviate slightly from the tetrahedral angle if the four substituent groups are not identical.

The atoms of other elements, such as oxygen and nitrogen, are sp³ hybridized in order to form the strongest possible bonds in their saturated compounds. The structures of the water and ammonia molecules, for example, are shown in Fig. 4.6, and in drawings of molecular models in Fig. 4.7. The oxygen atom has two unbonded pairs of electrons and nitrogen one.

The approximate shapes of most saturated organic molecules may be predicted from a knowledge of their bond angles. Drawings of models of the methanol, methoxymethane, propane and butane molecules are shown in Fig. 4.8.

Fig. 4.4   The tetrahedral sp³ hybridized orbitals of the carbon atom

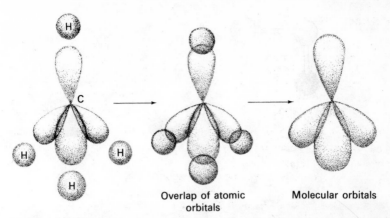

Fig. 4.5   *The structure of the methane molecule (the small lobes of the sp³ orbitals have been omitted for clarity's sake)*

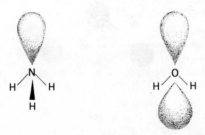

Fig. 4.6   *The structures of the molecules of ammonia and water*

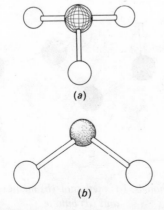

Fig. 4.7   *Molecular models: (a) ammonia and (b) water*

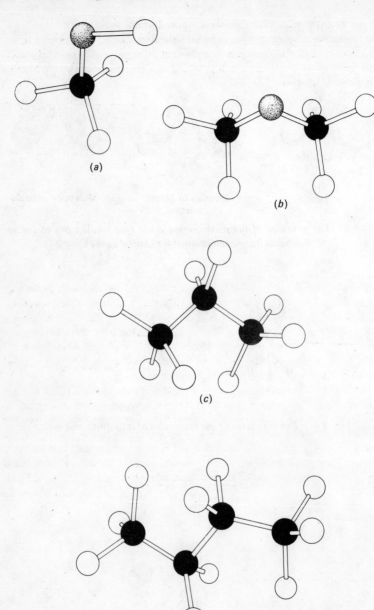

Fig. 4.8   Molecular models: (a) methanol, (b) methoxymethane, (c) propane
and (d) butane

(c) sp² Hybridization: the Carbon–Carbon Double Bond

The atomic orbitals of carbon can also hybridize to give three identical sp^2 orbitals arranged symmetrically in a plane at an angle of 120° to each other, with the remaining electron in a p orbital at right angles above and below this plane (Fig. 4.9).

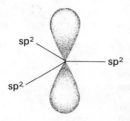

Fig. 4.9   The sp^2 hybridized orbitals of the carbon atom

In ethene (C_2H_4), for example, one of these sp^2 orbitals overlaps with an sp^2 orbital of a second carbon atom to form a σ bond. The other sp^2 orbitals of the two carbon atoms each overlaps with the 1s orbital of a hydrogen atom, to form four σ bonds. The 2p orbitals of the carbon atoms now overlap above and below the plane to form a π (Greek letter, pi) bond (Fig. 4.10). Carbon–oxygen ($>C{=}O$), carbon–nitrogen ($>C{=}N{-}$) and other double bonds are formed in the same way.

The two bonds (one σ and one π) making up the double bond are not equivalent to two single (σ) bonds. A σ bond is stronger than a π bond, as it is formed between the line of centres of the bonding atoms and greater orbital overlap is possible than in a π bond formed by lateral overlap of the p orbitals. A carbon–carbon double bond is both shorter and considerably stronger than a single bond, but it is not twice as strong. Typical bond dissociation energies (bond strengths) and bond lengths are listed in Table 4.2.

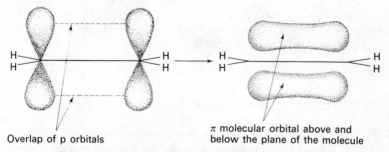

Overlap of p orbitals

π molecular orbital above and below the plane of the molecule

Fig. 4.10   Structure of the ethene molecule

Table 4.2 Bond lengths and bond dissociation energies

Bond	Compound	Bond length (nm)	Dissociation energy (kJ mol^{-1})
C—H	general	0.109	413
C—C	C_2H_6	0.154	345
C=C	C_2H_4	0.133	611
C≡C	C_2H_2	0.121	835
C—F	general	0.135	485
C—Cl	general	0.177	339
C—Br	general	0.191	285
C—I	general	0.214	215
C—N	CH_3NH_2	0.147	305
C=N	general	0.130	615
C≡N	HCN	0.116	890
C—O	CH_3OH	0.143	340
C=O	general	0.122	740
O—H	H_2O	0.096	464
N—H	NH_3	0.101	390

(d) sp^1 Hybridization: the Triple Bond

The hybrid formed from the 2s and one of the 2p orbitals consists of two identical co-linear sp^1 orbitals with lobes directed in diametrically opposite directions on either side of the nucleus. The two remaining unpaired electrons are in p orbitals (Fig. 4.11). In the ethyne molecule one of these sp^1 orbitals overlaps with an sp^1 orbital of the second carbon atom to form a

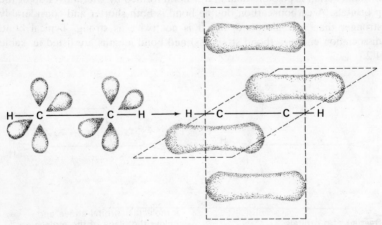

Fig. 4.11   *Structure of the ethyne molecule: the p orbitals overlap to give π bonds above, below and on either side of the linear molecule*

σ bond, while the two remaining sp^1 orbitals (one on each carbon atom) form σ bonds with hydrogen atoms. The unhybridized p orbitals overlap and two π bonds are obtained in planes at right angles above, below and on either side of the linear molecule. These π bonds draw the carbon atoms closer together, making the C≡C bond both shorter and stronger than the carbon–carbon double and single bonds (see Table 4.2).

(e) Rotation about Carbon–Carbon Bonds

In general, there is free rotation about a carbon–carbon and other single (σ) covalent bonds. In ethane, for example, the two methyl groups are able to turn freely about the axis between them and there is an infinite number of positions in which the hydrogen atoms on one carbon atom can be arranged relative to those of the second methyl group. Different arrangements of atoms within a molecule whose interconversion does not involve bond fission are known as *conformations*. The two extreme conformations in the ethane molecule—the *eclipsed* and *staggered conformations*—are shown in Figs. 4.12(a) and (c); Figs. 4.12(b) and (d) show the two conformations of the molecule viewed end-on along the line of the carbon–carbon bond.

The two conformations do not have the same energy. The hydrogen atoms in the two groups tend to repel one another and the staggered conformation, in which the separation of the hydrogen atoms is a maximum, is the more stable form. As the groups are rotated through an angle of 60° to the eclipsed form the potential energy increases to a maximum (see Fig. 4.13). The energy difference is approximately 12 kJ mol^{-1}. This is too small to allow the two conformations to be isolated as the energy from the thermal collisions of the molecules is sufficient to overcome this barrier and bring about interconversion of the two forms. Rotation about carbon–carbon single bonds is hindered, however, by the presence of large substituents on neighbouring groups. For example, two conformational isomers have been detected in 1,1,2,2-tetrabromoethane at low temperatures.

The barrier to rotation about carbon–carbon double bonds, on the other hand, is extremely high (c. 170 kJ mol^{-1} in ethene) and is too large to overcome except under very vigorous conditions. Alkenes substituted on

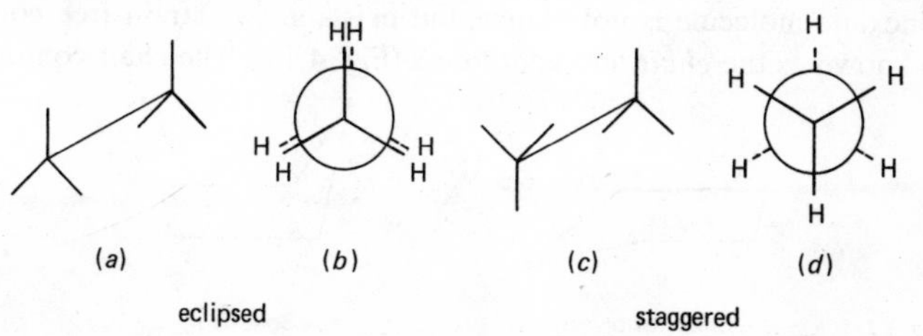

(a)   (b)   (c)   (d)

eclipsed   staggered

Fig. 4.12   *Eclipsed and staggered configurations of ethane*

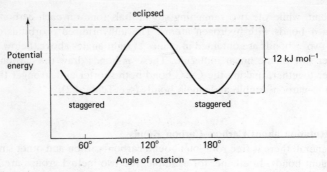

Fig. 4.13   *Potential energy changes for rotation about the carbon–carbon bond of ethane*

different sides of the double bond

A   H   A   H
 \   /   \   /
  C   C
  ‖   ‖
  C   C
 /   \   /   \
H   A   A   H

trans-isomer   *cis*-isomer

do not interconvert, but may be obtained as separate *geometrical isomers* (see Unit 19.2(*a*)).

(*f*) Saturated Cyclic Compounds

The angles between the bonds of an sp^3 hybridized carbon atom are 109°28′. Thus there is considerable strain in three- and four-membered ring structures, such as cyclopropane and cyclobutane, in which the bond angles for planar molecules are 60° and 90° respectively. This strain is reflected in the greater reactivity of these compounds compared with the higher cyclic alkanes.

CH_2
CH_2————CH_2
cyclopropane

CH_2—CH_2
| |
CH_2—CH_2
cyclobutane

Strain is minimized in larger rings by *puckering*. For example, the cyclohexane molecule is not planar, but exists in two strain-free conformations known as the *chair* and *boat forms* (Fig. 4.14). The chair conformation

Chair form   Boat form

Fig. 4.14   *Chair and boat conformations of cyclohexane*

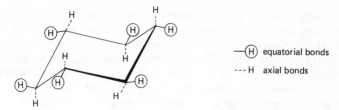

—(H) equatorial bonds

--- H axial bonds

Fig. 4.15   Cyclohexane axial and equatorial bonds

is markedly less crowded and is the more stable form. The energy difference between the two forms is too small to permit their separation, however, and they undergo rapid interconversion at room temperature by rotation of the carbon–carbon bonds.

In the chair form six of the hydrogen atoms are attached to the carbon atoms by bonds parallel to the ring. These bonds are known as the *axial bonds*, and the remaining six bonds (one to each carbon atom) are known as *equatorial bonds* (Fig. 4.15).

Ring structures also hinder rotation about carbon–carbon bonds, and 1,2-disubstituted cycloalkanes may be obtained in two geometrically isomeric forms (see Unit 19.2(*b*)).

4.5 Bond Fission and Formation

The covalent bond between two atoms may be broken in three possible ways (the bonding electrons being represented by dots):

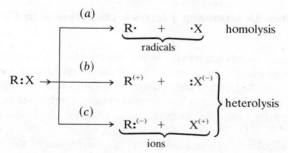

In (*a*) the two electrons of the bond are divided equally, one electron passing to R and one to X. This is known as *homolysis* or *homolytic fission* and the species obtained are highly reactive *free radicals* or *atoms*. Radical reactions and homolytic fission occur mainly in the gas phase or in non-polar solvents. They are initiated by light, especially ultra-violet light, and by the presence of peroxides. Examples of radical reactions are discussed in Units 5.5(*b*) and 7.6(*b*)(i).

In (b) and (c) unequal sharing of the electrons (*heterolysis* or *heterolytic fission*) gives rise to an *ion pair*. This process occurs mainly in solution where the resulting ions may be stabilized by solvation, particularly with polar solvents such as water. The charge on the ions may also be stabilized by *delocalization*, that is, by spreading it over a part or the whole of the molecule by *inductive* and *mesomeric* effects (see Unit 4.6). Ions in which the positive or negative charge is localized on the carbon atom are known as *carbonium ions* and *carbanions* respectively.

Covalent bonds are formed by the reverse of these processes, by the combination either of free radicals,

$$CH_3\cdot + \cdot CH_3 \longrightarrow CH_3CH_3$$

$$\underbrace{}_{\text{methyl radicals}} \qquad \text{ethane}$$

or of oppositely charged ions:

$$\underset{\substack{\text{1,1-dimethylethyl}\\ \text{cation}}}{CH_3-\overset{\overset{\displaystyle CH_3}{|}}{\underset{\underset{\displaystyle CH_3}{|}}{C^+}}} + \underset{\substack{\text{chloride}\\ \text{anion}}}{Cl^-} \longrightarrow \underset{\text{2-chloro-2-methylpropane}}{CH_3-\overset{\overset{\displaystyle CH_3}{|}}{\underset{\underset{\displaystyle CH_3}{|}}{C}}-Cl}$$

Carbonium ions, carbanions and radicals are too reactive to exist in large concentrations for any length of time. Their presence as transient intermediates is important in the mechanisms of many chemical reactions, however, as they provide a route for the transformation of the reactant molecules into molecules of the reaction products.

4.6 Factors Determining Electron Distribution in Covalent Bonds

While covalent bonds are formed by the sharing of electrons between two atoms, this sharing is rarely equal. One of the atoms forming the bond is generally associated with a higher electron density than the other. These regions of relatively high and low electron density, represented by $\delta -$ and $\delta +$ respectively, give the molecule as a whole a *dipole moment* (see Fig. 4.16).

The principal effects which determine the distribution of the electronic charge in a covalent bond are the *inductive effect*, the *inductomeric effect* and *mesomerism*; we shall discuss these one by one.

(a) Inductive Effect

If the two atoms forming the bond have different electronegativities (as with carbon and chlorine in a chloroalkane), then one (in this example the chlorine atom) will have a greater share of the electrons and hence a higher electron density than the other. This is known as the *inductive effect* and is

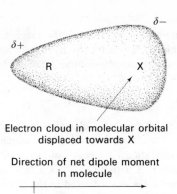

Electron cloud in molecular orbital
displaced towards X

Direction of net dipole moment
in molecule

Fig. 4.16   The dipole moment of a molecule R—X

generally indicated by an arrow showing the direction of displacement of the electronic charge:

$$\overset{\delta +}{\underset{}{-}}\overset{}{C} \longrightarrow \overset{\delta -}{Cl}$$

This effect can be transmitted from one carbon atom to the next in a chain as the electron-deficient ($\delta +$) carbon atom attracts the electrons in the σ bond linking it to the next carbon atom:

$$C \text{——} C \overset{\delta\delta\delta +}{\longrightarrow} C \overset{\delta\delta +}{\longrightarrow} C \overset{\delta +}{\longrightarrow} C \overset{\delta -}{\longrightarrow} Cl$$

where $\delta +$, $\delta\delta +$, $\delta\delta\delta +$ indicate diminishing effects. The effect is usually negligible after the second carbon atom.

Atoms such as halogens and groups such as nitro-, —CHO or —CHCl$_3$ groups, which attract the bonding electrons more strongly than does the hydrogen atom, are said to have a $-I$ or *electron-withdrawing effect*. Alkyl groups have the opposite effect:

$$\begin{array}{c} \overset{\delta +}{CH_3} \\ H_3C \overset{\delta +}{\longrightarrow} \overset{\delta -}{C} \longrightarrow \\ \underset{\delta +}{CH_3} \end{array}$$

and are *electron-releasing* compared with hydrogen and thus have a $+I$ effect.

The inductive effect is a permanent one, and the presence of a dipole in the molecule influences such physical properties as boiling-point, melting-point, and acid or basic strength (see Units 16.5(a) and 18.5(a)), as well as the rate of reaction and site of attack by reactant molecules.

(b) **Inductomeric Effect**

This effect occurs only on the approach of the reagent. A chloroalkane, for example, is susceptible to attack by the hydroxide ion which is attracted towards the electron-deficient carbon atom attached to the chlorine:

$$HO^- \cdots\cdots\rightarrow \overset{\delta+}{CH_3}\rightarrow\overset{\delta-}{Cl}$$

The approach of the anion repels the electrons in the carbon–chlorine bond towards the chlorine atom, thus increasing the inductive effect and aiding the reaction. This polarization disappears and the electrons return to their ground state if the anion is withdrawn. It is a time-variable effect; it can only help the reaction and is not reflected in the physical properties of the molecule.

(c) **Mesomerism (Resonance)**

The *mesomeric* (or +M or −M) effect denotes the shift of π electrons in multiple bonds and is analogous to the inductive effect in single bonds. In the carbonyl group, for example, the oxygen atom has a higher electron density than the carbon owing to polarization of the double bond:

$$\text{C}{=}\text{O}, \qquad \text{that is,} \qquad \text{C}{=}\text{O}$$

The curved arrow indicates the direction in which the electron pair moves. This structure may be represented as a *resonance hybrid* of the following *canonical forms*:

$$\text{C}{=}\text{O} \longleftrightarrow \overset{(+)}{\text{C}}{-}\overset{(-)}{\text{O}}$$

The double-headed arrow indicates that the actual structure is intermediate between the structures of the canonical forms, that is:

$$\overset{\delta+}{\text{C}}{\cdots}\overset{\delta-}{\text{O}}$$

where $\cdots$ represents a partial double bond. Canonical forms are not in equilibrium—the actual structure does not oscillate between them—but each makes some contribution to it.

Mesomerism is fairly common in organic chemistry and plays an important part in the structure and stability of many compounds and reactive intermediates, such as carbonium ions and carbanions. For example, the carboxylate anion is a resonance hybrid:

In this anion the two carbon–oxygen bonds are identical (0.127 nm) and are intermediate in length between the single and double bond (the values for C—O and C=O are 0.143 nm and 0.122 nm respectively). The π orbital covers *both* carbon–oxygen bonds (Fig. 16.1) and may be written as:

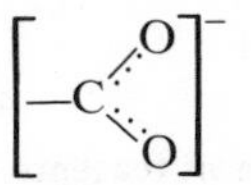

$$\left[-C\underset{\diagdown O}{\overset{\diagup O}{\diagdown}} \right]^{-}$$

Resonance or delocalization stabilization is particularly powerful when, as in this instance, the canonical forms are of equal energy and there is no charge separation to confer opposite charges on different parts of the molecule (*cf.* benzene, discussed in Unit 9.5).

(d) Electromeric Effect

The electromeric effect is a temporary reversible polarization of a multiple bond produced on the approach of the reagent and has the effect of increasing the reaction rate (*cf.* inductive and inductomeric effects, which apply to single covalent bonds):

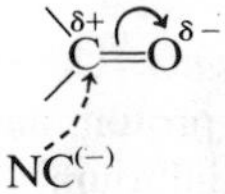

$$\underset{/}{\overset{\diagdown}{C}}\overset{\delta+}{=}\overset{\delta-}{O}$$

$NC^{(-)}$ approach of anion to electron-deficient carbon atom enhances mesomeric effect

This electromeric effect is also important in aromatic compounds as it governs the ease and position of substitution of halogeno-, hydroxy-, amino- and other monosubstituted benzene derivatives (see Unit 9.9).

(e) Conjugation

The conjugative effect applies to systems containing alternate double and single bonds. Buta-1,3-diene, CH_2=CHCH=CH$_2$, for example, is more stable than would be expected from its structure. The reason is that the two double bonds are not isolated and there is a partial overlap of the p orbitals over all four carbon atoms, thus extending the π bond over the whole molecule and conferring some double bond character to the central carbon–carbon bond (Fig. 4.17).

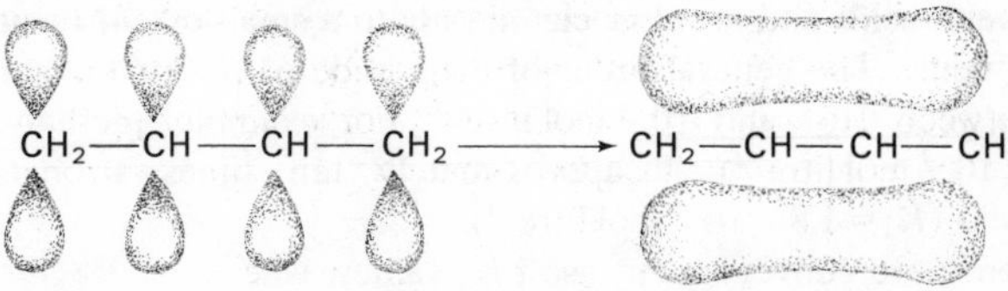

Fig. 4.17   Structure of the buta-1,3-diene molecule

4.7 Classification of Reagents

Reagents are classed as either *electrophiles* or *nucleophiles* depending on whether they attack regions of relative higher electron density ($\delta -$) or electron deficiency ($\delta +$) respectively. Examples of both classes are listed in Table 4.3.

Table 4.3 Classification of reagents

Electrophiles	Nucleophiles
H^+, H_3O^+, D^+	F^-, Cl^-, Br^-, I^-
$Br^{\delta +}$ or Br^+	OH^-, OR^-, NH_2^-
NO_2^+, HSO_3^+, SO_3	NH_3, NHR, NR_2 etc.
R^+ or $R^{\delta +}, RCO^+$	$CN^-, NO_2^-, RCO_2^-, HSO_3^-$
ArN_2^+	BH_4^-, AlH_4^-, H^-

4.8 Acids and Bases

The Bronsted Theory defines an *acid* as a *proton donor*. The strength of an acid is thus a measure of its readiness to donate a proton, and in aqueous solution it is determined by the position of the equilibrium:

$$HY \; + \; H_2O \rightleftharpoons H_3O^+_{(aq)} \; + \; Y^-_{(aq)}$$
$$\text{acid}$$

or,

$$HY_{(aq)} \rightleftharpoons H^+_{(aq)} \; + \; Y^-_{(aq)}$$

The magnitude of the equilibrium constant for this reaction provides information about the concentration of hydrated protons in solution (represented in the first equation as oxonium or hydroxonium ions, H_3O^+) and hence of the degree of ionization of the acid, HY. The acid dissociation constant, K_a, is defined as

$$K_a = \frac{[H^+_{(aq)}][Y^-_{(aq)}]}{[HY_{(aq)}]}$$

and is a constant for a particular acid at a given temperature. Most organic acids are weak acids and are dissociated only to a small extent (usually less than 2 per cent). The general order of magnitude of K_a for the carboxylic acids is between 10^{-6} and 10^{-4} mol litre^{-1}. For example, methanoic acid ($K_a = 1.8 \times 10^{-4}$ mol litre^{-1}) is approximately ten times stronger than ethanoic acid ($K_a = 1.8 \times 10^{-5}$ mol litre^{-1}).

It is often more convenient to use pK_a values, where

$$pK_a = -\log K_a$$

as these do not involve the negative powers of numbers: the higher the value of K_a, the stronger the acid and the smaller the value of pK_a.

Similarly, a base is defined as a *proton acceptor*:

$$\text{B} \quad + \quad H_2O \rightleftharpoons BH^+_{(aq)} \quad + \quad OH^-_{(aq)}$$

base

and the dissociation constant of a base, K_b, is defined as

$$K_b = \frac{[BH^+_{(aq)}][OH^-_{(aq)}]}{[B_{(aq)}]},$$

and

$$pK_b = -\log K_b$$

The relationship between a compound's structure and its relative strength as an acid or base is discussed in Units 16.5(*a*) and 18.5(*a*).

4.9 Classification of Reactions

The reactions of organic compounds may be divided into four main types: *substitution* (or *displacement*), *addition*, *elimination* and *rearrangement*. Examples of the four classes include:

(*a*) The *substitution* of hydrogen atoms in alkanes or aromatic hydrocarbons by halogen atoms:

$$CH_4 + Cl_2 \xrightarrow[\text{u.v. light}]{\text{heat or}} CH_3Cl + HCl$$

methane   chloromethane

and the hydrolysis of chloromethane to methanol (see Unit 10.6(*a*)(i)).

(*b*) The *addition* of hydrogen to a multiple bond:

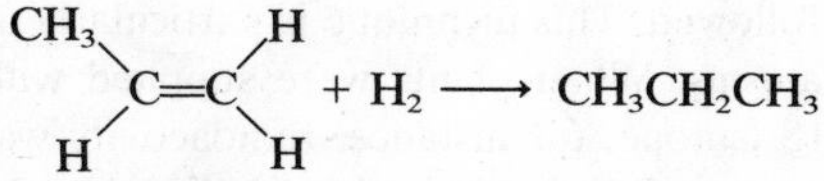

propene   propane

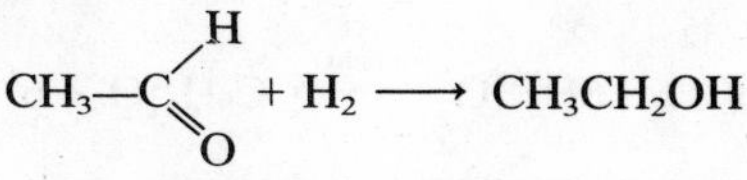

ethanal   ethanol

(*c*) The *elimination* of bromine from 1,2-dibromoethane to form ethene:

$$CH_2BrCH_2Br + Zn \xrightarrow{\text{heat}} CH_2{=}CH_2 + ZnBr_2$$

1,2-dibromoethane   ethene

(d) The *rearrangement* (*isomerization*) of alkanes on heating with aluminium chloride:

$$CH_3CH_2CH_2CH_3 \xrightarrow{AlCl_3/300°} CH_3\overset{\overset{\displaystyle CH_3}{|}}{C}HCH_3$$

butane   2-methylpropane

Occasionally an addition reaction is accompanied by the elimination of a small molecule such as water or ammonia; for example, ethanal forms an oxime on treatment with hydroxylamine with the elimination of water (see Units 15.5 and 15.6(b)):

$$CH_3C\overset{\displaystyle H}{\underset{\displaystyle O}{\big<}} + H_2NOH \longrightarrow \left[CH_3-\overset{\overset{\displaystyle H}{|}}{\underset{\underset{\displaystyle NHOH}{|}}{C}}-OH \right] \xrightarrow[H_2O]{\text{elimination of}} CH_3CH{=}N{-}OH$$

ethanal   hydroxylamine   unstable addition   ethanal oxime
                                compound
                            (an intermediate)

Such a process is known as a *condensation reaction*.

4.10 Isotopic Labelling

Atoms of isotopes differ in mass but have the same atomic number; they thus have the same number of protons but different numbers of neutrons. As the chemical properties of an element are determined by the electronic configuration of its atoms, the replacement of certain atoms in an organic molecule by their isotopes does not alter the compound's chemistry, though there may be changes in reaction rates owing to the difference in atomic mass. The less-common isotopes may therefore be used to *label* parts of a molecule. By analysing the products to determine the position of the isotopic label, the path taken by a particular group or atom in a sequence of reactions may be followed. This technique is particularly useful in the study of reaction mechanisms. When plants were supplied with water enriched with the oxygen-18 isotope, for instance, radioactivity was detected in the liberated oxygen rather than in their tissues, showing that this oxygen is derived from the water and not from the carbon dioxide:

$$6CO_2 + 6H_2{}^{18}O \xrightarrow{sunlight} C_6H_{12}O_6 + 6{}^{18}O_2$$

Isotopic labelling was also used to determine the position of bond fission in ester hydrolysis (see Unit 17.5(d)).

Studies of reaction mechanisms use both stable isotopes such as deuterium, nitrogen-15 and oxygen-18, and radio-isotopes such as tritium, carbon-14, chlorine-36 and sulphur-35. Isotopic labels may be detected by mass spectrometry, by density measurement or by spectroscopy; radioactive isotopes, however, are most easily traced using a Geiger–Müller counter.

Test Yourself on Unit 4

1. Indicate which of the values A to E

$$A = 60°; B = 90°; C = 110°; D = 120°; E = 180°$$

is closest to the appropriate bond angle in the following compounds:
   (a) Cl—C—C in C_2Cl_4;
   (b) (i) H—C—H and (ii) C—C—C in $CH_3C{\equiv}CH$;
   (c) O—C—O in CO_2;
   (d) Cl—C—Cl in $COCl_2$;
   (e) (i) O—C—N and (ii) H—N—H in CH_3CONH_2;
   (f) C—C—C in (i) cyclobutane, (ii) cyclopropane and (iii) cyclopentane.

2. Arrange the following acids in order of increasing strength: A, methanoic acid ($K_a = 1.7 \times 10^{-4}$); B, phenol ($K_a = 1.05 \times 10^{-10}$); C, ethanoic acid ($K_a = 1.8 \times 10^{-5}$).

3. Arrange the following bases in order of increasing strength: A, NH_3 ($pK_b = 4.74$); B, $C_6H_5NH_2$ ($pK_b = 9.38$); C, $(CH_3)_3N$ ($pK_b = 4.20$); D, CH_3NH_2 ($pK_b = 3.36$); E, $C_6H_5NHCH_3$ ($pK_b = 9.15$).

4. Calculate the pK_b value for ethylamine ($K_b = 5.4 \times 10^{-4}$ mol litre^{-1}).

5. Classify the following reactions:

(a) $(CH_3)_2CO + HCN \longrightarrow (CH_3)_2C{\bigg\langle}{\substack{OH \\ CN}}$

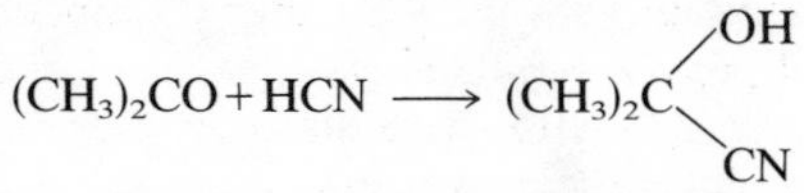

(b) $Cl_2 + CH_3CO_2H \longrightarrow ClCH_2CO_2H + HCl$

(c) $CH_3CH_2OH \longrightarrow CH_2{=}CH_2 + H_2O$

(d) $3CH_3COCH_3 \longrightarrow$ $+ 3H_2O$

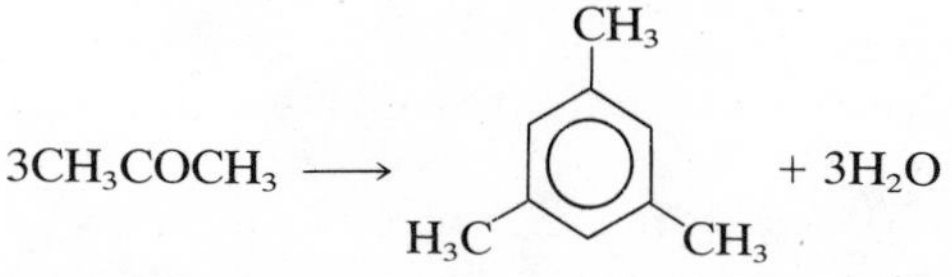

Indicate whether the statements in Questions 6–12 are true or false.

6. A carbon–carbon double bond is twice as strong as a carbon–carbon single bond.

7. Degenerate orbitals have identical energies.

8. Although the carbon atom has only *two* unpaired electrons it achieves greater stability in forming *four* covalent bonds.

9. The order of strength of the carbon–halogen bond is C—F > C—Cl > C—Br > C—I.

10. The C—C—C bond angle in cyclohexane is 120° as the molecule is a regular hexagon.

11. The structures of alkenes and alkynes make them susceptible to electrophilic attack.

12. Bromine can act both as an electrophile and as a nucleophile.

13. Carbonium ions are formed by the homolysis of a carbon–carbon σ bond.

14. Compounds whose molecules possess a dipole moment tend to be highly volatile.

15. The two carbon–oxygen bonds in the ethanoate anion,

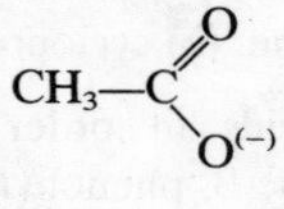

$$CH_3-C{\overset{\textstyle O}{\underset{\textstyle O^{(-)}}{<}}}$$

are of equal length.

Unit Five

Alkanes

5.1 General Formula and Nomenclature

The alkanes are the simplest of the organic compounds: they are saturated hydrocarbons, that is, they contain only carbon–carbon and carbon–hydrogen single bonds. The general formula of the alkanes is $C_n H_{2n+2}$.

The names and formulae of the first members of the homologous series are given in Table 1.1 (in Unit 1.4(a)(i)) and their boiling-points and melting-points are summarized in Fig. 1.4. Branched-chain alkanes are named as alkyl derivatives of the alkane with the longest possible carbon chain; for example, the following isomers of pentane (C_5H_{12})

$$CH_3-\underset{\underset{H}{|}}{\overset{\overset{CH_3}{|}}{C}}-CH_2-CH_3 \quad \text{and} \quad CH_3-\underset{\underset{CH_3}{|}}{\overset{\overset{CH_3}{|}}{C}}-CH_3$$

are 2-methylbutane (not 2-ethylpropane) and 2,2-dimethylpropane respectively. The tridecane $(C_{13}H_{28})$

$$CH_3-\overset{6}{C}H-\overset{5}{C}H_2-\overset{4}{C}H-\overset{3}{C}H_2-\overset{2}{C}-\overset{1}{C}H_3$$

is named as an octane derivative, as the longest chain in the structure includes the two carbon atoms of the ethyl group on carbon atom 6. The substituent groups are listed in alphabetical order, irrespective of the number of each in the molecule, and the carbon atoms in the chain are numbered in the direction that gives the lowest numbers to the positions of the substituents. Thus this compound is 4-ethyl-2,2,6-trimethyloctane, rather than 5-ethyl-3,7,7-trimethyloctane.

The carbon atoms in alkanes, as in other organic compounds, are classified according to the number of other carbon atoms that are attached to them. A carbon atom which is attached to only one other is classified as a *primary* (1°) carbon atom; while *secondary* (2°) and *tertiary* (3°) carbon atoms are attached to two and three other carbon atoms respectively. For example, 2-methylbutane contains one secondary, one tertiary and three primary carbon atoms:

$$\underset{\underset{1°}{CH_3}-\underset{2°}{CH_2}-\underset{3°}{CH}-\underset{1°}{CH_3}}{\overset{\overset{1° CH_3}{|}}{}}$$

Hydrogen, nitrogen and halogen atoms are classified according to the type of carbon atom to which they are attached (see, for instance, Unit 10.1).

5.2 Methods of Preparation

Owing to their ready availability from natural gas and petroleum (see Unit 6.3) it is rarely necessary to prepare alkanes; the following preparations are, however, of interest:

(a) From Alkenes

In the *Sabatier–Senderens reduction* a mixture of the alkene and hydrogen is passed under pressure over a nickel catalyst at 200–300°:

$$C_nH_{2n} + H_2 \xrightarrow[\text{pressure}]{\text{Ni}/200-300°} C_nH_{2n+2}$$

alkene   alkane

Other catalysts may be used for this reaction. When *Raney nickel* is used, the hydrogenation can often be carried out at room temperature and atmospheric pressure; the catalyst is prepared by dissolving away the aluminium in a nickel–aluminium alloy with aqueous sodium hydroxide, leaving a residue of powdered nickel. Like many of the reactions, methods and reagents in organic chemistry, it is named after its discoverer. Other suitable catalysts include finely divided platinum (known as *platinum black*), palladium and mixtures of platinum black and platinum oxide (*Adams' catalyst*).

The extremely large surface area of these metal catalysts is important, as they act by adsorbing the reactant molecules on their surface. This brings the alkene and hydrogen molecules close together and enables bonds to be broken and rearranged to form the alkane (Fig. 5.1). Alkenes are readily adsorbed via their π bonds, but alkane molecules have little affinity for the metal and immediately leave the surface free to adsorb further molecules of the alkene and hydrogen.

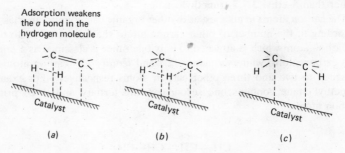

Fig. 5.1   Catalytic hydrogenation of alkenes

Hydrogenation is an exothermic process; for instance,

$$CH_2{=}CH_2 + H_2 \rightarrow C_2H_6 \quad (\Delta H = -124\ kJ\ mol^{-1})$$
$$\text{ethene} \qquad\qquad\quad \text{ethane}$$

(b) From Halogenoalkanes

A dissolving metal, such as zinc in ethanoic or hydrochloric acid or a zinc–copper couple in aqueous alcohol, will reduce a halogenoalkane to an alkane. The metal provides the electrons required for the reduction:

$$Zn \rightarrow Zn^{2+} + 2e$$
$$R{-}X + e \rightarrow R{\cdot} + X^-$$
$$R{\cdot} + e \rightarrow R{:}^{(-)} \xrightarrow{H^+} R{-}H$$

Yields are generally high (between 70 and 90 per cent). The zinc–copper couple is prepared by treating metallic zinc with an aqueous solution of copper(II) sulphate to coat part of it with copper:

$$Zn_{(s)} + Cu^{2+}_{(aq)} \rightarrow Zn^{2+}_{(aq)} + Cu_{(s)}$$

Halogenoalkanes may also be reduced to alkanes using lithium tetrahydridoaluminate(III), $LiAlH_4$ (lithium aluminium hydride), or by catalytic hydrogenation in alkaline solution with a palladium–carbon catalyst:

$$R{-}X + H_2 \xrightarrow[Pd/C]{NaOH} R{-}H + NaX$$

The Wurtz synthesis. A solution of a halogenoalkane (preferably the bromo- or iodo-derivative) in anhydrous ethoxyethane is treated with sodium:

$$2R{-}I + 2Na \xrightarrow{\text{ethoxyethane}} R{-}R + 2NaI$$
$$\text{alkane}$$

The Wurtz synthesis is most suitable for the preparation of higher alkanes containing an even number of carbon atoms. Although alkanes containing an odd number of carbon atoms may be prepared using a mixture of two different halogenoalkanes, as, for example:

$$CH_3I + 2Na + C_2H_5I \xrightarrow{\text{ethoxyethane}} CH_3CH_2CH_3 + 2NaI$$
$$\text{propane}$$

yields are low owing to the formation of ethane, CH_3CH_3, and butane, $C_2H_5C_2H_5$, as by-products.

(c) From Grignard Reagents

A Grignard reagent is an alkylmagnesium(II) halide or an aryl analogue, RMgX or ArMgX (see Unit 10.6(c)(iii)). An alkylmagnesium(II) halide yields an alkane on treatment with aqueous hydrochloric or sulphuric acid:

$$RMgX + H_2O \xrightarrow{H^+_{(aq)}} R\!-\!H + MgX(OH)$$

or by the action of a halogenoalkane:

$$RMgX + R'\!-\!I \xrightarrow[\text{ethoxyethane}]{\text{anhyd.}} R\!-\!R' + MgI_2$$

(d) Kolbe Electrolysis

When an aqueous solution of the sodium or potassium salt of an aliphatic acid is electrolysed, hydrogen is evolved at the cathode and a mixture of an alkane and carbon dioxide at the anode:

$$2RCO_2^-K^+ + 2H_2O \xrightarrow{\text{electrolysis}} \underbrace{R\!-\!R + 2CO_2}_{\text{at anode}} + \underbrace{2KOH + H_2}_{\text{at cathode}}$$

The reaction involves the formation of a free radical as the alkanoate ion is discharged at the anode:

$$RCO_2^- \;\rightarrow\; RCO_2\!\cdot + e$$
$$RCO_2\!\cdot \;\rightarrow\; R\!\cdot + CO_2$$

The alkyl radicals then dimerize to yield the alkane:

$$2R\!\cdot \;\rightarrow\; R\!-\!R$$

Some ester is also formed by combination of the alkyl and alkanoate radicals,

$$RCO_2\!\cdot + R\!\cdot \;\rightarrow\; RCO_2R$$
$$\text{ester}$$

(e) From Carbonyl Compounds

Ketones are reduced to the corresponding alkanes by the action of zinc amalgam and concentrated hydrochloric acid:

$$\underset{\text{ketone}}{RCOR'} \xrightarrow[\text{(Zn/Hg—HCl)}]{e,\,H^+_{(aq)}} \underset{\text{alkane}}{RCH_2R'}$$

This reaction is known as the *Clemmensen reduction*. Aldehydes (RCHO) react in the same way but the yield of alkane is considerably lower.

The carbonyl group may also be reduced by heating the aldehyde or ketone (or, equally, a carboxylic acid) with concentrated hydriodic acid in the presence of red phosphorus:

$$CH_3COCH_3 \xrightarrow[150°]{red\ P/HI} CH_3CH_2CH_3$$

propanone   propane

$$RCO_2H \xrightarrow[200°]{red\ P/HI} RCH_3$$

alkane

5.3 Preparation of Methane

Methane cannot be prepared by the reactions in Units 5.2(a), (d) and (e), because the molecule only contains one carbon atom; the other general methods do, however, apply. Methane may be prepared in the laboratory by:

Hydrolysis of aluminium carbide:

$$Al_4C_3 + 12HCl_{(aq)} \rightarrow 4AlCl_{3(aq)} + 3CH_4$$

Decarboxylation of sodium ethanoate with soda-lime:

$$CH_3CO_2Na + \text{'NaOH'} \xrightarrow{heat} CH_4 + Na_2CO_3$$

sodium   soda-   meth-
ethanoate   lime   ane

Soda-lime is quicklime (CaO) slaked with aqueous sodium hydroxide. It is a solid which behaves like sodium hydroxide, but has the advantages of a higher melting-point and that it is not deliquescent. Other sodium carboxylates react similarly with soda-lime, but the yields of alkane are low.

5.4 Physical Properties of Alkanes

Methane (b.p. −162°), ethane (b.p. −89°), propane (b.p. −42°) and butane (b.p. −0.5°) are colourless, odourless gases at room temperature. The boiling-points of the unbranched-chain alkanes increase steadily throughout the homologus series (see Fig. 1.4(a)). The alkanes from pentane (b.p. 36°) to $C_{17}H_{36}$ are colourless liquids at ordinary temperatures, while the higher homologues are waxy solids with a density of approximately 0.79 g cm^{-3}. Branched-chain isomers are more volatile than the corresponding unbranched compounds. Other physical properties of the alkanes (such as viscosity) also vary uniformly with molecular mass. They are insoluble in water (except methane, which is slightly soluble), but dissolve readily in non-polar solvents such as benzene and ethoxyethane.

5.5 Reactions of Alkanes

The alkanes are relatively unreactive chemically; the term 'paraffins', formerly the generic name of the alkanes, is derived from the Latin words *parum affinis* meaning 'little affinity'. Alkalis, acids and oxidizing agents such as potassium manganate(VII) or dichromate(VI) have no effect at room temperature. But since petroleum, which is a mixture of alkanes, is the source of about 90 per cent of all manufactured organic chemicals, the few reactions which the alkanes do undergo are of great importance.

(a) Combustion

The alkanes burn readily in an excess of air or oxygen to form carbon dioxide and water. The combustion proceeds via a high-temperature free-radical mechanism. The reaction is highly exothermic (hence the use of natural gas and the higher alkanes as fuels); for example:

$$CH_4 + 2O_2 \rightarrow CO_2 + 2H_2O_{(l)} \quad (\Delta H = -890 \text{ kJ mol}^{-1})$$
$$C_3H_8 + 5O_2 \rightarrow 3CO_2 + 4H_2O_{(l)} \quad (\Delta H = -2\,220 \text{ kJ mol}^{-1})$$

Methane burns with a non-luminous flame, but the larger the number of carbon atoms (and hence the percentage carbon content) in an alkane molecule, the more luminous is its flame. Carbon monoxide and carbon black (soot) are formed when alkanes burn in a limited amount of air.

(b) Halogenation

Alkanes do not react when mixed with chlorine or bromine in the dark at room temperature. If, however, the mixture is heated to 300–400° or is irradiated by ultra-violet light with a wavelength of about 300 nm, or if a suitable catalyst is present, the hydrogen atoms in the alkane are successively replaced by chlorine (or bromine) atoms to yield a mixture of halogenated alkanes. For example,

$$\underset{\text{methane}}{CH_4} + Cl_2 \rightarrow \underset{\text{chloromethane}}{CH_3Cl} + HCl$$

$$CH_3Cl + Cl_2 \rightarrow \underset{\text{dichloromethane}}{CH_2Cl_2} + HCl$$

$$CH_2Cl_2 + Cl_2 \rightarrow \underset{\text{trichloromethane}}{CHCl_3} + HCl$$

$$CHCl_3 + Cl_2 \rightarrow \underset{\text{tetrachloromethane}}{CCl_4} + HCl$$

Tetrachloromethane is the major product when the reaction is carried out using an excess of chlorine, while chloromethane predominates if an excess of methane is used.

The reaction proceeds via a free-radical mechanism. The substitution is strongly exothermic:

$$CH_4 + Cl_2 \rightarrow CH_3Cl + HCl \ (\Delta H = -100 \text{ kJ mol}^{-1})$$

and is initiated by the homolytic fission of the chlorine molecule by the action of heat or the absorption of radiation energy of ultra-violet light:

(i) $$Cl:Cl \xrightarrow[\text{light energy (h}\nu)]{\text{heat or}} Cl\cdot + \cdot Cl$$

(*thermal* or *photochemical*
initiation step)

Radiation of wavelength 300 nm has an energy of about $400\,kJ\,mol^{-1}$, which is more than enough to break the chlorine–chlorine bond (dissociation energy = $242\,kJ\,mol^{-1}$). The highly reactive chlorine atoms abstract hydrogen atoms from methane to form hydrogen chloride and methyl radicals:

(ii) $$Cl\cdot + CH_4 \rightarrow CH_3\cdot + HCl$$

This propagates the so-called *chain reaction* as the methyl radical can react with a chlorine molecule to form chloromethane and another free chlorine atom:

(iii) $$CH_3\cdot + Cl_2 \rightarrow CH_3Cl + Cl\cdot$$

Similar *chain-propagation steps* are repeated to yield CH_2Cl_2, $CHCl_3$ and CCl_4:

(iv) $$CH_3Cl + Cl\cdot \rightarrow \cdot CHCl_2 + HCl$$

(v) $$\cdot CHCl_2 + Cl_2 \rightarrow CHCl_3 + Cl\cdot$$

The chains are terminated when free radicals combine with each other:

(vi) $$Cl\cdot + \cdot Cl + Q \rightarrow Cl_2 + Q$$

(vii) $$Cl\cdot + \cdot CH_3 \rightarrow CH_3Cl$$

(viii) $$CH_3\cdot + \cdot CH_3 \rightarrow C_2H_6$$

The combination of the highly energetic chlorine atoms in (vi) takes place with the evolution of an enormous amount of energy. The presence of a 'third body', Q, is necessary to dissipate this energy, as otherwise the newly formed chlorine molecule breaks up at once. Q can be any of the other molecules present in the system (reactants or products), traces of impurities or the walls of the container.

Fluorination proceeds by a similar mechanism, but as the reaction takes place with explosive violence, the methane is usually diluted with an inert gas such as nitrogen. Iodination is reversible:

$$CH_4 + I_2 \rightleftharpoons CH_3I + HI$$

and requires the presence of an oxidizing agent (such as nitric acid, HNO_3, or iodic(v) acid, HIO_3) to remove the hydrogen iodide as it is formed in order to displace the equilibrium to the right:

$$5HI + HIO_3 \rightarrow 3H_2O + 3I_2$$

(c) **Nitration**

The alkanes react with concentrated nitric acid in the vapour phase at 150–450° to form nitro-compounds; for instance:

$$CH_4 + HNO_3 \rightarrow CH_3NO_2 + H_2O$$
$$\text{nitromethane}$$
$$\text{b.p. } 101°$$

The mechanism involves the participation of free radicals, and the higher alkanes yield a mixture of isomeric nitroalkanes and, especially at higher temperatures, of chain-fission products; for example:

$$CH_3CH_2CH_3 \xrightarrow[400°]{HNO_3} CH_3CH_2CH_2NO_2 + CH_3\underset{\underset{NO_2}{|}}{C}HCH_3 + C_2H_5NO_2 + CH_3NO_2$$

The nitroalkanes are colourless, pleasant-smelling liquids, which are used in industry as solvents for plastics, resins and dyes. Nitromethane is also used as a fuel for racing cars and other high-performance vehicles.

(d) **Cracking**

See Unit 6.6.

5.6 Cycloalkanes

Cycloalkanes (see Unit 4.4(f)) have the general formula C_nH_{2n}, and are isomeric with the alkenes. Their boiling-points are 10 to 20° higher than those of the corresponding alkanes. Their chemical and physical properties are similar to those of the acyclic compounds, except that cyclopropane and cyclobutane are slightly more reactive than propane and butane owing to strain in the ring system and are able to form addition products by *ring fission*; for example:

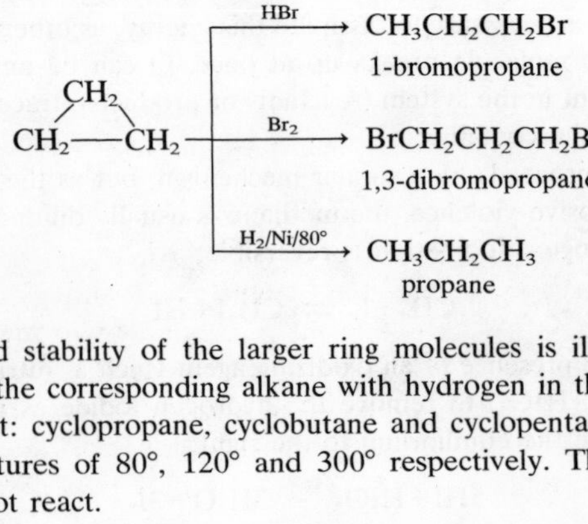

$$
\begin{array}{c}
CH_2 \\
CH_2{-}CH_2
\end{array}
\left\{
\begin{array}{ll}
\xrightarrow{HBr} & CH_3CH_2CH_2Br \\
& \text{1-bromopropane} \\
\xrightarrow{Br_2} & BrCH_2CH_2CH_2Br \\
& \text{1,3-dibromopropane} \\
\xrightarrow{H_2/Ni/80°} & CH_3CH_2CH_3 \\
& \text{propane}
\end{array}
\right.
$$

The increased stability of the larger ring molecules is illustrated by the reduction to the corresponding alkane with hydrogen in the presence of a nickel catalyst: cyclopropane, cyclobutane and cyclopentane require reaction temperatures of 80°, 120° and 300° respectively. The higher cycloalkanes do not react.

5.7 Uses of Alkanes

(a) Methane

Methane is the major constituent (about 95 per cent) of North Sea gas. It is used as a fuel and for the manufacture of chloro- and dichloro-methane (see Unit 5.5(b)) and of methanol (see Unit 12.4(a)). It is converted into ethyne by oxidation of some of the gas in a limited supply of air:

$$CH_4 + \tfrac{1}{2}O_2 \rightarrow CO + 2H_2$$

The heat liberated in this reaction is used to raise the temperature of the remaining methane to 1 500° for a very short time to form ethyne:

$$2CH_4 \xrightarrow{1\,500°} C_2H_2 + 3H_2$$

But the most important use of methane in the chemical industry is for the production of *synthesis gas*. Synthesis gas, a mixture of carbon monoxide and hydrogen, is manufactured by passing methane (or naphtha) and steam over a nickel catalyst at approximately 800°:

$$CH_4 + H_2O \xrightarrow[800°]{Ni} \underbrace{CO + 3H_2}_{\text{synthesis gas}}$$

It is used as a source of hydrogen and for the preparation of methanol (see Unit 12.4) and the higher alcohols. Methane is also used for the production of hydrogen cyanide:

$$CH_4 + NH_3 + 1\tfrac{1}{2}O_2 \xrightarrow[1000°]{\text{Pt/Rh catalyst}} HCN + 3H_2O$$

and carbon disulphide:

$$CH_4 + 4S \xrightarrow{\text{catalyst/heat}} CS_2 + 2H_2S$$

(b) Ethane

In the United States, ethane is an important source of ethene (see Unit 7.2). It is also used to prepare chloroethane for the manufacture of tetraethyl-lead (see Unit 6.4).

(c) The Higher Alkanes

These are used as petrol, fuel oils, lubricants, solvents, paraffin wax, Vaseline and bitumen and, like methane, are important raw materials for the large-scale preparation of both aliphatic and aromatic compounds. The vapour-phase nitration of propane (see Unit 5.5(c)) yields a mixture of nitro-compounds which, after fractional distillation, are used mainly as solvents.

Test Yourself on Unit 5

1. Give the systematic names for the following compounds:
   (a) $C(C_2H_5)_4$;
   (b) $CH_3CH_2CH_2C(CH_3)_3$;
   (c) $CH_3CH(CH_3)CH(CH_3)CH_3$;
   (d) $CH_3CH(C_2H_5)CH_2CH_2Cl$.

2. Give the structural formulae of:
   (a) 2,2,3-trimethylbutane;
   (b) 2,2-dimethylpropane;
   (c) 2,2-dichloro-5-methylhexane;
   (d) 1,3-dimethylcyclobutane.

3. Match the following named reactions with equations (i)–(vii):
   (a) Wurtz synthesis;
   (b) Kolbe synthesis;
   (c) Clemmensen reduction;
   (d) Sabatier–Senderens reaction;
   (e) Grignard reaction;
   (f) pyrolytic dehydrogenation.
   (i) $CH_3COCH_3 \rightarrow CH_3CH_2CH_3$
   (ii) $CH_3CH_2CH_2CH_3 \rightarrow CH_4 + C_2H_6 + CH_3CH{=}CH_2 + C_2H_4 + H_2$
   (iii) $CH_3MgI + C_2H_5I \rightarrow C_3H_8 + MgI_2$
   (iv) $2C_2H_5I + 2Na \rightarrow C_4H_{10} + 2NaI$
   (v) propene $\rightarrow$ propane
   (vi) potassium propanoate $\rightarrow$ butane
   (vii) $C_2H_5MgBr + HBr \rightarrow C_2H_6 + MgBr_2$

4. State how the following changes (a to g) may be carried out:

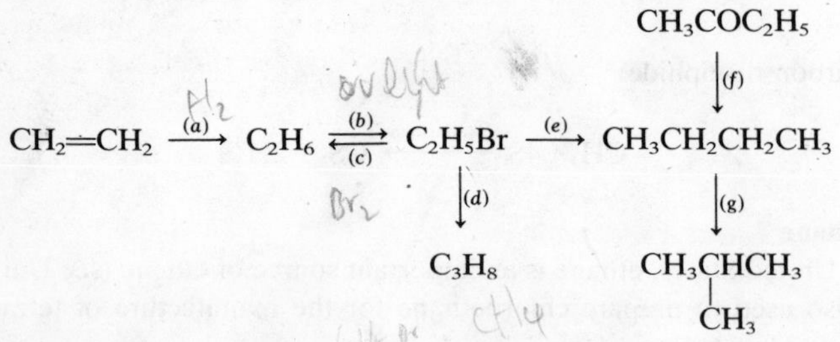

$$CH_3COC_2H_5$$

$$CH_2{=}CH_2 \xrightarrow{(a)} C_2H_6 \underset{(c)}{\overset{(b)}{\rightleftharpoons}} C_2H_5Br \xrightarrow{(e)} CH_3CH_2CH_2CH_3$$

(with arrows labelled (f), (d), (g))

$$C_3H_8 \qquad CH_3\underset{|}{CH}CH_3 \\ CH_3$$

5. Write an essay on the synthetic uses of methane.

6. Discuss the mechanisms of the following reactions:
   (a) the chlorination of methane;
   (b) the catalytic hydrogenation of ethene;
   (c) the reduction of iodoethane with zinc and ethanoic acid.

Petroleum

6.1 Introduction

Petroleum is a complex mixture of solid, liquid and gaseous hydrocarbons; other valuable substances may also be present, as well as a large number of impurities. Natural gas from Lacq in France, for example, contains about 15 per cent of hydrogen sulphide and is an important source of sulphur, while the gases from some American fields contain as much as 2 per cent of helium. North Sea gas is about 95 per cent methane. The principal oil deposits so far discovered are in the Middle East, Alaska, Canada, North Africa, the United States, Venezuela and under the North Sea. The composition of the petroleum varies; for example, petroleum from the Middle East consists mainly of alkanes, whereas Mexican and Californian oil is richer in aromatic hydrocarbons.

Evidence for the existence of some of these deposits has been apparent for thousands of years. The 'eternal fires of Baku' on the shores of the Caspian Sea and at Kirkuk in Iraq, which have been burning continuously since biblical times, are due to gas seepage from the oil-bearing rocks beneath and were probably originally ignited by lightning during a thunderstorm. Small amounts of oil and pitch have long been collected from such surface deposits for use in lamps and for waterproofing boats, water pipes and so on. Nevertheless it is only since 1895, when the first flowing oil well was sunk in Pennsylvania in the United States, that oilfields have really been exploited. Oil production has accelerated enormously during the last twenty or thirty years and hundreds of millions of tonnes are now consumed annually as fuels and as the source material for the manufacture of thousands of organic compounds. It seems probable that most of the world's major oilfields will be exhausted before the end of this century.

6.2 Petroleum Deposits

(a) The Origin of Oilfields

Petroleum is believed to have been formed over a period of millions of years by the bacterial decomposition of enormous numbers of minute marine plants and animals. Gradually layers of sediment were deposited on this organic material, subjecting it to enormous pressure, often at a high temperature, which eventually converted it into petroleum. The presence of salt strata from evaporated seas or of other impermeable layers prevented the oil and its associated natural gas from seeping away, while buckling of the earth's crust by earth movements has produced up-folds or *anticlines* that confine the oil beneath them (Fig. 6.1).

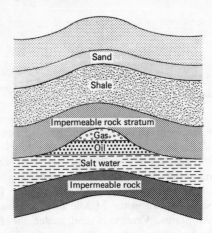

Fig. 6.1   An anticline

(b) Prospecting for Oil

The location of oilfields is determined by a combination of detailed geological survey and luck. Initial seismic exploration involves the generation of shock waves by firing explosive charges buried deep in the ground. These waves travel faster through hard compact rock formations than through relatively soft ground. Thus by recording the reflected shock waves at various sites and calculating the times taken for the waves to reach the recording stations, an indication of the position and depth of the different underground strata and the presence of promising oil-bearing pockets can be gained. Information may also be gained from aerial photography, while gravity and magnetic surveys detect minute variations in the earth's gravitational field or in the magnetic properties and electrical resistance of the rocks which may be due to the presence of oil-bearing strata.

The final test is exploratory drilling. Frequently holes more than three or four kilometres in depth have to be drilled into the earth or under the sea to reach the oil-bearing layers. Sometimes the pressure of the gas above the oil is sufficient to cause the crude oil to gush to the surface, making pumping unnecessary.

6.3 Distillation of Petroleum

Crude petroleum is usually a thick black liquid with a greenish sheen, but the colour varies from nearly colourless in some oil wells to red, brown, amber and fluorescent green in others. Its density varies between 0.82 and 0.95 g cm^{-3}.

After separation of the sand and water which is usually associated with it, the petroleum is transported directly to the refinery. The crude petroleum is

Table 6.1 Fractional distillation of crude petroleum

Boiling-point	Fraction	Number of carbon atoms	Use
<40°	Gas	C_1–C_4	LPG (e.g. Calor gas) and as fuel in the refinery
40–100°	Gasoline	C_4–C_7	Solvent, petrol
100–160°	Naphtha (ligroin)	C_7–C_{10}	Production of synthesis gas
160–250°	Kerosene	C_{10}–C_{16}	Liquid paraffin, heating oil, jet fuel, catalytic cracking
250–300°	Light gas oil	C_{16}–C_{20}	Catalytic cracking
300–350°	Heavy gas oil	C_{20}–C_{30}	Diesel fuel (DERV), Vaseline, fuel oil, paraffin wax
>350°	Residue	>C_{30}	Lubricating oils, grease, paraffin wax (some wax is cracked to yield unbranched-chain alkanes); bitumen, asphalt and coke

first heated to remove the dissolved natural gas (*stabilization*). It is then fractionally distilled in columns 40 or 50 m in height containing a large number of bubble-caps to bring the vapour and liquid phases into contact. The various fractions boiling over different temperature ranges are collected. A typical separation of crude petroleum is shown in Table 6.1, but the proportions of the different fractions vary widely from one oilfield to another.

The fractions are usually redistilled and are then subjected to further treatment to remove sulphur and other impurities.

6.4 Petrol (Gasoline): Octane Number

In an internal-combustion engine the fuel is sparked and ignited inside the working cylinder. In engines with high compression ratios the petrol tends to explode prematurely and burn unevenly, producing a series of sharp explosions known as 'knocking' or 'pinking' which decreases both the efficiency and the working-life of the engine. Knocking is particular apparent with unbranched alkanes such as n-heptane, but is reduced by the presence of branched-chain and cyclic hydrocarbons.

Petrol is graded using an arbitrary scale (or *octane rating*) based on n-heptane and the octane isomer 2,2,4-trimethylpentane. Heptane produces severe knocking and is assigned an octane number of zero, while 2,2,4-trimethylpentane causes little knocking and is given an octane value of 100.

The *octane number* of any fuel is the percentage of 2,2,4-trimethylpentane in a mixture with n-heptane which produces knocking under the same conditions as the fuel.

The octane number of petrol is improved by increasing the proportion of branched-chain and cyclic alkanes and by the addition of ethanol, methanol, aromatic hydrocarbons such as benzene, and tetraethyl-lead(IV), $Pb(C_2H_5)_4$, or its tetramethyl analogue. It is important to remove any traces of sulphur compounds from petrol, as these strongly inhibit the effect of tetraethyl-lead(IV). Lead compounds are toxic, however, and the amounts permitted in petrol are being decreased to reduce atmospheric pollution, while tetraethyl-lead(IV) is progressively being replaced by other additives. Most modern car engines run on 'three-star' or 'four-star' petrol, with an octane number of 95 to 99. As the petrol or gasoline fraction obtained from petroleum distillation has an octane number of only about 55 to 60, it needs considerable blending before it is suitable for use as a motor fuel.

6.5 Isomerization and Cyclization

Unbranched alkanes undergo rearrangement to yield their branched-chain isomers on heating in the presence of an aluminium chloride catalyst; 2-methylpropane, for example, may be obtained by isomerizing butane under these conditions (see Unit 4.9(*d*)).

Unbranched alkanes from the gasoline and naphtha fractions undergo *cyclization* and *dehydrogenation* (*catalytic reforming*) when they are passed over a heated catalyst of finely divided molybdenum(VI) oxide or platinum on aluminium oxide. The latter process is known as *platforming*. For example, hexane and heptane yield benzene and methylbenzene respectively under these conditions:

$$CH_3(CH_2)_4CH_3 \xrightarrow[500°]{Pt/Al_2O_3}$$

+ 4H_2

hexane   benzene

$$CH_3(CH_2)_5CH_3 \xrightarrow[500°]{Pt/Al_2O_3}$$

+ 4H_2

heptane

methylbenzene

The processes involve *bifunctional catalysis*: one of the components of the catalyst (the aluminium oxide) catalyses the cyclization, while the other (the platinum or molybdenum(VI) oxide) catalyses the dehydrogenation step. Some carbon is formed as a by-product, but the amounts may be reduced by carrying out the reaction in the presence of excess hydrogen (*hydroforming*). The catalyst is regenerated for re-use by burning off any carbon that has been produced.

6.6 Catalytic Cracking ('Cat-cracking')

The long-chain alkanes in the higher-boiling fractions of petroleum distillation, such as the kerosene and gas-oil fractions, are broken into smaller fragments by heating with steam to 400–600° under pressure in the presence of a catalyst. Such high-temperature fission processes are known as *cracking* or *pyrolysis* reactions. For example, the cracking of decane, $C_{10}H_{22}$, yields a mixture containing methane, ethane, ethene, hydrogen, propane, propene, butane and butene, as well as the longer-chain alkanes and alkenes:

$$\begin{array}{c}
\quad H\ \ H\ \ H\ \ H\ |\ H\ \ H\ \ H\ |\ H\ \ H\ |\ H \\
\quad |\ \ \ |\ \ \ |\ \ \ |\ \ |\ \ \ |\ \ \ |\ \ |\ \ \ |\ \ |\ \ \ | \\
H-C-C-C-C\!+\!C-C-C\!+\!C-C\!+\!C-H \\
\quad |\ \ \ |\ \ \ |\ \ \ |\ \ |\ \ \ |\ \ \ |\ \ |\ \ \ |\ \ |\ \ \ | \\
\quad H\ \ H\ \ H\ \ H\ |\ H\ \ H\ \ H\ |\ H\ \ H\ |\ H
\end{array}$$

catalytic cracking

$$RCH\!=\!CH_2 + RCH_2CH_3 + CH_4 + H_2 + C_4H_{10} + CH_2\!=\!CH_2$$
$$+ CH_3CH\!=\!CH_2 + C_2H_6 + C_3H_8 \text{ etc.}$$

The catalyst usually consists of a mixture of silicon(IV) oxide and metallic oxides, often aluminium or thorium oxide. It is generally in the form of a fine powder, which is allowed to flow out of the reactor into a second chamber (the *regenerator*) through which air is passed so that any carbon deposited on the catalyst may burn off. The reactivated catalyst is then returned to the reactor. The reaction proceeds by a free-radical mechanism with homolytic fission of carbon–carbon and carbon–hydrogen bonds:

$$RCH_2CH_2CH_3 \rightarrow RCH_2CH_2\!\cdot + \cdot CH_3 \qquad \begin{array}{l}\text{Chain initiation by thermal}\\\text{fission of carbon–carbon bond}\end{array}$$

$$\left.\begin{array}{r}
RCH_2CH_2CH_3 + \cdot CH_3 \rightarrow RCH_2\dot{C}HCH_3 + CH_4 \\
RCH_2CH_2\!\cdot \rightarrow RCH\!=\!CH_2 + H\cdot \\
RCH_2CH_2CH_3 + H\cdot \rightarrow RCH_2\dot{C}HCH_3 + H\cdot
\end{array}\right\} \begin{array}{l}\text{Chain-}\\\text{propagation}\\\text{steps}\end{array}$$

etc.

$$\left.\begin{array}{r}
2RCH_2CH_2\!\cdot \rightarrow RCH\!=\!CH_2 + RCH_2CH_3 \\
2RCH_2\dot{C}HCH_3 \rightarrow RCH_2CH\!=\!CH_2 + RCH_2CH_2CH_3
\end{array}\right\} \begin{array}{l}\text{Chain}\\\text{termination}\end{array}$$

The products of cracking are divided into three main fractions:

(i) *refinery gas*; this consists mainly of ethene and propene with varying amounts of hydrogen and the lower alkanes;

(ii) a liquid mixture, principally of branched-chain alkanes, alkenes, cycloalkanes and aromatic hydrocarbons, which is redistilled and used for making high-grade petrol;

(iii) a high-boiling residue which is used as a fuel oil.

In *hydrocracking* the kerosene and gas-oil fractions are passed over a platinum/sodium aluminosilicate catalyst with an excess of hydrogen. No alkenes are produced in this process and the mixture of saturated hydrocarbons obtained is rich in branched-chain alkanes which may be used in high-grade petrol.

6.7 The Petrochemical Industry

Natural gas and petroleum provide the raw materials for the manufacture of a huge range of chemicals, both organic and inorganic. The three principal primary sources are natural gas (see Unit 6.1), the naphtha fraction from the distillation of petroleum (see Unit 6.3) and refinery gas (see Unit 6.5). The synthetic uses of methane and natural gas were discussed in Unit 5.7. The syntheses of a number of important organic compounds are described elsewhere in this book, but those of some inorganic substances are discussed here.

(a) Carbon Monoxide and Hydrogen

These are obtained from synthesis gas (see Unit 5.7). The carbon monoxide can be separated from the hydrogen by absorption in an ammoniacal solution of a copper(I) salt. It is used for the synthesis of carbonyl chloride, $COCl_2$:

$$CO + Cl_2 \xrightarrow{\text{charcoal}/200°} COCl_2$$

and hence of the di-isocyano-compounds used in the manufacture of polyurethan resins and foams.

Hydrogen is obtained as a by-product of the cracking of petroleum (see Unit 6.5) and also by passing a mixture of synthesis gas and an excess of steam under pressure over heated iron:

$$\underbrace{CO + 3H_2}_{\text{synthesis gas}} + \underset{\text{steam}}{H_2O} \xrightarrow{\text{Fe}/400°/30 \text{ atm}} CO_2 + 4H_2$$

Carbon dioxide is removed by scrubbing with alkali.

Hydrogen is converted by the *Haber process* into ammonia:

$$N_2 + 3H_2 \underset{\text{Fe-Al}_2O_3/400°/300 \text{ atm}}{\rightleftharpoons} 2NH_3$$

which is used to manufacture inorganic fertilizers (such as ammonium nitrate and ammonium sulphate) and also provides a synthetic route to nitric acid:

$$4NH_3 + 5O_2 \xrightarrow[900°]{\text{Pt gauze}} 4NO + 6H_2O$$

$$\downarrow {2O_2 \text{ (air)}}$$

$$4NO_2$$

$$H_2O + 3NO_2 \longrightarrow 2HNO_3 + NO$$

and to nylon (see Unit 21.5) and carbamide (urea), which is used for the manufacture of resins and as fertilizer:

$$2NH_3 + CO_2 \xrightarrow[200°]{\text{high pressure}} O{=}C{\overset{NH_2}{\underset{NH_2}{\Big\langle}}} + H_2O$$

carbamide

Hydrogen is also used in oxy-hydrogen welding and in the large-scale production of methanol (see Unit 12.4(a)(ii)), margarine (see Unit 7.6(a)), cyclohexanol and other alcohols, and phenylamine (see Unit 18.3(b)).

(b) Sulphur

Sulphur is present in natural gas and petroleum as hydrogen sulphide and organic sulphur compounds, which themselves can be converted into hydrogen sulphide by hydrocracking. Hydrogen sulphide is absorbed in organic bases, and then converted into sulphur by the *Claus process*, in which part of the gas is burnt to yield sulphur dioxide which is then used to oxidize the remainder to sulphur:

$$H_2S + 1\tfrac{1}{2}O_2 \rightarrow H_2O + SO_2$$
$$2H_2S + SO_2 \rightarrow 2H_2O + 3S$$

The overall reaction is:

$$3H_2S + 1\tfrac{1}{2}O_2 \rightarrow 3H_2O + 3S$$

Sulphur is used for the manufacture of sulphuric acid, and this valuable acid is in turn used for a vast range of synthetic processes, including the manufacture of explosives such as nitroglycerine and TNT (see Units 12.8(b)(ii) and 9.7(a)), superphosphate and ammonium sulphate fertilizers, detergents (see Unit 17.9(b)) and rayon (see Unit 20.8(b)(ii)), and to 'pickle' iron and steel by removing oxide film before plating or galvanizing.

(c) Hydrogen Peroxide

Hydrogen is the starting material for the manufacture of hydrogen peroxide. An alkylanthraquinone is hydrogenated in the presence of a Raney nickel or palladium catalyst:

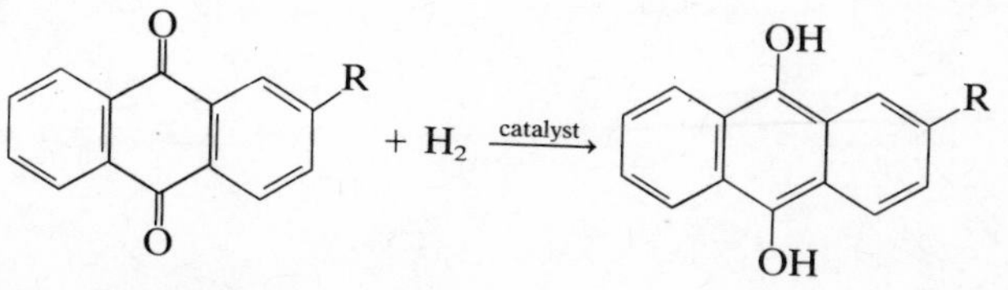

an alkylanthraquinone   an alkylanthraquinol

The product is then oxidized by oxygen or air to re-form the original alkyl-anthraquinone (which is then recycled) and hydrogen peroxide, which is extracted with water:

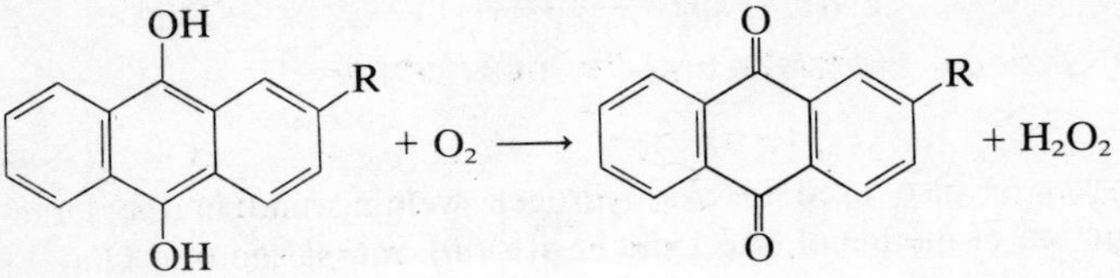

Test Yourself on Unit 6

1. Explain what is meant by the following terms: (a) anticline, (b) knocking (or pinking), (c) octane number, (d) catalytic cracking, (e) hydrocracking.

2. Write an essay discussing the origin, discovery and uses of petroleum.

3. Discuss the methods which are used to produce high-grade petrol from crude petroleum.

Alkenes

7.1 General Formula and Nomenclature

The general formula of the alkene homologous series is C_nH_{2n}. The compounds are unsaturated and contain one or more carbon–carbon double bonds. The name of an alkene is derived from that of the alkane with the same number of carbon atoms in its molecule by changing the suffix from -ane to -ene (see Unit 1.4(a)). The positions of the double bond and of any substituents are indicated by numbering the carbon atoms in the chain:

$$CH_2{=}CH_2 \qquad CH_3CH_2CH{=}CH_2 \qquad \overset{\displaystyle CH_3 \;\; CH_3}{CH_3CH{=}C{-}CHCH_2CH_3}$$

ethene   but-1-ene   3,4-dimethylhex-2-ene

7.2 Manufacture of Alkenes

Virtually all the alkenes required for industrial use in the United Kingdom (principally ethene and propene) are obtained as products of the cracking of the gas-oil and naphtha fractions of petroleum distillation (Units 6.3 and 6.5):

$$\text{Naphtha fraction} \xrightarrow{\text{steam/700–900°}} C_2H_4 + C_3H_6 + C_4H_8 + H_2 + CH_4 \text{ etc.}$$

(C_7–C_{10} alkanes) $\qquad\qquad\qquad\qquad\qquad$ + fuel oil + gasoline

The fuel oil and gasoline are separated and the gases are then compressed and cooled. As the temperature is progressively reduced the components liquefy according to their boiling-points and are drained off one after the other. The unwanted gases are burned as fuel.

In the United States many gas deposits contain high proportions of ethane and propane, and large amounts of ethene and propene are obtained by heating the corresponding alkane:

$$C_2H_6 \xrightarrow{700°/\text{catalyst}} C_2H_4 + H_2$$

$\qquad\qquad$ ethane $\qquad\qquad\qquad$ ethene

$$C_3H_8 \xrightarrow[700°]{Cr_2O_3/Al_2O_3} C_3H_6 + H_2$$

$\qquad\qquad$ propane $\qquad\qquad\qquad$ propene

7.3 General Methods of Preparation

(a) From Alcohols

The dehydration of alcohols is the principal method of preparing alkenes:

$$
\begin{array}{ccc}
\underset{\underset{\displaystyle H}{|}}{-C}-\overset{\displaystyle OH}{\underset{|}{C}}- & \xrightarrow{-H_2O} & >C=C< \\
\text{alcohol} & & \text{alkene}
\end{array}
$$

The alcohol may be vaporized and passed over heated alumina:

$$
C_2H_5OH \xrightarrow{Al_2O_3/350^\circ} \underset{\text{ethene}}{\overset{\displaystyle H}{\underset{\displaystyle H}{}}C=C\overset{\displaystyle H}{\underset{\displaystyle H}{}}} + H_2O
$$

or heated with an excess of concentrated sulphuric acid:

$$
C_2H_5OH + H_2SO_4 \rightarrow \underset{\text{ethyl hydrogen sulphate}}{C_2H_5HSO_4} + H_2O
$$

$$
C_2H_5HSO_4 + H_2SO_4 \xrightarrow[>170^\circ]{\text{excess of } H_2SO_4} \underset{\text{ethene}}{C_2H_4} + 2H_2SO_4
$$

Other suitable dehydrating agents include boric acid, phosphorus(v) oxide and phosphoric(v) acid (see Unit 12.6(g)). The method is also used for the preparation of cyclic alkenes; cyclohexene, for instance, is obtained by heating a mixture of cyclohexanol and concentrated phosphoric(v) acid (see Experiment 7.2):

$$
\underset{\text{cyclohexanol}}{\text{OH}} \xrightarrow[-H_2O]{\text{heat/phosphoric(v) acid}} \underset{\text{cyclohexene}}{\text{}}
$$

Experiment 7.1 *To prepare ethene by the dehydration of ethanol*

Set up the apparatus shown in Fig. 7.1 in a fume-cupboard. Place 15 cm³ of ethanol (use industrial methylated spirit, IMS) in the flask, together with some glass wool to ensure even boiling. Heat the aluminium oxide to approximately 350°, using a fish-tail burner or a tube furnace (this is well below red heat—ethoxyethane is obtained instead of ethene at low temperatures; see Unit 12.6(g)). Once the aluminium oxide is thoroughly hot, gently boil the ethanol in the flask and collect the ethene over water, placing corks in the test-tubes when they have been filled with gas. Carry out the tests for alkenes described in Experiment 7.3.

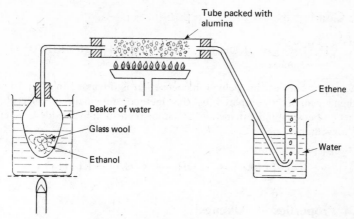

Fig. 7.1   Preparation of ethene

Experiment 7.2 *Preparation of cyclohexene*

Gently distil a mixture of cyclohexanol (10.5 cm³ = 10 g = 0.1 mol) and phosphoric(v) acid (5 cm³) in a 25 cm³ pear-shaped flask and collect the product in a test-tube. Transfer the distillate to a separating-funnel and shake with 3 or 4 cm³ of a saturated solution of sodium chloride. Discard the lower aqueous layer and transfer the upper layer to a small dry flask and add two or three lumps of fused calcium chloride (about 3 g) to remove any water present. Stopper the flask and allow it to stand, shaking it occasionally until the liquid is clear.

Decant the impure cyclohexene into a distillation flask and distil it, collecting the fraction boiling at 82–85° in a preweighed, dry sample tube. Weigh the tube and distillate and calculate the percentage yield of pure cyclohexene (see Foreword, p. xiii).

$$C_6H_{11}OH \quad \rightarrow \quad C_6H_{10}$$
$$\text{cyclohexanol} \qquad \text{cyclohexene}$$
$$\text{RMM} = 100 \qquad \text{RMM} = 82$$

Use the product for demonstrating the reactions of alkenes listed in Experiment 7.3.

(b) From Halogenoalkanes

Halogenoalkanes undergo *dehydrohalogenation* (that is, they lose a molecule of hydrogen halide) to yield an alkene when they are boiled with a solution of potassium hydroxide in alcohol (ethanol or IMS):

For instance,

$$CH_3CH_2CH_2Br + KOH_{(alcoholic)} \xrightarrow{\text{boil}} CH_3CH=CH_2 + KBr + H_2O$$

1-bromopropane   propene

The mechanism of this dehydrohalogenation is discussed in Unit 10.6(b). Ethene cannot be prepared by this method; the main product of the reaction between iodoethane and ethanolic potassium hydroxide is an ether (ethoxyethane):

$$C_2H_5I + KOH + C_2H_5OH \xrightarrow{\text{boil}} (C_2H_5)_2O + KI + H_2O$$

7.4 Properties of Alkenes

The first three members of the homologous series are gases at room temperature. Alkenes containing between 5 and 15 carbon atoms are colourless liquids and the higher alkenes are waxy solids. They are all insoluble in water, but dissolve readily in hydrocarbon solvents, thus following the general rule in chemistry that compounds are soluble in substances of similar composition and structure ('like dissolves like'). The alkenes burn in air:

$$C_2H_4 + 3O_2 \rightarrow 2CO_2 + 2H_2O_{(1)} \qquad (\Delta H = -1\,410 \text{ kJ mol}^{-1})$$

The flame is luminous and smoky, indicating that the combustion is incomplete. The presence of soot in the flame is an indication of the relatively high carbon content of these compounds; alkynes and aromatic compounds also burn with a sooty flame.

7.5 Structure and Reactivity of Alkenes

The two carbon atoms forming the double bond are both sp^2 hybridized (see Unit 4.4(c)). The ethene molecule is thus flat, with a π molecular orbital above and below the plane (see Fig. 4.10). In the higher alkenes the portion of the molecule about the double bond is flat, while the shape of the remainder is determined by the nature and state of hybridization of the substituents.

Geometrical isomerism (see Units 1.6 and 4.4(e)) is possible in substituted alkenes and in alkenes having four or more carbon atoms; thus there are two but-2-enes:

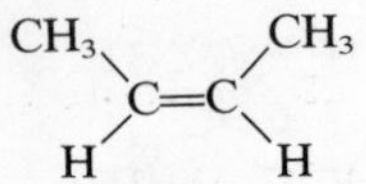

cis-isomer 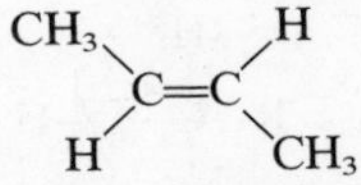   trans-isomer

Addition to the double bond of an alkene can occur *either* on one side *or* on opposite sides of the molecule. These two modes of addition are termed *syn* and *anti* respectively:

$$\diagdown C=C \diagup + X_2 \xrightarrow{\text{syn-addition}} \diagdown C - C \diagup$$
$$\qquad\qquad\qquad\qquad\qquad\qquad X \quad X$$

$$\diagdown C=C \diagup + X_2 \xrightarrow{\text{anti-addition}} \diagdown C - C \diagup$$
$$\qquad\qquad\qquad\qquad\qquad\qquad X$$

Alkenes are considerably more reactive than the alkanes, especially towards attack by *electrophiles* (see Unit 4.7) or *free radicals* (see Unit 4.5) which are attracted to the negative charge of the π orbital. They can also form polymeric products (see Unit 7.6(*j*)).

7.6 Reactions of Alkenes

(*a*) Hydrogenation

Alkenes are reduced to alkanes by the action of hydrogen in the presence of a metallic catalyst (see Unit 5.2(*a*)):

$$\diagdown C=C \diagup + H_2 \longrightarrow -C-C- $$
$$\qquad\qquad\qquad\qquad\quad H \quad H$$

Catalytic hydrogenation of the alkene bond is used to 'harden' unsaturated fats and oils to make margarine. These fats and oils are esters (see Unit 17.5) of long-chain carboxylic acids and the trihydric alcohol propane-1,2,3-triol (see Unit 12.8(*b*)). The presence of unsaturation in the oils lowers the melting-point and makes them too soft for commercial use. They are therefore heated with hydrogen in the presence of a nickel catalyst at about 200° under pressure (approximately 5 atmospheres); the double bonds are thus hydrogenated and a saturated solid ('hard') fat is obtained. Vitamins A and D, colouring matter and a preservative are added and the material is sold as the butter-substitute *margarine*.

(*b*) Halogenation

Alkenes form addition compounds with chlorine or bromine; for example:

$$CH_2{=}CH_2 + Br_2 \rightarrow CH_2BrCH_2Br$$
$$\text{ethene} \qquad\qquad\qquad \text{1,2-dibromoethane}$$

The mechanism is determined by the reaction conditions and can involve *either* a free-radical *or* a polar pathway.

(i) **Free-radical mechanism.** In the presence of ultra-violet light, the reaction is initiated by the photochemical fission of the chlorine or bromine molecule to yield atoms:

$$Cl_2 \xrightarrow{h\nu} 2Cl\cdot$$

This is followed by chain-propagation steps which result in the formation of 1,2-dichloroethane:

$$Cl\cdot + CH_2{=}CH_2 \rightarrow CH_2ClCH_2\cdot$$
$$CH_2ClCH_2\cdot + Cl_2 \rightarrow CH_2ClCH_2Cl + Cl\cdot$$

At high temperatures a *substitution* reaction takes place; for instance, ethene is substituted by chlorine at 600° to form chloroethene (see Unit 10.7(a)):

$$CH_2{=}CH_2 + Cl_2 \xrightarrow{600°} CH_2CHCl + HCl$$
$$\text{chloroethene}$$

(ii) **Polar mechanism.** This mechanism operates in the absence of light. It requires a polar surface, such as glass; ethene and bromine, for example, will not react in a vessel whose walls have been coated with a non-polar substance like paraffin wax. The reaction, which is catalysed by inorganic halides, takes place in two stages:

1. The covalent bond in the halogen molecule becomes polarized, enabling one end to act as an electrophile which is attracted to the π bond of the alkene. Fission follows, to form a carbonium ion such as $^+CH_2CH_2Br$, or possibly a cyclic bromonium ion such as

$$\begin{array}{c} CH_2 \\ | \quad\quad Br^+ \\ CH_2 \end{array}$$

2. This ion is then readily attacked by the bromide anion or some other nucleophile.

Evidence for this mechanism is provided by the formation of 1-bromo-2-chloroethane, $ClCH_2CH_2Br$, in addition to 1,2-dibromoethane, when ethene is brominated in the presence of sodium chloride. This indicates that the probable initial reaction is the formation of a carbonium ion which can react either with a chloride or with a bromide ion or some other nucleophile, such as water:

$$\overset{+}{C}H_2CH_2Br \xrightarrow{Cl^-} ClCH_2CH_2Br$$
$$\text{1-bromo-2-chloroethane}$$

$$\xrightarrow{Br^-} BrCH_2CH_2Br$$
$$\text{1,2-dibromoethane}$$

$$\xrightarrow{H_2O:} \begin{array}{c} H \\ \backslash \\ O{-}CH_2CH_2Br \xrightarrow{-H^+} HOCH_2CH_2Br \\ / \\ H \end{array}$$
$$\text{2-bromoethanol}$$

Addition is *anti*, that is, the nucleophile approaches the side of the molecule *opposite* to that of the initial electrophilic attack.

The decolorization of bromine water resulting from this addition reaction may be used as a test for unsaturation (see Experiment 7.3).

(c) Addition of Hydrogen Halides

Alkenes react with hydrogen halides to yield the corresponding halogeno-alkanes. For example, bromoethane is obtained by the addition of hydrogen bromide to ethene:

$$CH_2{=}CH_2 + HBr \rightarrow CH_3CH_2Br$$

Hydrogen fluoride reacts only with difficulty, and a catalyst such as aluminium chloride is needed for the addition of hydrogen chloride. Hydrogen bromide and hydrogen iodide add more readily; the alkene reacts with the aqueous acid at 100°.

The addition is *anti* (see Unit 7.5). Theoretically, two addition products are possible with unsymmetrical alkenes; the reaction of hydrogen chloride with propene, for instance, could yield either 1- or 2-chloropropane depending on whether the proton adds on to carbon atom 2 or 1 respectively:

$$\begin{array}{c} CH_3CH{=}CH_2 \\ + \\ H{-}Cl \end{array} \xrightarrow{(a)} CH_3CH_2CH_2Cl$$

1-chloropropane

or

$$\begin{array}{c} CH_3CH{=}CH_2 \\ + \\ Cl{-}H \end{array} \xrightarrow{(b)} \underset{\underset{Cl}{|}}{CH_3CHCH_3}$$

2-chloropropane

In practice, the direction of addition is given by *Markownikoff's Rule*, which states that in the addition to an unsymmetrical alkene the more *negative* part of the addendum becomes attached to the carbon atom which is linked to the *smaller* number of hydrogen atoms. Thus in our example, the reaction follows path (b) and addition of hydrogen chloride to propene yields 2-chloropropane and not the 1-isomer.

The theoretical explanation of Markownikoff's Rule is largely based on the inductive effect (+I) of the methyl group (see Unit 4.6(a)):

$$CH_3 {\longrightarrow} CH{=}CH_2 \longleftrightarrow CH_3{-}\overset{+}{C}H{-}\overset{-}{C}H_2 \longrightarrow CH_3{-}\overset{+}{C}H{-}CH_3$$

$$\overset{\cdot}{H^+} \qquad\qquad H^+$$

$$\xrightarrow{X^-} CH_3{-}CHX{-}CH_3$$

The rule applies to the addition to unsymmetrical alkenes of water, sulphuric acid and chloric(I) and bromic(I) acids (hypohalous acids, HClO and HBrO), as well as to that of hydrogen halides.

In the presence of peroxides or oxygen, hydrogen bromide adds in the opposite direction to that predicted by Markownikoff's Rule; thus the product of the reaction with propene is 1-bromopropane:

$$CH_3CH{=}CH_2 + HBr \xrightarrow{\text{peroxide}} CH_3CH_2CH_2Br$$
$$\text{1-bromopropane}$$

This abnormal addition is known as the *peroxide* or *anti-Markownikoff effect*. It is not observed with hydrogen fluoride, hydrogen chloride or hydrogen iodide. The mechanism involves free radicals generated by the decomposition of the peroxide. For example, di(benzoyl) peroxide, $(C_6H_5CO_2)_2$, decomposes as follows:

$$(C_6H_5CO_2)_2 \rightarrow 2C_6H_5CO_2{\cdot} \rightarrow 2C_6H_5{\cdot} + 2CO_2$$

The radicals thus formed propagate chain reactions which result in the formation of the 'anti-Markownikoff' addition product:

$$C_6H_5{\cdot} + HBr \rightarrow C_6H_6 + Br{\cdot}$$
$$Br{\cdot} + CH_3CH{=}CH_2 \rightarrow CH_3\overset{\cdot}{C}HCH_2Br$$
$$CH_3\overset{\cdot}{C}HCH_2Br + HBr \rightarrow CH_3CH_2CH_2Br + Br{\cdot}$$

(d) Addition of Chloric(ɪ) Acid

Alkenes form addition compounds with chloric(ɪ) acid (HClO, hypochlorous acid). For example, 2-chloroethanol (ethylene chlorohydrin, $ClCH_2CH_2OH$) is obtained when ethene is bubbled through chlorine water:

$$CH_2{=}CH_2 + HOCl \longrightarrow \underset{\underset{\text{2-chloroethanol}}{Cl}}{CH_2CH_2OH}$$

An aqueous solution of bromine reacts similarly to yield 2-bromoethanol. The mechanism involves electrophilic attack by the polarized halogen molecule, followed by the reaction of the carbonium ion produced with water (*cf.* Unit 7.6(*b*)(ii)).

(e) Addition of Sulphuric Acid

Concentrated sulphuric acid absorbs alkenes to yield alkyl hydrogen sulphates, thus:

$$\underset{\text{ethene}}{CH_2{=}CH_2} + H_2SO_4 \xrightarrow{\text{warm/pressure}} \underset{\text{ethyl hydrogen sulphate}}{C_2H_5OSO_2OH}$$

This reaction may be used to separate alkanes from alkenes as the former do not react with cold concentrated sulphuric acid, while the latter are very slowly absorbed at atmospheric pressure. With unsymmetrical alkenes the addition follows Markownikoff's Rule (see Unit 7.6(c)); for example, propene yields 1-methylethyl hydrogen sulphate, $(CH_3)_2CHOSO_2OH$. Alkyl hydrogen sulphates are hydrolysed to the parent alkanols by heating with water, so that this reaction may be used to convert a primary alcohol into a secondary alcohol (see Unit 12.1); for instance:

$$CH_3CH_2CH_2OH \xrightarrow[\text{or } H_2SO_4/\text{heat}]{Al_2O_3/\text{heat}} CH_3CH{=}CH_2 \xrightarrow{H_2SO_4}$$
$$1° \text{ alcohol}$$

$$(CH_3)_2CHOSO_3H \xrightarrow{H_2O} CH_3CH(OH)CH_3$$
$$2° \text{ alcohol}$$

(f) Hydration

Alkenes are hydrated directly to form alcohols by the action of steam in the presence of a heated catalyst. Ethanol, for example, is manufactured by passing a mixture of ethene (from cracked petroleum, see Unit 7.2) and steam over phosphoric(v) acid on silicon(iv) oxide or Celite at 300°:

$$C_2H_4 + H_2O \xrightarrow[300°]{H_3PO_4/SiO_2} C_2H_5OH$$
$$\text{ethene} \quad \text{steam} \qquad\qquad \text{ethanol}$$

The hydration of unsymmetrical alkenes follows Markownikoff's Rule (see Unit 7.6(c)):

$$CH_3 \rightarrow CH{=}CH_2 + H^+ \longrightarrow CH_3\overset{+}{C}HCH_3 \xrightarrow{H_2O:} (CH_3)_2CH{-}\overset{+}{O}\overset{H}{\underset{H}{\diagdown}}$$

$$\longrightarrow (CH_3)_2CHOH + H^+$$

The higher alkenes thus yield secondary or tertiary alcohols on hydration.

(g) Hydroxylation

Alkenes add on *two* hydroxyl groups when they are treated with oxidizing agents such as alkaline potassium manganate(vii) or hydrogen peroxide:

$$\begin{array}{c} \diagdown\diagup \\ C \\ \| \\ C \\ \diagup\diagdown \end{array} \xrightarrow{H_2O/[O]} \begin{array}{c} \diagdown\diagup \\ C{-}OH \\ \\ C{-}OH \\ \diagup\diagdown \end{array}$$

where [O] represents an oxygen atom provided by the oxidizing agent.

Addition may be *syn* or *anti*, depending on the oxidizing agent used. Cold, dilute alkaline potassium manganate(vii) transfers the oxygen atoms required for the oxidation of the alkene via a cyclic intermediate to yield the *syn*-addition product. For example:

$$\begin{array}{c} CH_2 \\ \| \\ CH_2 \end{array} + MnO_4^- \longrightarrow \left[\begin{array}{c} CH_2{-}O \\ | \quad\quad Mn \\ CH_2{-}O \end{array} \overset{O}{\underset{O^-}{\diagup}} \right] \xrightarrow{\text{hydrolysis}} \begin{array}{c} CH_2OH \\ | \\ CH_2OH \end{array} + MnO_3^-$$

$$2MnO_3^- \xrightarrow{\text{alkaline solution}} MnO_4^{2-} + MnO_2$$

By using potassium manganate(VII) labelled with the oxygen-18 isotope (see Unit 4.10) it has been shown that *both* oxygen atoms in the product are derived from the oxidizing agent.

The disappearance of the purple manganate(VII) colour on treating alkenes with alkaline or acidified potassium manganate(VII) is used as a test for unsaturation (see Experiment 7.3.2).

(*h*) Oxidation

Alkenes are oxidized by peroxo-acids to form epoxides. This oxidation is carried out industrially by passing ethene mixed with oxygen over a silver catalyst at 250°:

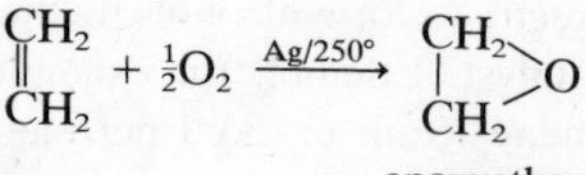

$$\begin{matrix} CH_2 \\ \| \\ CH_2 \end{matrix} + \tfrac{1}{2}O_2 \xrightarrow{\text{Ag/250°}} \begin{matrix} CH_2 \\ | \quad \diagdown \\ CH_2 \diagup \end{matrix} O$$

epoxyethane

The product, epoxyethane (see Unit 14.8), is a cyclic ether, b.p. 13°.

(*i*) Addition of Trioxygen

Alkenes add trioxygen (ozone) to yield unstable *ozonides*:

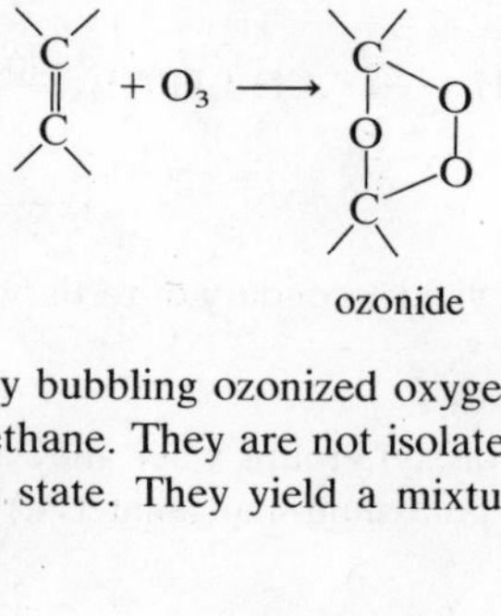

ozonide

Ozonides are prepared by bubbling ozonized oxygen through a solution of the alkene in trichloromethane. They are not isolated from solution as they are explosive in the free state. They yield a mixture of aldehydes and/or ketones on hydrolysis:

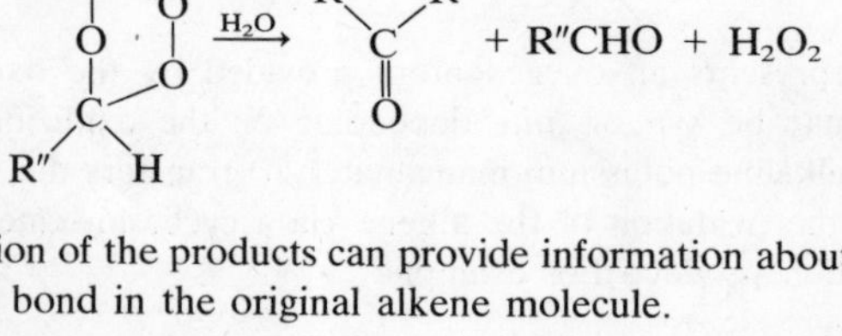

The composition of the products can provide information about the position of the double bond in the original alkene molecule.

(*j*) Addition Polymerization

Alkenes polymerize in the presence of a suitable catalyst to yield a product of very high relative molecular mass (between 10^4 and 10^6). For example, *polyethene* (or *polythene*) is formed by the polymerization of ethene in the presence of triethylaluminium and titanium(IV) chloride:

$$n\,CH_2{=}CH_2 \xrightarrow[70°/pressure]{Al(C_2H_5)_3/TiCl_4} \quad \leftarrow CH_2{-}CH_2 \rightarrow_n$$

where n is a large number.

This is an example of *addition polymerization*, during which a large number of *monomer* molecules (in this case the unsaturated alkene) join together to form a giant molecule known as a *polymer*:

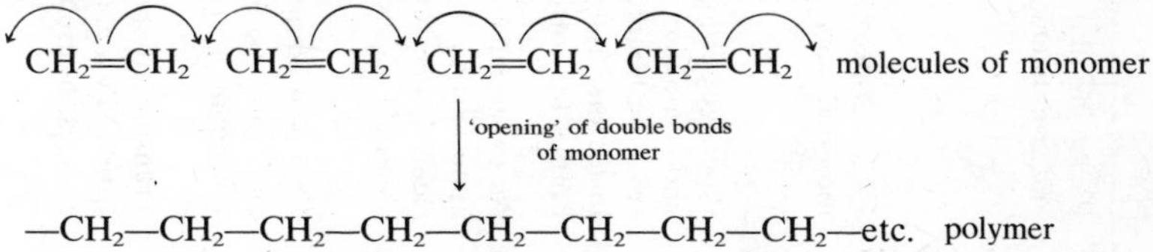

$$CH_2{=}CH_2 \quad CH_2{=}CH_2 \quad CH_2{=}CH_2 \quad CH_2{=}CH_2 \quad \text{molecules of monomer}$$

'opening' of double bonds of monomer

$$-CH_2{-}CH_2{-}CH_2{-}CH_2{-}CH_2{-}CH_2{-}CH_2{-}CH_2{-}\text{etc.} \quad \text{polymer}$$

Other alkenes and substituted alkenes behave similarly:

$$n\,CH_2{=}\underset{Y}{CH} \longrightarrow \left[CH_2{-}\underset{Y}{CH} \right]_n$$

$$\qquad\qquad \text{monomer} \qquad\qquad\qquad \text{polymer}$$

where Y is a substituent such as a chlorine atom or a methyl or phenyl group. For example:

$$n\,CH_2{=}\underset{CH_3}{CH} \xrightarrow[100°/10\,atm]{Al(C_2H_5)_3/TiCl_4} \left[CH_2{-}\underset{CH_3}{CH} \right]_n$$

$$\text{propene} \qquad\qquad\qquad \text{polypropene (polypropylene)}$$

$$n\,CH_2{=}CHCl \xrightarrow[heat]{di(benzoyl)\ peroxide} \left[CH_2{-}\underset{Cl}{CH} \right]_n$$

$$\text{chloroethene} \qquad\qquad\qquad \text{polychloroethene}$$
$$\text{(vinyl chloride)} \qquad\qquad\qquad \text{(poly(vinyl chloride),}$$
$$\text{PVC)}$$

$$n\,CF_2{=}CF_2 \xrightarrow[heat/pressure]{(NH_4)_2S_2O_8} \leftarrow CF_2{-}CF_2 \rightarrow_n$$

$$\text{tetrafluoroethene} \qquad\qquad \text{polytetrafluoroethene}$$
$$\text{(PTFE or Teflon)}$$

Table 7.1 summarizes the properties and uses of these valuable plastics, which comprise only a fraction of the enormous range in daily use.

A number of different polymerization methods are used industrially. Ethene, for example, may be polymerized by heating to 200° at 1 500 atmospheres in the presence of a trace of oxygen, acting as a radical

Table 7.1 Properties and uses of some polyalkenes

Polymer	Formula	Properties	Uses
Polyethene (polythene)	$\{CH_2CH_2\}_n$	Wax-like solid; chemical-resistant; electrical insulator; high-density form ($d = 0.95$) has higher softening temperature than low-density ($d = 0.92$, softening temperature = 120°)	Packaging film and sheet, piping, bottles and containers, household articles
Polypropene (polypropylene)	$\left\{CHCH_2 \atop CH_3\right\}_n$	Higher softening point and stiffer and harder than polythene	Fibres, rope, carpet backing, injection-moulded car components and household goods
Polychloroethene (poly(vinyl chloride) or PVC)	$\left\{CH_2CH \atop Cl\right\}_n$	Rigid (unplasticized) or flexible (plasticized)	Pipes, guttering, waterproof clothing and containers, floor tiles, vinyl wall covering, records, electrical insulators, upholstery, transparent bottles for soft drinks
Polyphenylethene (polystyrene)	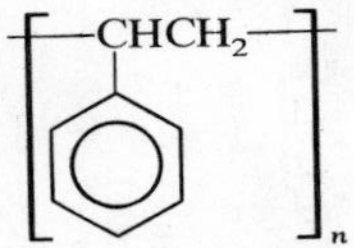 $\{CHCH_2\text{–}C_6H_5\}_n$	Strong but brittle; chemical-resistant	As expanded polystyrene, as packaging material and thermal insulator; also as clear sheets, refrigerator parts, electrical goods, yogurt pots, toys
Polytetrafluoroethene (PTFE or Teflon)	$\{CF_2CF_2\}_n$	High softening point (c. 327°); heat-resistant and inert to chemicals; lowest known coefficient of friction	Chemical equipment, frictionless joints and bearings, non-stick surfaces (e.g. saucepans, frying-pans)
Poly(methyl 2-methyl-propenoate) (Perspex)	$\left\{CH_2CHCH_2 \atop {CO \atop OCH_3}\right\}_n$	Tough, transparent, softening temperature c. 100°.	Transparent sheet used as glass substitute (Plexiglas); protective goggles, household goods.

initiator, to yield a product known as *low-density polythene* ($d = 0.92 \text{ g cm}^{-3}$) which has a considerably lower formula weight (between 50 000 and 300 000) and lower softening point (120°) than the *high-density polythene* ($d = 0.95 \text{ g cm}^{-3}$, formula weight up to 3×10^6) prepared by the *Ziegler–Natta process* in which triethylaluminium and titanium(IV) chloride are used as the catalyst.

Alkene polymerization occurs via either a free-radical or an ionic mechanism depending on the reaction conditions. Free radicals are generated by the presence of peroxides or of traces of oxygen, which is itself a *diradical* ($\cdot O{-}O\cdot$). For example,

$$(RCO_2)_2 \rightarrow 2RCO_2\cdot \rightarrow 2R\cdot + 2CO_2$$

$$R\cdot + CH_2{=}CH_2 \rightarrow RCH_2CH_2\cdot$$

$$RCH_2CH_2\cdot + CH_2{=}CH_2 \rightarrow RCH_2CH_2CH_2CH_2\cdot \xrightarrow{CH_2=CH_2} \text{ etc.}$$

$\left.\right\}$ Chain-propagation steps

The chain reactions are terminated by combination of two free radicals:

$$RCH_2CH_2\cdot \begin{cases} \xrightarrow{R\cdot} RCH_2CH_2R \\ \\ \xrightarrow{R(CH_2CH_2)_xCH_2CH_2\cdot} RCH_2CH_2(CH_2CH_2)_xCH_2CH_2R \end{cases}$$

or by *disproportionation*, in which one radical is reduced and the other oxidized:

$$2RCH_2CH_2\cdot \rightarrow RCH_2CH_3 + RCH{=}CH_2$$

or by combination with impurities:

$$RCH_2CH_2\cdot + HQ \rightarrow RCH_2CH_3 + Q$$
$$\text{(impurity)}$$

Polymerization in the presence of acids or metal halides, such as aluminium chloride or boron trifluoride, occurs via an ionic mechanism. The first step is the formation of a carbonium ion:

$$R{\rightarrow}CH{=}CH_2 + H^+ \rightarrow R\overset{+}{C}HCH_3$$

Aluminium chloride dissociates:

$$Al_2Cl_6 \rightleftharpoons 2AlCl_3$$

followed by

$$R{\rightarrow}CH{\overset{\frown}{=}}CH_2 + \overset{\delta+}{AlCl_3} \longrightarrow R{-}\overset{+}{C}H{-}CH_2{-}A\bar{l}Cl_3$$

The carbonium ion initiates a chain reaction by attacking further alkene molecules, thus:

$$R-\overset{+}{C}H \overset{\frown}{\quad} CH_2\!\!=\!\!CHR \longrightarrow R-CH-CH_2-\overset{+}{C}H$$
$$\underset{CH_3}{|} \qquad\qquad \underset{CH_3}{|} \quad \underset{R}{|}$$

$$\xrightarrow{RCH=CH_2} R-CH-CH_2-CH-CH_2-\overset{+}{C}H \xrightarrow{RCH=CH_2} \text{etc.}$$
$$\underset{CH_3}{|} \qquad \underset{R}{|} \qquad \underset{R}{|}$$

Experiment 7.3 *To demonstrate the reactions of alkenes*
These tests may be carried out with the alkenes prepared in Experiments 7.1 and 7.2.
1. Ignite a few drops of cyclohexene in an evaporating basin. Note the colour of the flame (*cf.* Unit 7.4).
2. Bubble ethene from Experiment 7.1 through test-tubes containing 5 to 10 cm^3 of the following solutions:
    (i) aqueous 1 per cent potassium manganate(vii) made alkaline by the addition of 0.3–0.5 g potassium carbonate;
    (ii) aqueous 1 per cent potassium manganate(vii) acidified with 1 or 2 cm^3 of dilute sulphuric acid;
    (iii) bromine water.
In each case note any change in colour or precipitate formation. Add a few drops of liquid bromine (**Care!**) to (iii) at the end of the experiment and then continue bubbling ethene through the solution. What is the dense oily liquid which is eventually formed at the bottom of the tube?
3. Repeat (2) above, shaking a few drops of cyclohexene with 2 or 3 cm^3 of each of the three reagents.

7.7 Dienes

A diene is a compound that contains two double bonds in its molecule. The most important of the dienes is *buta*-1,3-*diene*, $CH_2\!\!=\!\!CHCH\!\!=\!\!CH_2$, b.p. $-3°$, which is used to manufacture synthetic rubber (see Unit 21.8(*b*)). 2-*Methylbuta*-1,3-*diene* (isoprene), $CH_2\!\!=\!\!C(CH_3)CH\!\!=\!\!CH_2$, b.p. 35°, also polymerizes to form a rubbery substance when heated with sodium at 60° or with a Ziegler-type catalyst (see Unit 7.6(*j*)):

$$nCH_2\!\!=\!\!C(CH_3)CH\!\!=\!\!CH_2 \longrightarrow \left[CH_2-\underset{\underset{CH_3}{|}}{C}\!\!=\!\!CH-CH_2\right]_n$$

Manufacture. Buta-1,3-diene is prepared on an industrial scale by dehydrogenating butane or but-1-ene (from cracked petroleum) over a heated catalyst of chromium(iii) oxide on an alumina support:

$$\left.\begin{array}{l} CH_3CH_2CH_2CH_3 \\ \text{or} \\ CH_3\!\!=\!\!CHCH_2CH_3 \end{array}\right\} \xrightarrow[600°]{Cr_2O_3/Al_2O_3} CH_2\!\!=\!\!CHCH\!\!=\!\!CH_2 + 2H_2$$
$$\text{buta-1,3-diene}$$

7.8 Uses of Alkenes

Alkenes, and particularly ethene, are important starting compounds in the chemical industry. They are sources of alcohols, especially ethanol and propanol (see Unit 7.6(f)), plastics (see Unit 7.6(j)), ethanal and propanone (see Unit 15.3) and epoxyethane (see Unit 14.8)—and hence of ethanediol and a wide range of solvents and detergents.

Test Yourself on Unit 7

1. Name the following compounds:
   (a) 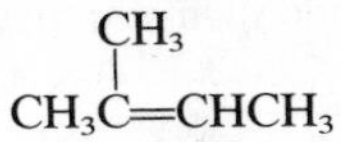
   $$CH_3C=CHCH_3$$
   with CH_3 attached above
   (b) $CH_2=CHBr$
   (c) $CH_3CH=CHCH=CH_2$
   (d) $CH_2=CHCH_2C(CH_3)_3$
   (e) CH_3CH_2, H and C=C and H, CH_2CH_3

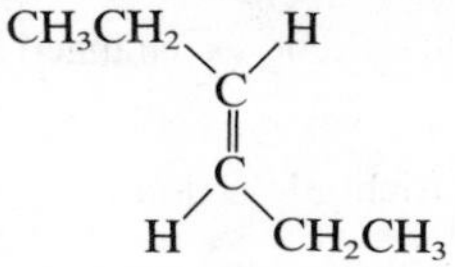

2. Write structural formulae for the following compounds:
   (a) cyclobutene;
   (b) 2,3,3,4,4-pentamethylpent-1-ene;
   (c) 2-methylpropene;
   (d) methylbuta-1,3-diene;
   (e) 3-phenylprop-1-ene.

3. Explain what is meant by the following:
   (a) Markownikoff's Rule;
   (b) peroxide effect;
   (c) addition polymerization.

4. 'Addition to alkenes can proceed via an ionic or a free-radical mechanism depending on the reaction conditions'. Discuss this statement with respect to the polymerization and bromination of ethene.

5. Compare and contrast the structure and reactions of the alkanes and alkenes.

Indicate whether the statements 6 to 16 are true or false.

6. The alkenes are isomeric with cycloalkanes.

7. There is free rotation about the carbon–carbon double bond of alkenes.

8. An alcohol such as ethanol may be dehydrated to form either an alkene or an ether.

9. Propan-1-ol may be obtained from propan-2-ol by the following sequence of reactions:

$$CH_3CHOHCH_3 \xrightarrow[-H_2O]{Al_2O_3/heat} CH_3CH{=}CH_2 \xrightarrow[+H_2O]{steam/catalyst} CH_3CH_2CH_2OH$$

10. The melting-points of unsaturated fats and oils are increased by catalytic hydrogenation.

11. Ethene can undergo either substitution or addition with chlorine depending on the reaction conditions.

12. Ethene reacts more readily with hydrogen chloride than with hydrogen iodide.

13. Di(benzoyl) peroxide is an initiator of radical reactions.

14. Ethene may be prepared in the laboratory by boiling iodoethane with an ethanolic solution of potassium hydroxide.

15. The hybridization of the carbon atoms in ethene is changed by an addition reaction.

16. Polytetrafluoroethene is used for making 'frictionless' joints.

Unit Eight

Alkynes

8.1 General Formula and Nomenclature

The *alkynes* were once known as the *acetylenes* and this name is still widely used (especially in industry) for the first member of the series, C_2H_2:

$$H—C\equiv C—H$$

ethyne (acetylene)

The general formula of the alkynes is C_nH_{2n-2}. The compounds contain a carbon–carbon triple bond and are highly unsaturated. They are named by changing the suffix of the name of the alkane with the same number of carbon atoms from -*ane* to -y*ne*; for example,

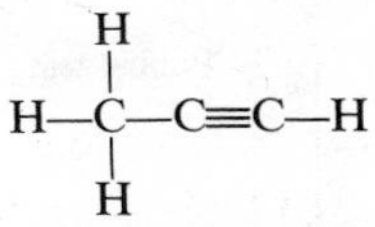

$$\begin{array}{c} H \\ | \\ H—C—C\equiv C—H \\ | \\ H \end{array}$$

C_3H_4, propyne

There are two isomeric butynes (C_4H_6) and the position of the triple bond is indicated by the numbering of the carbon atoms in the chain:

$$CH_3CH_2C\equiv CH \quad \text{and} \quad CH_3C\equiv CCH_3$$
but-1-yne but-2-yne

Ethyne is the most important member of the homologous series. Although many of the preparative methods and reactions described in this Unit apply to any member of the series, the higher alkynes are of trivial commercial importance compared with ethyne, and the rest of this Unit is devoted almost entirely to the chemistry of this compound.

8.2 Manufacture of Ethyne

(a) Pyrolysis of Methane
See Unit 5.7.

(b) Hydrolysis of Calcium Dicarbide
Calcium dicarbide is prepared at Niagara (and in other parts of the world where hydroelectric power is cheap) by heating a mixture of calcium oxide and coke in an electric furnace:

$$CaO \quad + \quad 3C \quad \xrightarrow[2\,500-3\,000°]{\text{electric furnace}} \quad CaC_2 \quad + \quad CO$$
calcium oxide coke calcium dicarbide

The action of water on this compound produces ethyne:

$$CaC_2 + 2H_2O \rightarrow Ca(OH)_2 + C_2H_2$$
$$\text{ethyne}$$

8.3 Preparation of Ethyne

There is rarely any need to prepare ethyne in the laboratory but, if required, it may be obtained by the action of water on calcium dicarbide.

Experiment 8.1 *Preparation of ethyne*
Set up the apparatus shown in Fig. 8.1. Add water drop by drop from the dropping pipette to small lumps of calcium dicarbide and collect the ethyne produced in test-tubes over water. These samples may be used to carry out the general reactions of alkynes described in Experiment 8.2; alternatively, the gas may be bubbled directly through solutions of the reagents.

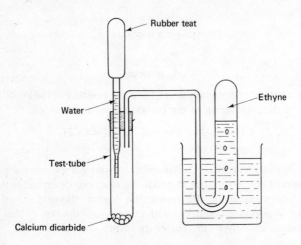

Fig. 8.1   Preparation of ethyne

The gas obtained by this method is impure and contains traces of hydrogen sulphide, phosphine and arsine. These impurities may be removed by passing the gas through aqueous copper(II) sulphate. Very pure ethyne is produced by the action of dilute nitric acid on silver or copper dicarbide (see Unit 8.6(g)). Alkynes are also obtained by the dehydrohalogenation of dihalogenoalkanes:

$$\underset{\text{dihalogenoalkane}}{\overset{\displaystyle -\overset{\displaystyle H}{\underset{\displaystyle H}{C}}-\overset{\displaystyle X}{\underset{\displaystyle X}{C}}-}{}} \quad \xrightarrow[\text{X=Cl, Br or I}]{-2HX} \quad \underset{\text{alkyne}}{-C{\equiv}C-}$$

Both 1,1- and 1,2-dibromoethane, for instance, yield ethyne on boiling with an ethanolic solution of potassium hydroxide:

$$CH_3CHBr_2 \ + 2^-OC_2H_5 \xrightarrow{\text{boil}} C_2H_2 + 2Br^- + 2C_2H_5OH$$
1,1-dibromoethane

$$CH_2BrCH_2Br \ + 2^-OC_2H_5 \xrightarrow{\text{boil}} C_2H_2 + 2Br^- + 2C_2H_5OH$$
1,2-dibromoethane

8.4 Properties of Ethyne

Ethyne is a colourless gas (b.p. $-84°$) which has a sweet 'ethereal' odour when pure. The boiling-points of the first members of the alkyne series are similar to those of the corresponding alkanes (see Fig. 1.4(a)). Ethyne is only sparingly soluble in water, but dissolves readily in propanone (acetone), especially under pressure; it is usually stored in propanone solution absorbed on a suitable inert porous material such as kieselguhr at about 12 atmospheres, as it is explosive in both the compressed and the liquid states. Ethyne burns incompletely in air with a smoky luminous flame which indicates the compound's high carbon content (see Unit 7.4). The combustion is strongly exothermic, and flame temperatures in excess of 3 000° may be reached by burning ethyne in controlled amounts of oxygen. The gas is widely used in 'oxy-acetylene' welding.

8.5 Structure and Reactivity of Ethyne

The two carbon atoms in ethyne are sp^1 hybridized and the molecule is linear, with π bonds at right angles to one another above, below and on either side of the molecule (see Unit 4.4(d) and Fig. 4.11). This structure is highly susceptible to electrophilic attack and its principal reactions, like those of ethene (see Unit 7.6), involve addition to the multiple bond to form a saturated compound; Markownikoff's Rule (see Unit 7.6(c)) applies to the addition of unsymmetrical reactants (such as water or hydrogen halides) to unsymmetrical alkynes.

A hydrogen atom attached to an alkynic carbon is very weakly acidic ($pK_a = 26$ approximately):

$$\text{B:} + \text{H—C} \equiv \text{C—H} \ \rightleftharpoons \ \text{B} \overset{+}{\text{H}} + \text{H—C} \equiv \overset{-}{\text{C}}$$
base

and may be replaced by some metals (see Unit 8.6(g)).

8.6 Reactions of Ethyne

(a) Hydrogenation
Ethyne is reduced by hydrogen in the pressure of a suitable catalyst, such as

nickel at 150° or platinum or palladium at room temperature:

$$H-C\equiv C-H \xrightarrow{H_2/catalyst} \begin{array}{c} H \\ \diagdown \\ \end{array} C=C \begin{array}{c} H \\ \diagup \\ \end{array} \xrightarrow{H_2/catalyst} H-\underset{\underset{H}{|}}{\overset{\overset{H}{|}}{C}}-\underset{\underset{H}{|}}{\overset{\overset{H}{|}}{C}}-H$$

ethyne   ethene   ethane

The hydrogenation proceeds via the formation of ethene. The reaction can be stopped at this intermediate stage by using the calculated amount of hydrogen in the presence of Adams' catalyst (see Unit 5.2(a)).

(b) Addition of Halogens

The reaction between ethyne and chlorine is explosive in the absence of a catalyst (especially in sunlight) and yields a mixture of carbon and hydrogen chloride:

$$C_2H_2 + Cl_2 \xrightarrow[\text{no catalyst}]{\text{sunlight}} 2C + 2HCl$$

The reaction is moderated by mixing the ethyne and chlorine in the dark or allowing them to react in the presence of kieselguhr and iron filings or a metal halide catalyst such as antimony trichloride. Under these conditions electrophilic addition occurs:

$$H-C\equiv C-H \xrightarrow[\text{catalyst}]{Cl_2} CHCl = CHCl \xrightarrow[\text{catalyst}]{Cl_2} CHCl_2CHCl_2$$

1,2-dichloroethene   1,1,2,2-tetrachloroethane

Bromine reacts less violently than chlorine; bromine water yields the dibromo-adduct, CHBr=CHBr, and an excess of bromine in the absence of a solvent yields 1,1,2,2-tetrabromoethane (see Unit 8.6(b)):

$$C_2H_2 + 2Br_{2(l)} \rightarrow CHBr_2CHBr_2$$
1,1,2,2-tetrabromoethane

(c) Addition of Hydrogen Halides

Alkynes react with hydrogen halides via the same electrophilic addition mechanism described for alkenes (see Unit 7.6(c)). The order of reactivity is $HF < HCl < HBr < HI$ and the addition is catalysed by metal halides or light, although it will take place in the dark. Hydrogen iodide reacts with ethyne at room temperature, hydrogen bromide at 100°, while hydrogen chloride requires a catalyst such as mercury(II) chloride on activated charcoal. Markownikoff's Rule is obeyed in the addition of hydrogen halide to the ethene intermediate, and hydrogen bromide, for example, yields first bromoethene and then 1,1-dibromoethane:

$$H-C\underset{\underset{H^+}{}}{\equiv}C-H \longrightarrow H-C=C-H \xrightarrow{Br^-} H-\overset{}{C}=\overset{\overset{Br}{|}}{C}\diagdown_H$$
$$\underset{H^+}{|}$$

$$\xrightarrow{H^+} CH_2 \overset{\delta+}{=\!\!=} \overset{\delta-}{CH} \rightarrow Br \longrightarrow H_2C-\overset{+}{C}HBr \xrightarrow{Br^-} CH_3CHBr_2$$
$$\underset{H^+}{|} \qquad\qquad \underset{H}{|} \qquad\qquad\qquad\qquad \text{1,1-dibromoethane}$$

Under the same conditions, propyne yields 2,2-dibromopropane:

$$CH_3 \rightarrow C \equiv \overset{\delta-}{C} \overset{\delta+}{-H} \xrightarrow{\text{2HBr}} CH_3CBr_2CH_3$$

$$\underset{H^+}{} \qquad\qquad \text{2,2-dibromopropane}$$

The reaction can be stopped at the 'half-way' stage when only one mole of hydrogen halide has been added; for example:

$$H-C\equiv C-H \xrightarrow{\text{Hg}^{2+}\text{ catalyst/HCl}_{(aq)}} CH_2=CHCl$$

$$\text{chloroethene}$$

thus illustrating the stability of chloro- or bromo-ethene. This reaction has been used to prepare chloroethene (vinyl chloride) for the manufacture of poly(chloroethene) (see Unit 7.6(j)).

The 'peroxide' or 'anti-Markownikoff' effect on the addition of hydrogen bromide to alkynes operates as for alkenes; for example:

$$H-C\equiv C-H + HBr \xrightarrow{\text{peroxide}} CH_2BrCH_2Br$$

$$\text{1,2-dibromoethane}$$

(d) Hydration

Ethyne reacts with water at 60° in the presence of dilute sulphuric acid and mercury(II) sulphate to yield ethanal:

$$C_2H_2 + H_2O \xrightarrow[60°]{\text{H}^+/\text{HgSO}_4} [CH_2=CHOH] \longrightarrow CH_3-C\overset{H}{\underset{O}{<}}$$

$$\underset{\text{intermediate}}{\text{unstable}}$$

(e) Oxidation

When ethyne is bubbled into aqueous alkaline potassium manganate(VII) solution it is oxidized to ethanedioic acid:

$$\begin{matrix} CH \\ \| \\ CH \end{matrix} \xrightarrow{\text{[O]/NaOH}} \begin{matrix} CO_2Na \\ | \\ CO_2Na \end{matrix}$$

In acidified potassium manganate(VII) solution, however, further oxidation takes place:

$$\begin{matrix} CH \\ \| \\ CH \end{matrix} \xrightarrow[\text{H}^+/\text{KMnO}_4]{\text{[O]}} \begin{matrix} CO_2H \\ | \\ CO_2H \end{matrix} \xrightarrow{\text{[O]}} 2CO_2 + H_2O$$

The purple manganate(VII) solution is decolorized, thus confirming the presence of carbon–carbon unsaturation in ethyne (see Unit 7.6(g)).

(f) Polymerization
(i) Ethyne trimerizes at 400° to form benzene:

$$3C_2H_2 \xrightarrow{400°} C_6H_6$$
benzene

but the reaction is of no practical value (see Unit 9.3(c))
(ii) Ethyne dimerizes in the presence of copper(I) chloride, ammonium chloride and hydrochloric acid to yield but-1-en-3-yne:

$$2H-C\equiv C-H \rightarrow H-C\equiv C-CH=CH_2$$
but-1-en-3-yne

This compound undergoes addition across the triple bond with one molecule of hydrogen chloride to form 2-chlorobuta-1,3-diene (chloroprene):

$$H-C\equiv C-CH=CH_2 + HCl \rightarrow CH_2=CCl-CH=CH_2$$
2-chlorobuta-1,3-diene

which readily polymerizes to form the important synthetic rubber, neoprene (see Unit 21.8(b)).

(g) Formation of Dicarbides
The hydrogen atoms in ethyne are weakly acidic (see Unit 8.5) and may be replaced by a metal. A red precipitate of copper(I) dicarbide is formed when ethyne is bubbled into an ammoniacal solution of copper(I) chloride:

$$C_2H_2 + 2Cu^+ + 2NH_3 \rightarrow \quad Cu_2C_{2(s)} \quad + \quad 2NH_4^+$$
(red precipitate of
copper(I) dicarbide)

Ammoniacal silver nitrate, $[Ag(NH_3)_2]^+NO_3^-$, under similar conditions yields a white precipitate of silver(I) dicarbide, Ag_2C_2. Both these dicarbides are dangerous when dry as they explode on heating or on being subjected to mechanical shock. They dissolve in dilute nitric acid to yield pure ethyne:

$$Ag_2C_2 + 2HNO_3 \rightarrow C_2H_2 + 2AgNO_3$$

The acid hydrogen atoms of ethyne may also be replaced by sodium in liquid ammonia medium:

$$H-C\equiv C-H \xrightarrow[\text{liquid NH}_3]{\text{Na}} H-C\equiv \bar{C}Na^+ \xrightarrow[\text{liquid NH}_3]{\text{Na}} Na^+\bar{C}\equiv \bar{C}Na^+$$
sodium dicarbide

Sodium dicarbide can be used to synthesize the higher alkynes; for example, it reacts with iodomethane to yield propyne:

$$H-C\equiv \bar{C}Na^+ + CH_3I \rightarrow H-C\equiv C-CH_3 + NaI$$
propyne

Alkynes with the general formula R—C≡C—R' do not react with sodium or with aqueous ammoniacal solutions of silver(ɪ) or copper(ɪ) ions. These reactions may therefore be used as a test for the presence of a terminal triple bond.

Experiment 8.2 *Reactions of alkynes*
Carry out the following tests on ethyne prepared as described in Experiment 8.1. Compare your results with those obtained for the alkenes (Experiment 7.3).
Care: ethyne forms explosive mixtures with air. These tests should be carried out on small amounts of the gas only. Safety goggles must be worn and the use of a safety screen is recommended.

1. Bubble the gas through a few cm^3 of a solution of bromine in tetrachloromethane. **(Care: Do not inhale the vapour or allow bromine to come into contact with your skin or eyes.)**

2. Pass ethyne through an alkaline 1 per cent aqueous solution of potassium manganate(vɪɪ).

3. Bubble ethyne through a solution of copper(ɪ) chloride (0.1–0.2 g) in dilute aqueous ammonia. After the experiment dissolve the precipitate obtained in an excess of dilute nitric acid and wash away down the sink with plenty of water.

4. Prepare an ammoniacal solution of silver nitrate (see Appendix II) and pass ethyne into this solution. Dispose of the products of the reaction immediately after the experiment as described in (3).

8.7 Uses of Ethyne

Prior to the development of the petrochemical industry, ethyne (acetylene) was a major starting material for the manufacture of organic compounds. Its synthetic importance is now decreasing, however, as more ethene derivatives are made directly from the alkenes. Chloroethene, for example, is now prepared commercially by the chlorination of ethene (see Unit 7.6(b)(i)), ethanal is increasingly manufactured by the Wacker process (see Unit 15.3(b)) and propenonitrile for the production of acrylic fibres and synthetic rubber is obtained from propene (see Unit 17.8(b)(iv)).
Ethyne is used to prepare chlorinated solvents and for 'oxy-acetylene' welding.

Test Yourself on Unit 8

1. Name the following compounds:
    (a) $(CH_3)_3CCH_2C{\equiv}CCH_3$;
    (b) $CH_3CHClC{\equiv}CH$;
    (c) $CH_3CH{=}CHC{\equiv}CH$;
    (d) $CH_3CH_2C{\equiv}CCH_2CH_3$

2. Write structural formulae for the following compounds:
  (a) 4-chlorobut-1-yne;
  (b) 3-methylpent-3-en-1-yne;
  (c) hexa-1,5-dien-3-yne;
  (d) 5,5-dimethylhex-2-yne.

3. Suggest methods of preparing the following compounds using coke as the sole source of carbon:
  (a) ethane;
  (b) ethanal;
  (c) chloroethene;
  (d) 1,2-dibromoethane.

4. 'Ethyne has been largely superseded by ethene as a starting material for organic synthesis.' Discuss this statement.

5. 8.4 cm^3 of a gaseous hydrocarbon, A, were exploded with 50 cm^3 of oxygen. After cooling to room temperature the volume of the gaseous products was 37.4 cm^3 which contracted to 3.8 cm^3 on treatment with potassium hydroxide. A forms a red precipitate with ammoniacal copper(ɪ) chloride, and a dense oily liquid, B, with boiling aqueous hydrogen bromide.

Identify A and B and write equations for the reactions.

6. Discuss the meaning of the term *unsaturation*. Illustrate your answer with reference to the structure and reactions of ethane, ethene and ethyne.

Unit Nine

Aromatic Hydrocarbons

9.1 Introduction

Organic compounds are divided for convenience into two main classes: the *aliphatic* and the *aromatic*. The molecules of both saturated and unsaturated aliphatic compounds are open-chain structures or simple rings (see Unit 1.4). Those of aromatic compounds, on the other hand, contain highly stable, unsaturated ring structures, and were so named because they were first isolated from balsams, gums, resins and other sweet-smelling or 'aromatic' oils. These compounds were found to be derivatives of benzene, an unsaturated, but nevertheless stable, cyclic molecule containing six carbon atoms. The term *aromatic compound* is now used to describe both benzene and its derivatives (the *benzenoid compounds*) and also other substances having similar stable unsaturated structures; aromatic hydrocarbons are sometimes called *arenes*.

Benzene has the molecular formula C_6H_6 and is represented as a regular hexagon

of which each corner represents a carbon atom linked to an atom of hydrogen. Benzene derivatives are formed by the replacement of one or more of these hydrogen atoms by other atoms or groups of atoms. For example:

Cl CH_3

chlorobenzene methylbenzene (toluene)

The positions of the substituents attached to the ring are indicated by numbering the carbon atoms of the benzene nucleus (or, for disubstituted benzene derivatives, by using the older-style prefixes *ortho-*, *meta-* or *para-*, often abbreviated to *o*-, *m*- and *p*-). The three isomeric dichlorobenzenes, for example, are:

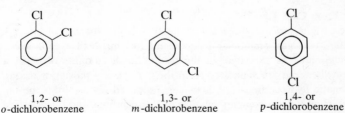

1,2- or   1,3- or   1,4- or
o-dichlorobenzene *m*-dichlorobenzene *p*-dichlorobenzene

1,2- and 1,6-dichlorobenzene are clearly the same compound, and 1,3- and 1,5-dichlorobenzene are similarly identical.

9.2 Manufacture of Benzene and its Homologues

(a) From Petroleum

Aromatic hydrocarbons occur in petroleum, from which they can be separated by fractional distillation (see Unit 6.3); in practice, however, they are principally prepared from the non-aromatic constituents. Unbranched-chain alkanes undergo cyclization and dehydrogenation (*catalytic reforming*) when heated under pressure with a suitable catalyst (see Unit 6.5):

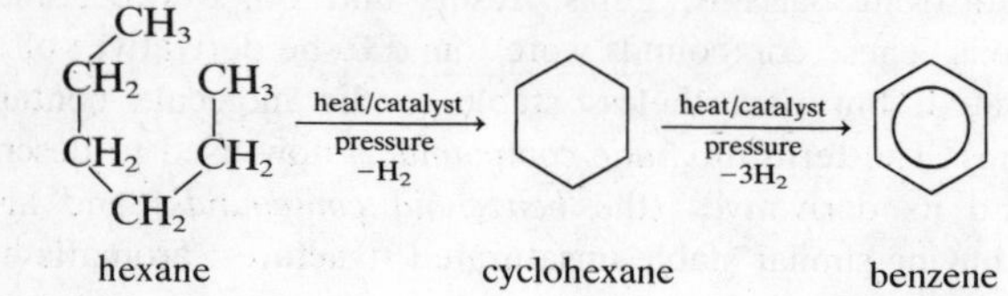

hexane   cyclohexane   benzene

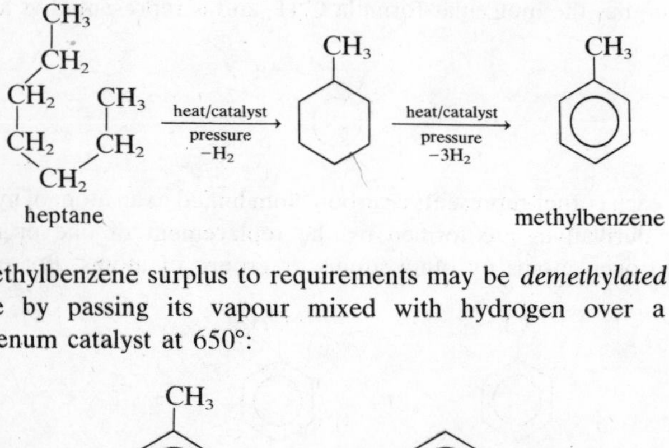

heptane   methylbenzene

Any methylbenzene surplus to requirements may be *demethylated* to yield benzene by passing its vapour mixed with hydrogen over a cobalt–molybdenum catalyst at 650°:

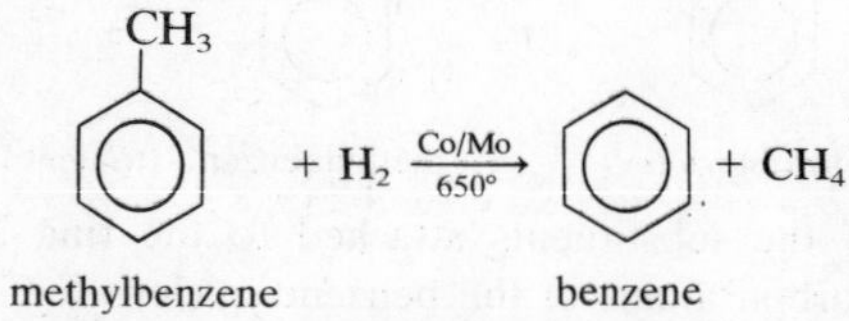

methylbenzene   benzene

Catalytic reforming is now the principal commercial source of benzene and its homologues in the United Kingdom.

(b) From Coal Tar

If coal is *destructively distilled* by heating in the absence of air at 1 000–1 200°, coal gas, ammoniacal liquor and coal tar distil over in succession, leaving coke as a residue in the retort. Small amounts of benzene and methylbenzene are separated from the coal gas by passing it through oil; aromatic hydrocarbons are, however, produced mainly from the tar fraction. Coal tar is a complex mixture of hydrocarbons and phenols (see Unit

13), the precise composition of which depends on the conditions used for carbonization. After removing any water present, the coal tar is fractionally distilled and the first fraction, after further purification, is redistilled to yield benzene and methylbenzene.

9.3 Preparation of Benzene and its Homologues

There is rarely any need to prepare benzene or methylbenzene in the laboratory, as both compounds are readily available from commercial sources; the following reactions have some 'synthetic' interest, however.

(a) From Salts of Aromatic Acids

Benzene and methylbenzene are obtained when sodium benzoate and sodium methylbenzoate respectively are heated with soda-lime:

$$ArCO_2^-Na^+ + \text{`NaOH'} \xrightarrow{heat} ArH + Na_2CO_3$$
$$\text{soda-lime}$$

Compare the preparation of methane described in Unit 5.3.

(b) From Phenol

Phenol is reduced to benzene on distillation with zinc dust:

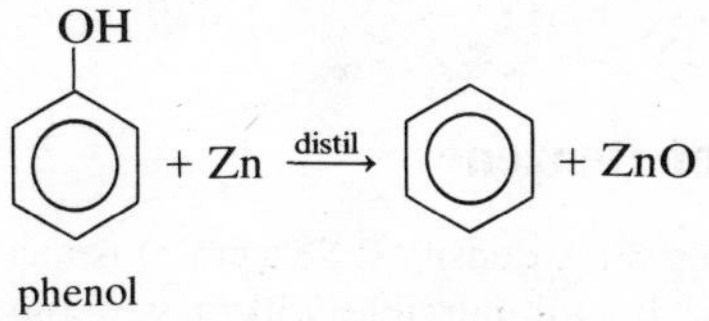

phenol

The yields from this reaction are poor.

(c) From Ethyne

Ethyne polymerizes to form benzene (plus a large number of other products) when it is passed through a red-hot tube:

$$3C_2H_2 \xrightarrow{400°} C_6H_6$$

Yields are poor and the method has little preparative use, except for the synthesis of isotopically labelled benzene, in which the hydrogen atoms have been replaced by deuterium (D):

$$CaC_2 + 2D_2O \rightarrow C_2D_2 + Ca(OD)_2$$
calcium
dicarbide

$$3C_2D_2 \xrightarrow[catalyst]{heat} C_6D_6$$
hexadeuterobenzene

Hexadeuterobenzene can also be prepared by isotopic exchange of the hydrogen atoms with deuterium bromide:

$$C_6H_6 + 6DBr \xrightarrow{\text{boil}} C_6D_6 + 6HBr$$
$$\text{(excess)}$$

(d) The Wurtz–Fittig Reaction

This is analogous to the Wurtz reaction for the preparation of alkanes from halogenoalkanes (see Unit 5.2(b)). In the Wurtz–Fittig reaction, benzene homologues are obtained when a mixture of a halogenoalkane and a halogenoarene in ethoxyethane is treated with sodium; for instance:

bromobenzene   bromoethane   ethylbenzene

Yields are often low, however, owing to the formation of biphenyl, butane and other by-products.

(e) Friedel–Crafts Reaction

See Unit 9.6(b)(iv).

9.4 Properties of Benzene

Benzene (m.p. 5°, b.p. 80°; density $0.88\,\text{g cm}^{-3}$) is a colourless liquid with a characteristic odour. It is immiscible with water, but is readily soluble in organic solvents and is itself a useful solvent for phosphorus, iodine, oils, fats and resins. Like all aromatic compounds, it burns with a smoky, luminous flame which indicates its high carbon content. Benzene vapour is toxic if inhaled over long periods and can induce anaemia.

9.5 Structure of Benzene

The molecular formula of benzene, C_6H_6, implies a high degree of unsaturation (compare the saturated alkane C_6H_{14}). Benzene will, for example, add hydrogen or chlorine to yield C_6H_{12} and $C_6H_6Cl_6$ respectively. This indicates the presence of three double bonds, which is confirmed by the formation of a triozonide, $C_6H_6(O_3)_3$ (cf. Unit 9.6(a)(iii)). Benzene does not, however, exhibit the addition reactions typical of alkenes and alkynes: it does not react with hydrogen chloride, hydrogen bromide, chloric(I) acid or with cold alkaline potassium manganate(VII) or other oxidizing agents. Sulphuric acid reacts by *substitution* and not by addition, and the reactions of benzene with nitric acid, and with chlorine, bromine and iodine in the absence of ultra-violet light, also proceed via substitution. What kind of structure, apparently containing three double bonds, can account for this unexpected stability?

The existence of only one monosubstituted derivative, C_6H_5X, ruled out all linear structures, such as

$$HC\equiv C-CH_2-CH_2-C\equiv CH \text{ or } CH_2=CH-C\equiv C-CH=CH_2$$

and is evidence for a cyclic molecule like that suggested by Kekulé in 1865:

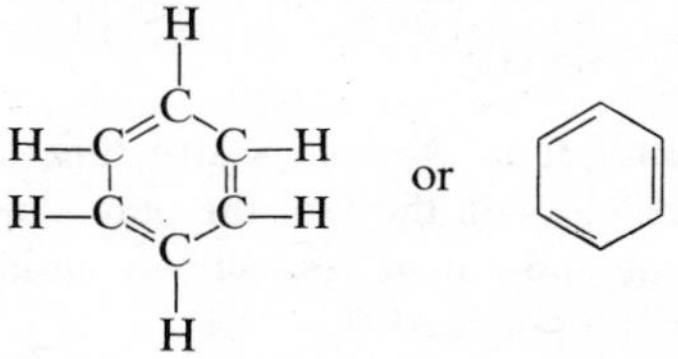

But this structure did not account for the existence of only three disubstituted derivatives, $C_6H_4X_2$:

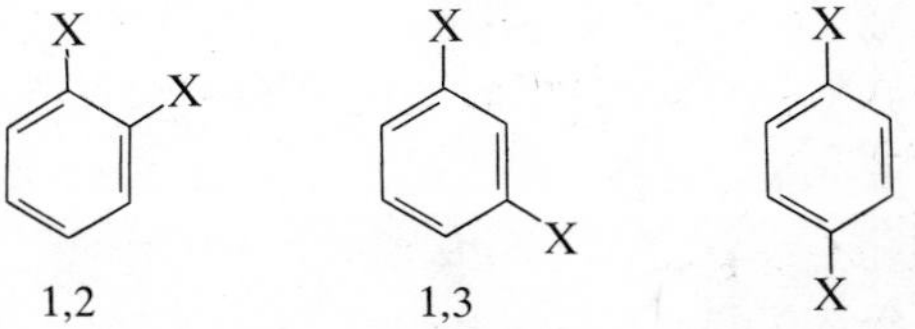

In 1869, Ladenberg pointed out that if Kekulé's proposed structure were correct, two 1,2-isomers should exist:

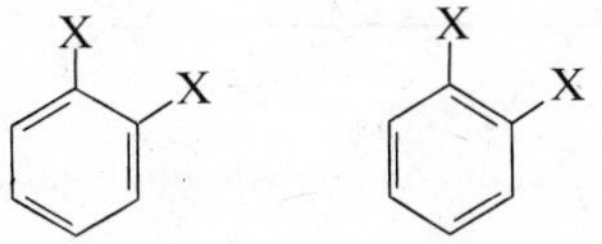

To meet this objection, Kekulé suggested that a benzene molecule rapidly alternates between two forms in equilibrium with each other:

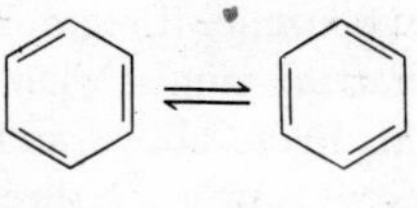

Even this modification, however, did not explain why benzene does not undergo the addition reactions characteristic of alkenes.

Much later, the *resonance theory* suggested that the actual distribution of the electrons in a benzene molecule could not be accurately represented by a single structural diagram, and that the true structure was a hybrid of several canonical forms (see Unit 4.6(c)), each containing the same number of electrons. Thus benzene is a *resonance hybrid* of the two Kekulé

formulae

with smaller contributions from structures such as

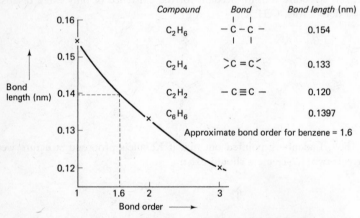

All six carbon–carbon bonds in such a structure are identical and by comparing the bond length with those of the pure single, double and triple bonds in ethane, ethene and ethyne respectively an indication of the bond order for benzene can be obtained (Fig. 9.1).

Compound	Bond	Bond length (nm)
C_2H_6	$-C-C-$	0.154
C_2H_4	$>C=C<$	0.133
C_2H_2	$-C\equiv C-$	0.120
C_6H_6		0.1397

Approximate bond order for benzene = 1.6

Fig. 9.1   Correlation of bond length and bond order for benzene

The Molecular Orbital Theory

This theory (see Units 4.3 and 4.4) gives a more satisfactory explanation of the structure and reactivity of benzene. It regards all six carbon atoms in the ring as sp^2 hybridized, so that the ring is planar with the six $2p_y$ atomic orbitals at right angles to this plane above and below the ring. These p_y orbitals do not overlap in pairs to form the three double bonds alternating with three single bonds of either of the Kekulé structures, but all six interact together to form a continuous π molecular orbital above and below the ring. A very stable structure is thus obtained in which the six delocalized electrons from the p orbitals are free to move over the entire ring and any substitutents attached to it (Fig. 9.2).

This stable π layer is lost when benzene undergoes addition reactions; thus its hydrogenation, for example, is more difficult than that of alkenes

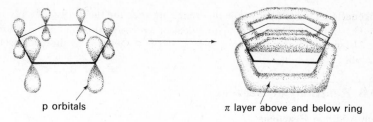

p orbitals   π layer above and below ring

Fig. 9.2   Structure of the benzene molecule

and the addition of chlorine or bromine only occurs in the presence of ultra-violet light (*cf.* Unit 7.6(*b*)). Benzene and its derivatives react predominantly by substitution of the hydrogen atoms attached to the ring. Electrophiles (see Unit 4.7) are attached to the π layer and the reaction proceeds with overall retention of the aromatic character of the ring.

The positive charge in the intermediate I is spread over the remaining five carbon atoms via the π molecular orbital. The structure of the intermediate is a resonance hybrid of the canonical forms:

It is sufficiently stable to have been isolated as a salt in some reactions at low temperatures.

Resonance (or delocalization) energy. An indication of the enhanced stability conferred by the delocalization of the electrons is given by the resonance energy. If either of the Kekulé canonical forms represented the true structure of benzene, and if there were no interaction between the three separate double bonds, the heat of hydrogenation of benzene to form cyclohexane would be expected to be three times that of cyclohexene.

cyclohexene $\xrightarrow[\Delta H = -120 \text{ kJ mol}^{-1}]{+H_2}$ cyclohexane $\xleftarrow{+3H_2}$ benzene

The experimental value ($\Delta H = -208 \text{ kJ mol}^{-1}$) is considerably less than this, showing that benzene is a more stable structure than one containing three alkene-like double bonds. The difference between the theoretical $(3 \times 120 = 360 \text{ kJ mol}^{-1})$ and the experimental heat of hydrogenation (i.e. $360 - 208 = 152 \text{ kJ mol}^{-1}$) is the *resonance energy* and is a measure of this increased stability.

9.6 Reactions of Benzene

(a) Addition Reactions
(i) **Hydrogenation.** Benzene vapour reacts with hydrogen to yield cyclohexane:

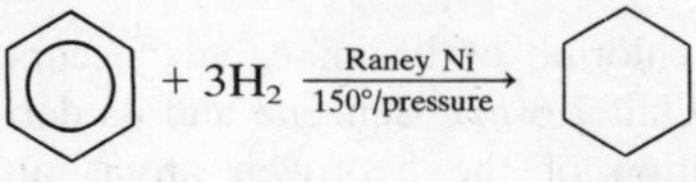

cyclohexane

(ii) **Halogenation.** In the presence of ultra-violet light, benzene reacts with chlorine by addition:

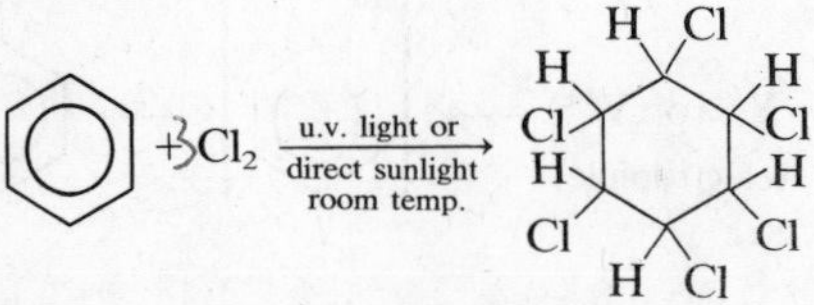

The white crystalline product is a mixture of geometrical isomers, one of which is an important insecticide, 'Gamma-HCH', which is sold commercially as *Gammexane* or *lindane*. The reaction proceeds via a free-radical mechanism (*cf.* Units 5.5(*b*) and 7.6(*b*)(i)):

$$\cdot Cl_2 \xrightarrow{h\nu} 2Cl\cdot \qquad \text{(photochemical initiation)}$$

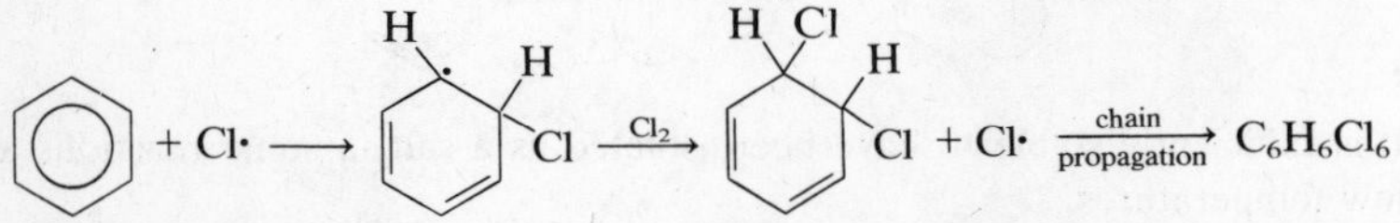

Bromine reacts similarly.

(iii) **Reaction with trioxygen (ozone).** Benzene forms a triozonide (see Unit 7.6(*i*)) which can be hydrolysed to form a dialdehyde:

$$C_6H_6 + 3O_3 \longrightarrow C_6H_6(O_3)_3 \xrightarrow{\text{hydrolysis}} 3 \begin{array}{c} CHO \\ | \\ CHO \end{array}$$

ethanedial

(b) Electrophilic Substitution Reactions
(i) **Halogenation.** Substitution takes place when chlorine (or bromine) reacts with benzene at room temperature in the presence of a suitable catalyst or *halogen carrier.*

$$C_6H_6 + Cl_2 \rightarrow \overset{\cdot}{C}_6H_5Cl + HCl$$

chlorobenzene

The halogen carrier (which may be iron filings, iodine or aluminium chloride or bromide) acts as a Lewis acid or electrophile (see Unit 4.7) which polarizes the halogen molecule and begins a series of reactions which culminates in the formation of chloro- (or bromo-)benzene and regeneration of the catalyst:

$$Al_2Cl_6 \rightleftharpoons 2AlCl_3$$

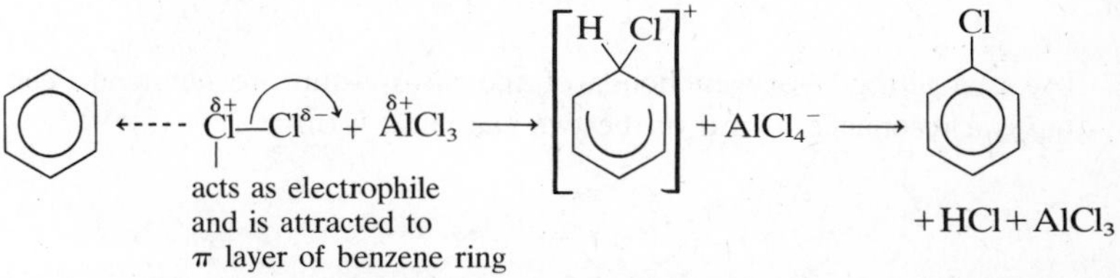

acts as electrophile
and is attracted to
π layer of benzene ring

$+ HCl + AlCl_3$

Iron filings react first with the halogen to form an iron(III) halide which acts similarly to aluminium chloride. Further halogenation of the product is more difficult than the reaction with benzene, and results in a mixture of the 1,2- and the 1,4-disubstituted isomers.

Benzene reacts with iodine to form iodobenzene, but the yield is low unless a base (such as sodium carbonate) or an oxidizing agent (such as nitric acid) is added to remove the hydrogen iodide as it is formed, so as to displace the equilibrium to the right:

$$C_6H_6 + I_2 \rightleftharpoons C_6H_5I + HI$$

(ii) **Nitration.** Benzene reacts with a mixture of equal volumes of concentrated nitric and sulphuric acids to form nitrobenzene. The reaction is exothermic and the temperature must be kept below 55 or 60° to prevent further nitration to 1,3-dinitrobenzene.

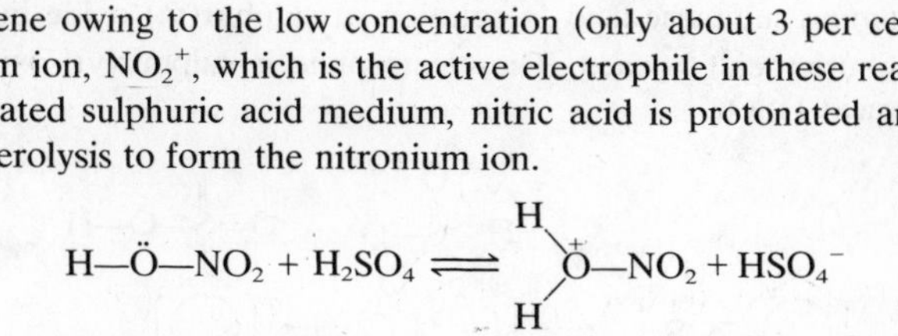

nitrobenzene

Concentrated nitric acid in the absence of sulphuric acid has little effect on benzene owing to the low concentration (only about 3 per cent) of the nitronium ion, NO_2^+, which is the active electrophile in these reactions. In concentrated sulphuric acid medium, nitric acid is protonated and undergoes heterolysis to form the nitronium ion.

Net reaction: $HNO_3 + 2H_2SO_4 \longrightarrow H_3O^+ + NO_2^+ + 2HSO_4^-$

and the mechanism then follows the general pattern of electrophilic substitution:

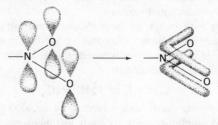

The two nitrogen–oxygen bonds of the nitro-group are identical. The group is a resonance hybrid of the two canonical forms:

that is, the π orbital extends over the nitrogen and both the oxygen atoms (Fig. 9.3).

Fig. 9.3   Structure of the nitro-group

Nitrobenzene (b.p. 211°) is a dense pale-yellow liquid with a characteristic almond-like odour. It is insoluble in water; it is steam-volatile and its vapour is poisonous. Aromatic nitro-compounds are the starting materials for the manufacture of primary aromatic amines and hence of azo-dyes and a wide range of other synthetic products (see Units 18.2(a) and 18.6).

(iii) **Sulphonation.** Benzenesulphonic acid is formed when benzene is heated under reflux for several hours with sulphuric acid. The reaction is faster if fuming sulphuric acid (a solution of sulphur(VI) oxide in concentrated sulphuric acid) is used. The electrophile is sulphur(VI) oxide or its conjugate acid HSO_3^+:

The reaction is reversible, and the aromatic hydrocarbon may be regenerated by heating the sulphonic acid with aqueous hydrochloric acid at 150° under pressure in a sealed tube. The sulphur atom in the aromatic sulphonic acids (general formula: $ArSO_2OH$) is linked directly to a carbon atom, whereas the esters of sulphuric acid, by contrast, contain carbon–oxygen–sulphur groups; for example:

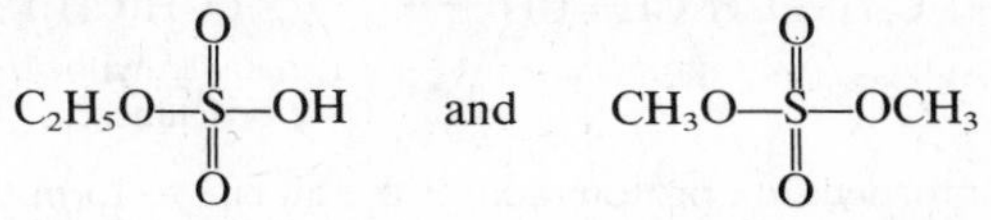

$$C_2H_5O-\overset{\displaystyle O}{\underset{\displaystyle O}{\overset{\|}{\underset{\|}{S}}}}-OH \quad \text{and} \quad CH_3O-\overset{\displaystyle O}{\underset{\displaystyle O}{\overset{\|}{\underset{\|}{S}}}}-OCH_3$$

ethyl hydrogen sulphate   dimethyl sulphate

Benzenesulphonic acid is a colourless, crystalline, deliquescent solid, m.p. 44°, and is a very strong acid, about as strong as sulphuric acid ($pK_a = 0.70$).

(iv) **Friedel–Crafts reaction.** Aromatic hydrocarbons react with halogeno-alkanes or acyl halides in the presence of aluminium chloride to form the corresponding alkyl-substituted hydrocarbon or aromatic ketone respectively:

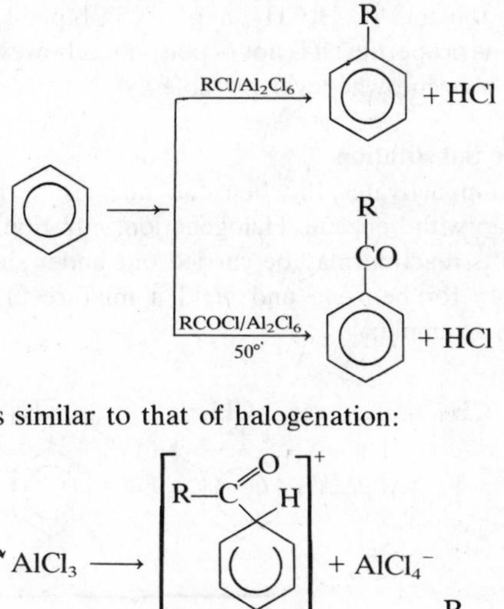

The mechanism is similar to that of halogenation:

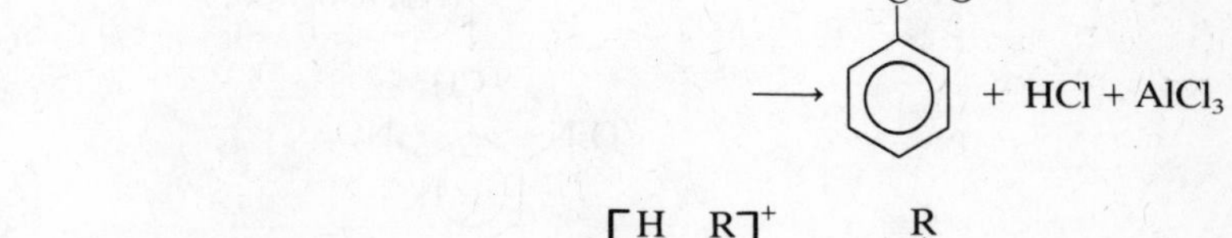

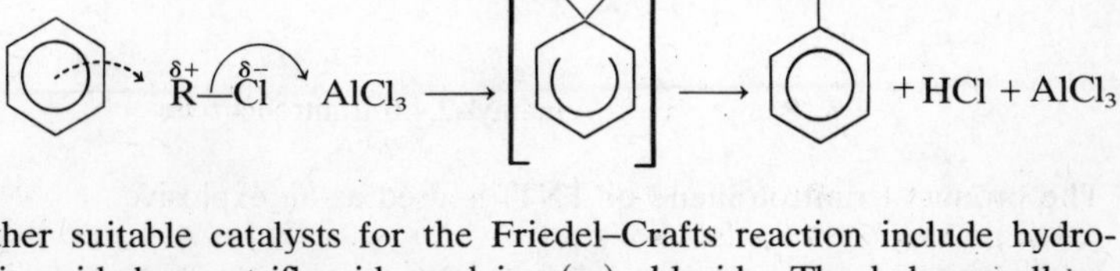

Other suitable catalysts for the Friedel–Crafts reaction include hydro-fluoric acid, boron trifluoride and iron(III) chloride. The halogenoalkane or acyl halide can be replaced by an alkene, an alcohol or an acid anhydride; for example:

$$C_6H_6 + CH_3CH{=}CH_2 \xrightarrow{H^+} C_6H_5CH(CH_3)_2$$

propene   (1-methylethyl)benzene
(cumene)

The reaction proceeds via protonation of the alkene to form the carbonium ion, $(CH_3)_2CH^+$, which acts as the electrophile. (1-Methylethyl)benzene (cumene) is prepared on a large scale using propene from cracked petroleum (see Units 6.6 and 7.2), and is an important source of phenol (C_6H_5OH) and propanone (CH_3COCH_3; see Unit 13.3).

9.7 Methylbenzene

Methylbenzene (toluene) ($C_6H_5CH_3$; m.p. $-95°$, b.p. $111°$) resembles benzene in many of its properties; it is not as poisonous, however, and is therefore used instead of benzene whenever possible.

(a) Electrophilic Substitution

The methyl group activates the benzene nucleus to make electrophilic attack easier than with benzene. Halogenation, nitration, sulphonation and the Friedel–Crafts reaction may be carried out under similar conditions to those appropriate for benzene and yield a mixture of the 1,2- and the 1,4-isomers. For example:

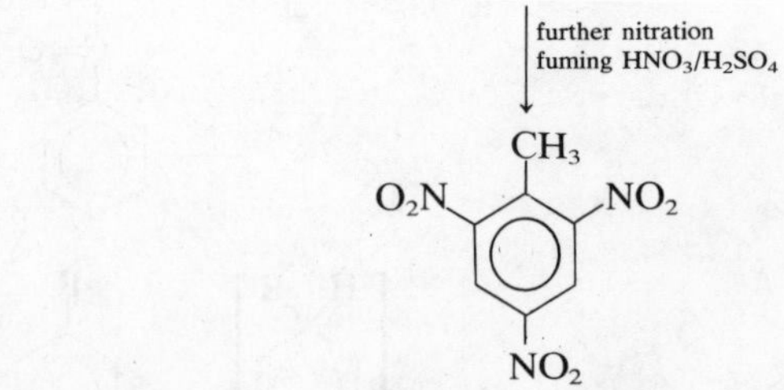

methyl-2,4,6-trinitrobenzene

The product (trinitrotoluene or TNT) is used as an explosive.

(b) Addition to the Ring

Methylbenzene is reduced to methylcyclohexane on reaction with hydrogen in the presence of nickel at 150°:

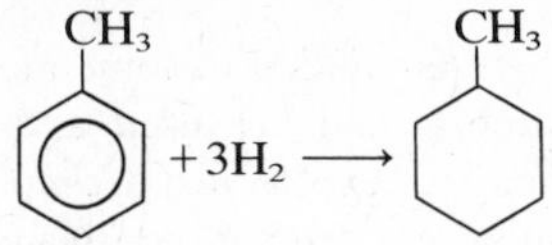

$$CH_3 + 3H_2 \longrightarrow CH_3$$

As might be expected, methylbenzene reacts with trioxygen (ozone) to form a triozonide; chlorine, however, tends to substitute in the methyl side-chain in the presence of ultra-violet light, rather than add on to the benzene ring (see reaction (c)(ii) below).

(c) Reactions of the Side-chain
(i) **Oxidation.** When methylbenzene is heated with acidic or alkaline potassium manganate(vii) or acidified potassium dichromate(vi) solution, the side-chain is oxidized with the formation of a carboxy-group:

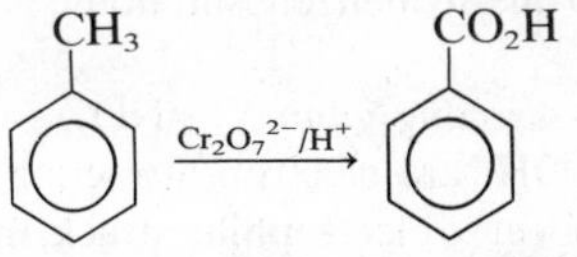

$$CH_3 \xrightarrow{Cr_2O_7^{2-}/H^+} CO_2H$$

benzoic acid

Milder oxidizing agents, such as chromium(vi) dichloride dioxide, CrO_2Cl_2, or manganese(iv) oxide only partially oxidize methylbenzene, yielding benzaldehyde, C_6H_5CHO.

(ii) **Chlorination.** The hydrogen atoms of the side-chain are progressively replaced when chlorine is passed into boiling methylbenzene in ultra-violet light. The reaction may be stopped at any stage when the theoretical mass increase has been attained. No catalyst is required; the reaction proceeds by a free-radical mechanism similar to that described for the chlorination of methane (see Unit 5.5(b)). The change in oxidation state in each of these stages is apparent when the hydrolysis products of the chlorinated derivatives are considered.

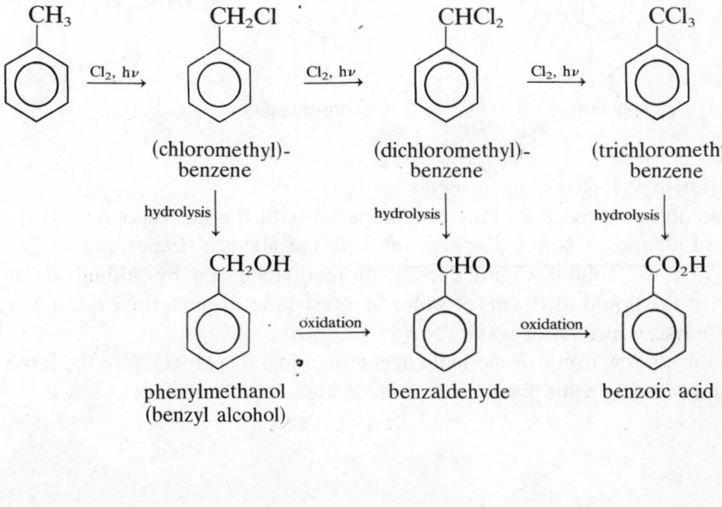

$$CH_3 \xrightarrow{Cl_2,\ h\nu} CH_2Cl \xrightarrow{Cl_2,\ h\nu} CHCl_2 \xrightarrow{Cl_2,\ h\nu} CCl_3$$

| (chloromethyl)-benzene | (dichloromethyl)-benzene | (trichloromethyl)-benzene |

hydrolysis ↓ hydrolysis ↓ hydrolysis ↓

$$CH_2OH \xrightarrow{oxidation} CHO \xrightarrow{oxidation} CO_2H$$

phenylmethanol (benzyl alcohol)   benzaldehyde   benzoic acid

9.8 Uses of Benzene and its Homologues

Benzene and methylbenzene are added to some motor fuels to increase the octane number (see Unit 6.4) and are used as solvents and as the raw materials for the manufacture of explosives, dyes, plastics, insecticides and a large number of other important aromatic derivatives.

9.9 Substitution of Monosubstituted Benzene Derivatives

Three disubstituted products are possible when a monosubstituted benzene is subjected to further attack. Both the orientation of the product and the relative ease of reaction with the attacking electrophile are determined by the substituent already attached to the ring, and *not* by the nature of the attacking group. On sulphonation, for example, nitrobenzene yields *m*-nitrobenzenesulphonic acid; methylbenzene, on the other hand, forms a mixture of the *o*- and *p*-methylbenzenesulphonic acids, and chlorobenzene reacts analogously.

In general, the *meta-directing groups* (—NO_2, —CN, —CO_2H, --CHO, —COR, —CCl_3, —SO_2OH) are electron-attracting ($-I$ effect) and deactivate the nucleus with respect to electrophilic attack, making substitution more difficult than in benzene itself.

The *ortho-/para-directing groups* (alkyl, halogeno-, —O^-, —OH, —OR, —NH_2, —NHR, —NR_2) on the other hand, are *either* electron-releasing ($+I$ effect) *or*, having a $-I$ effect, possess an unshared pair of electrons. Except for halogen, the *ortho-/para*-directing groups strongly activate the benzene nucleus. For example, the aromatic ring in the phenol and phenylamine molecules is so susceptible to electrophilic substitution that these compounds react with bromine water at room temperature in the absence of a halogen carrier to form the tribromo-derivative; for example:

phenol   2,4,6-tribromophenol

Experiment 9.1 *Reactions of methylbenzene*
The results of these tests may be compared with the corresponding reactions of alkanes, alkenes (Experiment 7.3) and alkynes (Experiment 8.2).

1. Test the solubility and density of methylbenzene by adding about 1 cm^3 of the liquid to 10 cm^3 of water in a test-tube. Repeat the experiment using ethanol instead of water.

2. Burn a few drops of methylbenzene on a metal spatula. Note the large amount of soot in the flame, indicating a high carbon content.

3. Add 1 cm³ of a solution of bromine in tetrachloromethane to half a dozen drops of methylbenzene in a test-tube.

4. Add 5 drops of bromine to 1 cm³ of methylbenzene in a dry test-tube. Allow the mixture to stand for a few minutes and note whether any gas is evolved. Now add some iron filings to the tube. Test any gas evolved with ammonia and with moist blue litmus paper. How do you account for the effect of the iron filings?

5. *Nitration*. Add 2 cm³ of methylbenzene slowly to a boiling-tube containing 10 cm³ of a mixture of equal volumes of concentrated sulphuric acid and nitric acid. Shake the mixture well for two or three minutes, cooling the tube, meanwhile under a cold tap, and then pour the contents into a beaker of water. Note whether a solid or a new liquid is obtained. Decant the supernatant liquid (**Care: this solution is strongly acidic**) and wash the residue with water. Note the smell and colour of the organic product.

6. *Sulphonation*. Add 1 cm³ of methylbenzene slowly to 2 cm³ of fuming sulphuric acid (oleum) (**Care!**) in a test-tube. Allow the test-tube to stand in a beaker of water at about 70° for two or three minutes and observe whether a separate organic layer is obtained. (Liquid alkanes under similar conditions float unchanged on the surface of the acid.) Pour the mixture into 20 cm³ of cold water, stirring meanwhile; a clear solution of the highly soluble aromatic sulphonic acid is obtained.

Test Yourself on Unit 9

Indicate whether the following statements are true or false:

1. The chemistry of aromatic hydrocarbons is characterized by easy elimination and addition reactions.

2. Benzene burns in air with a smoky flame owing to its high carbon content.

3. Ethylbenzene is isomeric with the three dimethylbenzenes.

4. The benzene ring is resistant to oxidation.

5. All the bond angles in benzene are 120°.

6. The terms *ortho-*, *para-* and *meta-* refer respectively to the 1,2-, 1,3- and 1,4-isomers of disubstituted benzene.

7. All the properties of benzene can be explained if it is assumed that it consists of an equilibrium mixture of the two structures:

8. The benzene ring is formed by the overlap of the sp³ hybridized atomic orbitals of the six carbon atoms.

9. Compounds having delocalized electrons tend to be less reactive than their structural formulae might suggest, as the electrons have greater freedom of movement, thus lowering their energy and increasing the stability of the molecule.

10. The carbon–carbon bond is shorter in benzene than in ethene.

11. The symbol ↔ between two structures indicates that they are in equilibrium with one another.

12. Benzene has a lower heat of hydrogenation than would be expected if the molecule had three double bonds.

13. Iodine acts as a catalyst in the chlorination of benzene by polarizing the chlorine molecule and enabling it to act as an electrophile.

14. Nitric acid can ionize to form either NO_3^- or NO_2^+ ions.

15. Except for the aryl and alkyl groups, benzenesulphonic acid and ethyl hydrogen sulphate have the same structure.

16. Light-catalysed chlorination of methylbenzene results in side-chain substitution while benzene, under the same conditions, undergoes an addition reaction.

17. 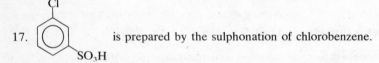   is prepared by the sulphonation of chlorobenzene.

18. Methyl-4-nitrobenzene may be prepared by the reaction of chloromethane with nitrobenzene in the presence of anhydrous aluminium chloride.

Unit Ten

Halogen Compounds: Aliphatic

10.1 General Formula and Nomenclature

The halogenoalkanes are formed by the replacement of one or more hydrogen atoms in an alkane molecule by halogen atoms. The general formula for a monohalogenoalkane is therefore $C_nH_{2n+1}X$ (or R—X) where R— is an alkyl group and X a halogen atom. Fluorine often behaves differently from the other halogens; in this and the following Unit, therefore, X refers to chlorine, bromine or iodine only, unless otherwise stated.

Halogenoalkanes are named as derivatives of the corresponding alkanes; the positions of the halogen atoms are indicated (if necessary) by the numbering of the carbon atoms of the chain. For example:

$$C_2H_5Br \qquad\qquad CH_3CHClCH_3 \qquad\qquad CH_3{-}\overset{\displaystyle CH_3}{\underset{\displaystyle Cl}{\overset{|}{\underset{|}{C}}}}{-}CH_3$$

bromoethane   2-chloropropane   2-chloro-2-methylpropane

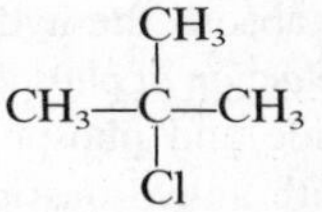

Classification of halogen compounds. Halogen compounds are classified as *primary*, *secondary* or *tertiary* depending on the number of alkyl (or aryl) groups attached to the carbon atom linked to the halogen:

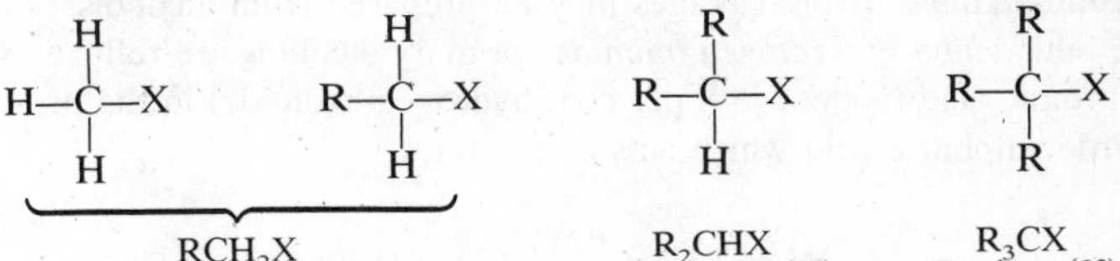

RCH_2X Primary (1°)		R_2CHX Secondary (2°)	R_3CX Tertiary (3°)

10.2 Preparation of Halogenoalkanes

The monohalogenoalkanes are prepared from alcohols, alkenes or alkanes.

(a) From Alcohols
(i) **Chloroalkanes.** The hydroxy-group of an alcohol (ROH) is replaced by chlorine:

1. *by the action of hydrogen chloride* in the presence of anhydrous zinc chloride which acts as a catalyst (*Grove's process*):

$$C_2H_5OH + HCl_{(g)} \xrightarrow{\;ZnCl_2\;} C_2H_5Cl + H_2O$$

ethanol   chloroethane

Tertiary alcohols react readily with concentrated aqueous hydrochloric acid to form the corresponding chloride, even in the absence of a catalyst; for instance:

$$(CH_3)_3COH + HCl_{(aq)} \xrightarrow{\text{no catalyst}} (CH_3)_3CCl + H_2O$$

2-methylpropan-2-ol   2-chloro-2-methylpropane

2. *by the action of sulphur dichloride oxide (thionyl chloride):* sulphur dichloride oxide, $SOCl_2$, is a colourless, fuming liquid (b.p. 77°) which reacts readily with anhydrous alcohols to yield chloroalkanes with evolution of sulphur dioxide and hydrogen chloride. The general equation for the reaction is:

$$ROH + SOCl_2 \rightarrow RCl + SO_2 + HCl$$

An organic base, such as pyridine, is ometimes added to the reaction mixture to absorb the hydrogen chloride.

3. *by the action of phosphorus halides:* phosphorus trichloride, phosphorus pentachloride and phosphorus trichloride oxide (phosphorus oxychloride) all react with anhydrous alcohols to yield chloroalkanes:

$$3ROH + PCl_3 \rightarrow 3RCl + H_3PO_3$$
$$ROH + PCl_5 \rightarrow RCl + POCl_3 + HCl_{(g)}$$
$$3ROH + POCl_3 \rightarrow 3RCl + H_3PO_4$$

(ii) **Bromoalkanes.** Bromoalkanes may be prepared from alcohols:

1. *by the action of hydrogen bromide:* primary alcohols are refluxed with hydrobromic acid (aqueous 48 per cent hydrogen bromide) in the presence of a little sulphuric acid which acts as a catalyst:

$$ROH + HBr \xrightarrow{H_2SO_4} RBr + H_2O$$

When a secondary or tertiary alcohol is used the sulphuric acid is usually omitted, as such alcohols undergo dehydration under these conditions (*cf.* Units 7.3(*a*) and 12.6(*g*)):

$$(CH_3)_2CHOH \xrightarrow[-H_2O]{H_2SO_4} CH_3CH=CH_2$$

The hydrogen bromide for the preparation of a primary bromoalkane may be generated *in situ* by the action of concentrated sulphuric acid on sodium bromide:

$$NaBr + H_2SO_4 \rightarrow NaHSO_4 + HBr$$
$$CH_3CH_2CH_2CH_2OH + HBr \rightarrow CH_3CH_2CH_2CH_2Br + H_2O$$

butan-1-ol   1-bromobutane

2. *by the action of red phosphorus and bromine*:

$$2P + 3Br_2 \rightarrow 2PBr_3$$

$$3ROH + PBr_3 \rightarrow 3RBr + H_3PO_3$$

This reaction is analogous to the preparation of chloroalkanes by the action of the corresponding phosphorus chlorides (see Unit 10.2(*a*)(i)). The bromine reacts with the red phosphorus to yield phosphorus tribromide. (**Note:** *red* phosphorus is used in this preparation. The reaction must **not** be attempted with the highly reactive and toxic yellow allotrope.)

(iii) **Iodoalkanes.** The general methods of preparing iodoalkanes from alcohols are:

1. *by treatment with hydrogen iodide:* the alcohol is refluxed with constant-boiling hydriodic acid (aqueous 57 per cent hydrogen iodide):

$$ROH + HI \rightarrow RI + H_2O$$

Alternatively, the hydriodic acid may be prepared *in situ* by the action of phosphoric(v) acid on potassium iodide:

$$H_3PO_4 + 2KI \rightarrow 3HI + K_3PO_4$$

Sulphuric acid cannot be used for this reaction as hydrogen iodide, a powerful reducing agent, is oxidized to iodine by the acid.

(2) *by the action of red phosphorus and iodine:*

$$2P + 3I_2 \rightarrow 2PI_3$$

$$3ROH + PI_3 \rightarrow 3RI + H_3PO_3$$

(b) From Alkenes

Hydrogen halides add on to the double bond of alkenes to form halogeno-alkanes:

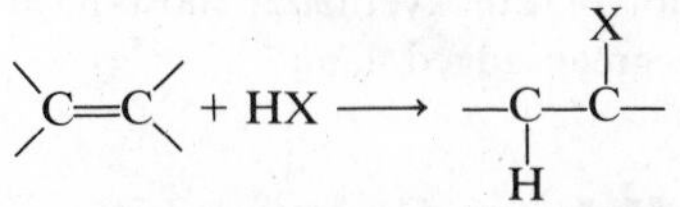

The order of reactivity is HCl < HBr < HI. The reaction conditions and mechanism of this addition were described in Unit 7.6(*c*).

(c) From Alkanes

Alkanes are progressively substituted by chlorine or bromine on heating, or in the presence of ultra-violet light or of a catalyst such as copper(ɪ) chloride for chlorination or iron(ɪɪɪ) bromide for bromination. The mechanism of this reaction was discussed in Unit 5.5(*b*). The monohalogenoalkanes are obtained by using an excess of the alkane to minimize polyhalogenation; for instance:

$$CH_4 + Cl_2 \xrightarrow[\text{or } 400°]{\text{u.v. light}} CH_3Cl + HCl$$

chloromethane

10.3 Manufacture of Halogenoalkanes

Halogenoalkanes (especially the chloro-compounds) are prepared on an industrial scale by the halogenation of alkanes (see Unit 5.5(*b*)) or by the addition of hydrogen chloride to alkenes; for instance:

$$CH_2{=}CH_2 + HCl \longrightarrow \begin{cases} \xrightarrow[\text{Al}_2\text{Cl}_6\text{ at 150–250°}]{\text{vapour phase}} C_2H_5Cl \\[2em] \xrightarrow[\text{Al}_2\text{Cl}_6\text{ at 35–40°}]{\text{liquid phase}} C_2H_5Cl \end{cases}$$

In the United Kingdom chloromethane is obtained mainly by the reaction between methanol and hydrogen chloride in the presence of a zinc chloride or pumice catalyst:

$$CH_3OH + HCl \xrightarrow[\text{catalyst}]{\text{heat}} CH_3Cl + H_2O$$

10.4 Physical Properties of Halogenoalkanes

Chloromethane, bromomethane, chloroethane and chloroethene are colourless gases at room temperature. Most of the other important halogenoalkanes are colourless liquids, and the boiling-points and densities of derivatives of a given alkane, RH, increase in the order $RCl < RBr < RI$. Within a group of isomeric halogen compounds, the order of the boiling-points is tertiary $<$ secondary $<$ primary.

Halogenoalkanes are insoluble in water, but dissolve readily in organic solvents such as ethanol or ethoxyethane; most have a sweet, pleasant odour and burn with a green-edged flame.

10.5 Reactivity of Halogen Compounds

The order of reactivity of the halogen compounds is determined largely by the dissociation energy of the carbon–halogen bond (see Table 4.2). In general, the iodides are more reactive than the bromides, which in turn are more reactive than the chlorides or the fluorides.

The reactivity of the halogenoalkanes is mainly a result of the polarity of the carbon–halogen bond, $R^{\delta+}{-}X^{\delta-}$ (see Unit 4.6(*a*)). The high electronegativity of the halogen atom decreases the electron density on the carbon atom and thus makes it susceptible to *nucleophilic attack*. The principal reactions of the halogenoalkanes involve *substitution* of the halogen atom by nucleophiles, such as OH^-, CN^-, RO^-, NO_2^- and RCO_2^-; for example:

$$HO^- + R^{\delta+}{-}X^{\delta-} \rightarrow HO{-}R + X^-$$

Halogenoalkanes also undergo *elimination reactions* to yield unsaturated compounds; thus 1-bromopropane yields propene on warming with an ethanolic solution of potassium hydroxide:

$$CH_3CH_2CH_2Br + KOH_{(ethanolic)} \xrightarrow{\text{warm}} CH_3CH{=}CH_2 + KBr + H_2O$$

In general, the ease of elimination from halogenoalkanes is greatest for tertiary and least for primary compounds. Chloroethene, $CH_2{=}CHCl$, is unreactive, however; this lack of reactivity arises because the p orbitals of the halogen atom overlap with the π molecular orbitals of the alkene, conferring some double-bond character to the carbon–halogen bond:

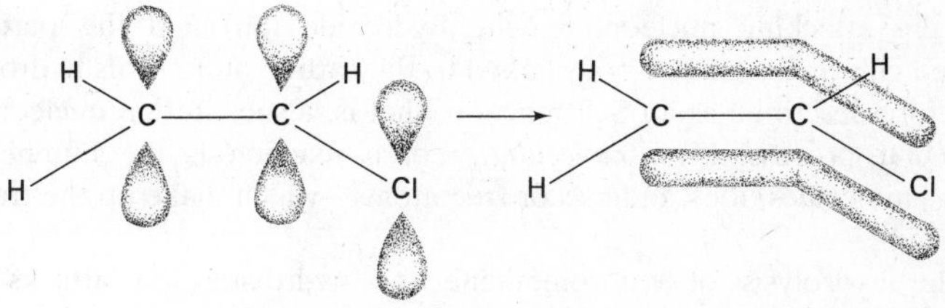

Fig. 10.1   Structure of the chloroethene molecule

This is reflected in a shorter bond length and a higher bond dissociation energy compared with the corresponding chloroalkane (see Table 10.1).

Table 10.1 Bond lengths and bond energies of the carbon–chlorine bond

Compound	Bond length (nm) C—Cl	Dissociation energy C—Cl (kJ mol^{-1})
C_2H_5Cl	0.178	340
$CH_2{=}CHCl$	0.174	435
C_6H_5Cl	0.169	365

10.6 Reactions of Halogenoalkanes

(a) Substitution Reactions
(i) **Hydrolysis.** The halogenoalkanes are hydrolysed to alcohols by boiling with aqueous alkalis or by the action of silver(I) oxide suspended in boiling water:

$$RX + OH^- \rightarrow ROH + X^-$$

The mechanism of this reaction is determined by the structure of the halogen compound. The alkaline hydrolysis of chloromethane and of many other primary halogenoalkanes is a *second-order reaction*—that is, the rate of the hydrolysis depends on the concentrations of both the halogenoalkane and the hydroxide ion:

$$CH_3Cl + OH^- \rightarrow CH_3OH + Cl^-$$

$$Rate = k[CH_3Cl][OH^-]$$

where k is a constant. Since the overall rate of a sequence of reactions is determined by the rate of the slowest step in the sequence—the *rate-determining step*—this equation implies that *both* reactants are involved in the rate-determining step and suggests a *transition state* or intermediate in which the attacking nucleophile (the hydroxide ion) and the partially displaced chlorine atom are both linked to the carbon atom. This hydrolysis is therefore described as an S_N2 reaction, that is, a substitution nucleophile **bi**molecular process. (The *molecularity* of a reaction is the number of species—molecules, ions, radicals or free atoms—which make up the transition state.)

In the hydrolysis of chloromethane the hydroxide ion attacks the electron-deficient carbon atom along the line of centres at the side opposite to the halogen atom:

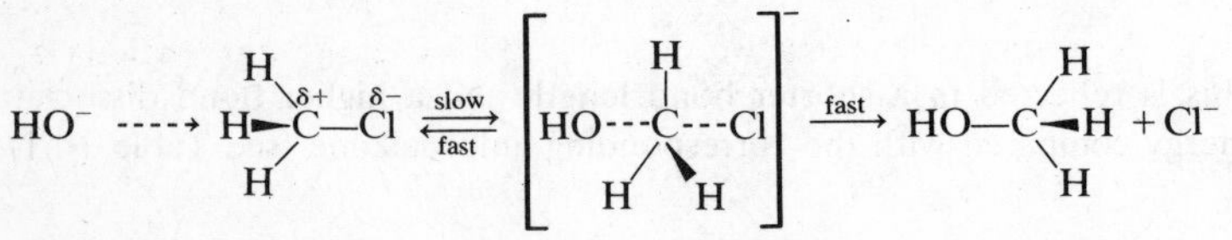

The bonds about the sp^3 hybridized carbon atom have a tetrahedral configuration. Hydrolysis by an S_N2 mechanism inverts this tetrahedron, which results in the inversion of the configuration of an optically active halogenoalkane (see Unit 19.8). In the transition state the alkyl group is planar; thus any structural factors which prevent the formation of a plane, such as the presence of bulky alkyl groups, makes the compound resistant to S_N2 hydrolysis.

The formation of the transition state usually requires energy in the form of heat; thus, although the overall reaction involves a decrease in free energy, an input of energy—the activation energy—is initially required to overcome the activation barrier and to enable the reaction to proceed at a reasonable rate (Fig. 10.2).

The alkaline hydrolysis of tertiary halogenoalkanes such as 2-chloro-2-methylpropane, $(CH_3)_3CCl$, takes place by a different mechanism. The reaction is first-order and the rate of hydrolysis depends only on the concentration of the halogenoalkane:

$$(CH_3)_3CCl + OH^- \rightarrow (CH_3)_3COH + Cl^-$$

$$Rate = k[(CH_3)_3CCl]$$

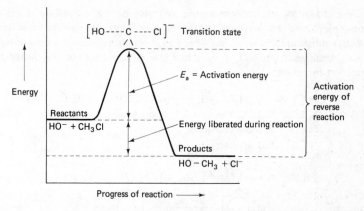

Fig. 10.2   Energy diagram for S_N2 hydrolysis

and is unaffected by the hydroxide ion concentration. The rate-determining step must therefore involve only the halogenoalkane and the reaction is *unimolecular*. The hydrolysis is described as an S_N1 reaction.

A two-step mechanism has been proposed in which the rate-determining step is the ionization (heterolytic fission) of the carbon–halogen bond to yield a highly reactive *carbonium ion*. This intermediate will react rapidly with the hydroxide ion or any other nucleophile present, including the chloride anion or the solvent itself:

$$(CH_3)_3C\!:\!Cl \xrightarrow[\text{ionization}]{\text{slow}} (CH_3)_3C^+ + :Cl^-$$

$(CH_3)_3COH \xleftarrow[\text{v. fast}]{OH^-}$ $\xrightarrow[\text{v. fast}]{:Cl^-}$ $(CH_3)_3CCl$ $\xrightarrow[\text{(nucleophile)}]{X^-}$ $(CH_3)_3CX$ $\xrightarrow{H_2O:}$ $(CH_3)_3C\!:\!\overset{+}{\underset{H}{O}}\!\!\overset{H}{}$

$\xrightarrow{-H^+}$ $(CH_3)_3COH$

The carbonium ion intermediate is stabilized by the use of a polar solvent and by the presence of electron-donating groups: both act by delocalizing the charge on the ion. Secondary halogenoalkanes and the higher primary halogenoalkanes are hydrolysed by both S_N1 and S_N2 mechanisms, proceeding simultaneously in varying ratios. The contribution of each is determined by the degree of stabilization of the carbonium ion provided by the substituent alkyl groups; in the methyl-substituted halogenomethanes, for example, the relation between the reaction rates is shown by:

$$\underset{S_N2}{\overset{H}{\underset{H}{\overset{|}{C^+}}}\overset{H}{}} < \underset{\text{mainly } S_N2}{\overset{H}{\underset{CH_3}{\overset{|}{C^+}}}\overset{H}{}} < \underset{S_N1 + S_N2}{\overset{CH_3}{\underset{CH_3}{\overset{|}{C^+}}}\overset{CH_3}{}} < \underset{S_N1}{\overset{CH_3}{\underset{CH_3}{\overset{|}{C^+}}}\overset{CH_3}{}}$$

The charge on the carbonium ion may also be delocalized by resonance (mesomerism). This accounts for the rapid increase in reaction rates in the phenyl-substituted halogenomethanes as the hydrolysis mechanism progressively changes from S_N2 to S_N1 and the contribution of the faster S_N1 reaction increases:

$$CH_3Cl < C_6H_5CH_2Cl < (C_6H_5)_2CHCl < (C_6H_5)_3CCl$$

| S_N2 | $S_N2 + S_N1$ in aqueous propanone, S_N1 in water | predominantly S_N1 | S_N1 |

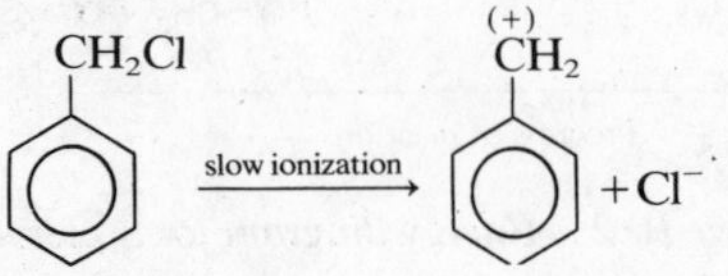

$$\xrightarrow{\text{slow ionization}}$$

This carbonium ion is resonance-stabilized by such forms as:

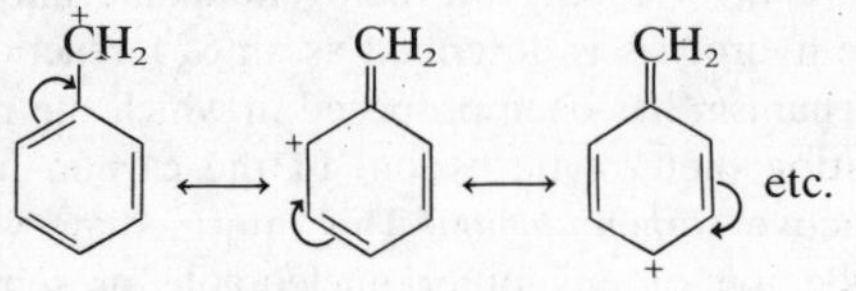

etc.

The carbonium ion from chlorotriphenylmethane, $(C_6H_5)_3CCl$, is so stable that a solution of the compound in liquid sulphur dioxide conducts electricity.

The high reactivity of 3-chloropropene, $CH_2{=}CHCH_2Cl$, is similarly explained by the resonance stabilization of the propenyl carbonium ion:

$$CH_2{=}CHCH_2Cl \xrightarrow{\text{ionization}} [CH_2{=}CH{-}\overset{+}{C}H_2 \leftrightarrow \overset{+}{C}H_2{-}CH{=}CH_2] + Cl^-$$

The alkaline hydrolysis of halogenoalkanes, particularly of the tertiary compounds, also yields some alkene as a by-product (see Unit 10.6(b)). This is formed from the *elimination reaction*:

$$(CH_3)_3C^+ \xrightarrow{\text{base, e.g. OH}^-} (CH_3)_2C{=}CH_2 + H^+$$

Alkene formation can be avoided by carrying out the hydrolysis with a suspension of moist silver(I) oxide in ethoxyethane:

$$2(CH_3)_3CBr + Ag_2O + H_2O \xrightarrow{\text{ethoxyethane}} 2(CH_3)_3COH + 2AgBr$$

(ii) **Ether formation.** An ether (see Unit 14.1) is obtained when a halogenoalkane is treated with a solution of a sodium alkoxide in the corresponding alcohol. The alkoxide, which acts as the nucleophile in this synthesis, is prepared by the action of sodium on the alcohol; for example,

$$2CH_3OH + 2Na \longrightarrow 2CH_3O^-Na^+ + H_{2(g)}$$

methanol   sodium methoxide

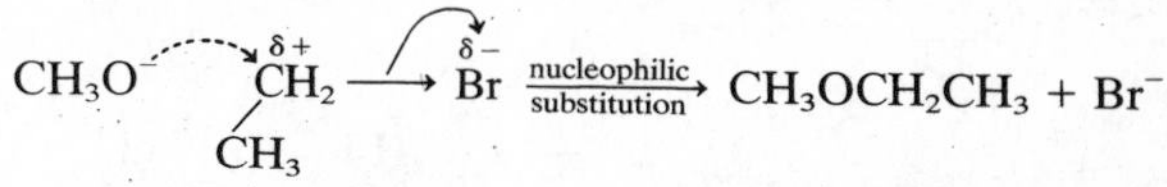

bromoethane   methoxyethane

This reaction is known as *Williamson's ether synthesis*. Ethers may also be prepared by the action of dry silver(I) oxide on halogenoalkanes:

$$2RBr + Ag_2O \rightarrow R—O—R + 2AgBr$$

an ether

(iii) **Reaction with inorganic salts.** Halogenoalkanes undergo double decomposition with silver or potassium salts to yield a wide range of useful compounds. The anion, Y^-, acts as the nucleophile and, depending on the structure of the halogenoalkane, the reaction proceeds via the S_N2 or S_N1 mechanisms described in Unit 10.6(*a*)(i):

$$Y^- + \overset{\delta+}{R}—\overset{\delta-}{X} \rightarrow [Y \cdots R \cdots X]^- \rightarrow Y—R + X^- \quad \mathbf{S_N2}$$

$$\left.\begin{array}{l} R_3C—X \rightarrow R_3C^+ + X^- \\ R_3C^+ + Y^- \rightarrow R_3CY \end{array}\right\} \quad \mathbf{S_N1}$$

The principal salts which react with halogenoalkanes are:

1. *Cyanides.* Nucleophilic substitution of halogen by cyanide occurs when an alcoholic solution of *potassium cyanide* is refluxed with the halogenoalkane. For example, propanonitrile, C_2H_5CN, is formed by the action of potassium cyanide on bromoethane:

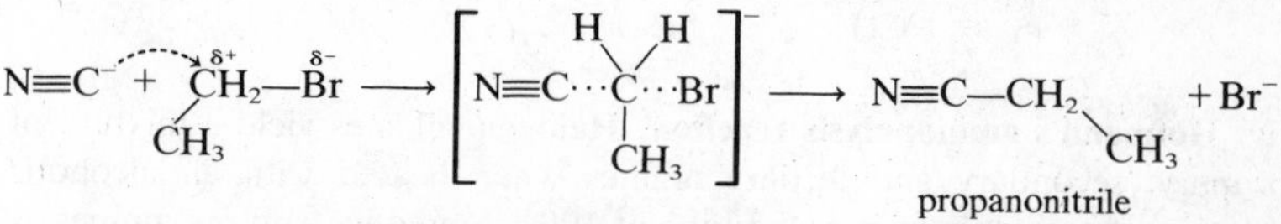

propanonitrile

With *silver cyanide*, a mixture of propanonitrile, C_2H_5CN, with the isomeric isocyanoethane, C_2H_5NC, is obtained:

$$AgCN + RI \rightarrow R—C{\equiv}N + R—N{\equiv}C + AgI$$

Nitriles are useful in organic syntheses as they may be converted into carboxylic acids by hydrolysis with boiling aqueous acids or alkalis:

$$RCN + 2H_2O \xrightarrow[\text{boil}]{H^+} RCO_2H + NH_4^+$$

$$RCN + H_2O \xrightarrow[\text{boil}]{OH^-} RCO_2^- + NH_3$$

and hence provide a synthetic route to a large number of other organic compounds.

2. *Silver nitrite* under the same conditions yields a mixture of the isomeric nitroalkane, R—NO$_2$, and alkyl nitrite, R—O—N=O. For example,

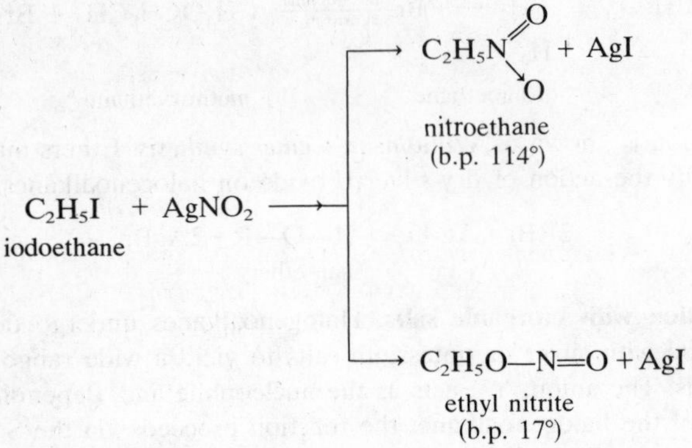

$$C_2H_5I + AgNO_2 \longrightarrow$$
iodoethane

$$\longrightarrow C_2H_5N \underset{O}{\overset{O}{<}} + AgI$$
nitroethane
(b.p. 114°)

$$\longrightarrow C_2H_5O—N=O + AgI$$
ethyl nitrite
(b.p. 17°)

The mixture may be separated by fractional distillation.

3. *Silver salts of carboxylic acids.* An ester is formed when an alcoholic solution of the silver salt of a carboxylic acid is heated with a halogeno-alkane. For example, bromoethane reacts with silver ethanoate to yield ethyl ethanoate and a precipitate of silver bromide:

$$CH_3CO_2^-Ag^+ + C_2H_5Br \xrightarrow[\text{heat}]{\text{ethanol}} CH_3CO_2C_2H_5 + AgBr$$
silver ethanoate   bromoethane   ethyl ethanoate

$$CH_3—\underset{O}{\overset{}{C}}—O^- \overset{\delta+}{CH_2}—\overset{\delta-}{Br} \longrightarrow CH_3\underset{O}{\overset{}{C}}—OCH_2CH_3 + Br^-$$
               CH_3

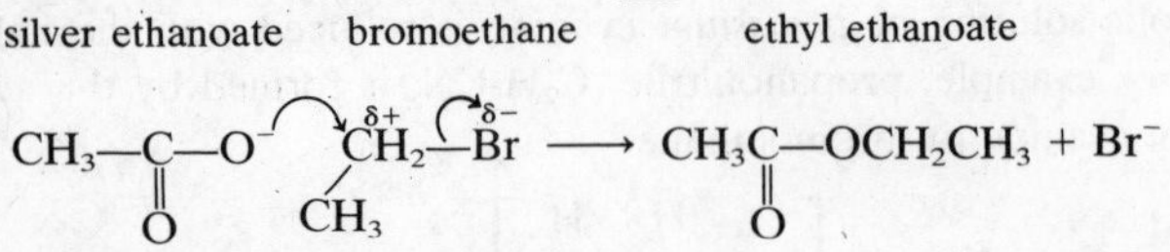

(iv) Hofmann's ammonolysis reaction. Halogenoalkanes yield a mixture of primary, secondary and tertiary amines when heated with an alcoholic solution of ammonia in a sealed tube at 100°. Ammonia, and the amines as they are formed, act as nucleophiles via the unbonded pair of electrons on the nitrogen atom:

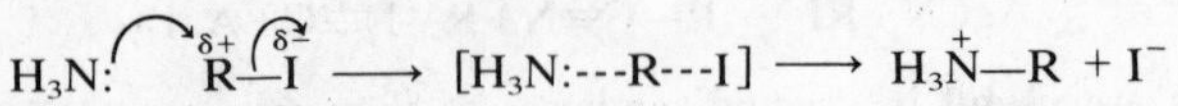

$$H_3N: \overset{\delta+}{R}—\overset{\delta-}{I} \longrightarrow [H_3N:\text{---}R\text{---}I] \longrightarrow H_3\overset{+}{N}—R + I^-$$

The primary amine, RNH$_2$, is liberated from its salt by warming with aqueous alkali:

$$R\overset{+}{N}H_3I^- + NaOH \rightarrow RNH_2 + NaI + H_2O$$

The reaction between ammonia and a halogenoalkane yields a mixture of products as the primary amine reacts further:

$$R\overset{+}{N}H_3I^- + NH_3 \rightleftharpoons RNH_2 + NH_4I$$
1° amine

$$R\overset{..}{N}H_2 + RI \rightarrow R_2\overset{+}{N}H_2I^- \xrightarrow{NH_3} R_2NH + NH_4I$$
2° amine

$$R_2\overset{..}{N}H + RI \rightarrow R_3\overset{+}{N}H_2I^- \xrightarrow{NH_3} R_3N + NH_4I$$
3° amine

$$R_3\overset{..}{N} + RI \rightarrow \qquad R_4N^+I^-$$
a tetra-alkylammonium salt

The order of reactivity of the halogenoalkanes in this reaction is $RI > RBr > RCl$.

(v) **Friedel–Crafts reaction** (see Unit 9.6(b)(iv)). The Friedel–Crafts reaction involves the electrophilic attack of a halogenoalkane on an aromatic hydrocarbon in the presence of anhydrous aluminium chloride:

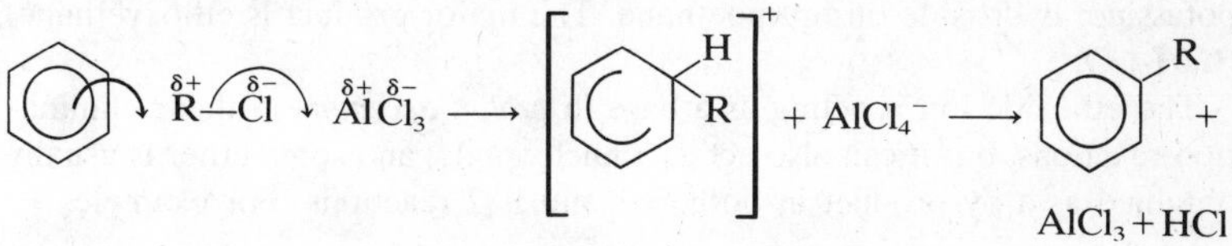

Equally, we can regard the aromatic hydrocarbon as acting as a nucleophile in the displacement of a halide ion from the halogenoalkane.

(b) Elimination Reactions

Halogenoalkanes undergo dehydrohalogenation on heating with an ethanolic solution of potassium hydroxide to yield an alkene:

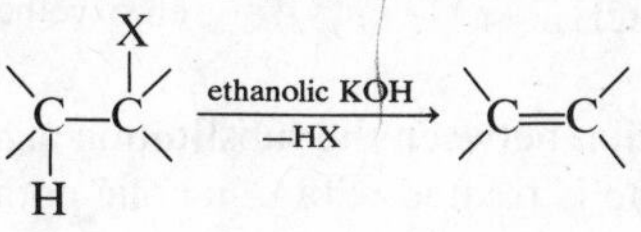

The elimination can occur via either a unimolecular (E1) or bimolecular (E2) mechanism; for example,

E1 mechanism:

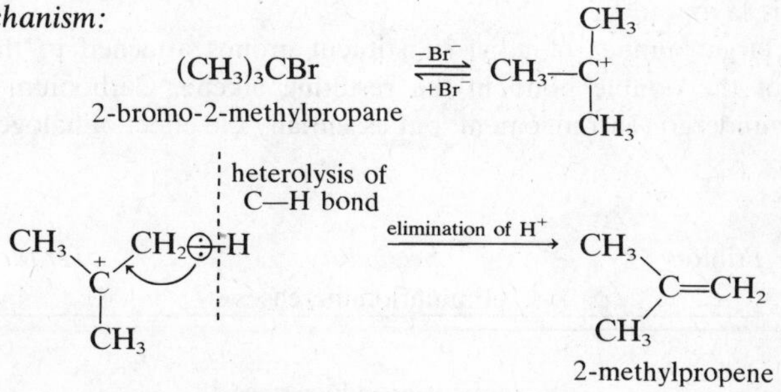

$$(CH_3)_3CBr \underset{+Br^-}{\overset{-Br^-}{\rightleftharpoons}} CH_3-\overset{\displaystyle CH_3}{\underset{\displaystyle CH_3}{\overset{|}{\underset{|}{C^+}}}}$$
2-bromo-2-methylpropane

$$C_2H_5O^- + H^+ \longrightarrow C_2H_5OH$$
ethoxide anion   ethanol

E2 mechanism:

$$C_2H_5OH + KOH \rightleftharpoons C_2H_5O^-K^+ + H_2O$$

ethanol

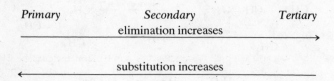

transition state

$$CH_3—CH{=}CH_2 + Br^-$$

propene

The halogenoethanes do not undergo this elimination reaction to any great extent; only 2 per cent of ethene is formed by the action of ethanolic potassium hydroxide on bromoethane. The major product is ethoxyethane, $(C_2H_5)_2O$.

The ethoxide ion is acting as a base (a *proton acceptor*) in these elimination reactions, but it can also act as a nucleophile, and some ether is usually obtained as a by-product in both S_N1 and S_N2 reactions. For example,

$$(CH_3)_3\overset{+}{C} \quad + \quad C_2H_5O^- \longrightarrow \quad (CH_3)_3COC_2H_5 \qquad \mathbf{S_N1}$$

2-methylpropyl   ethoxide   2-ethoxy-2-methylpropane
carbonium ion   ion

$$C_2H_5O^- \qquad \overset{\delta^+}{CH_2}{-}\overset{\delta^-}{X} \longrightarrow C_2H_5OCH_2CH_3 + X^- \quad \mathbf{S_N2}$$

CH_3 ethoxyethane

There is thus competition between the substitution and elimination reactions when a halogenoalkane is treated with ethanolic potassium hydroxide. The proportions of ether and alkene in the reaction products are determined by the structure of the halogenoalkane and by the reaction conditions. Elimination is favoured by:

(i) a large number of alkyl substituent groups attached to the carbon atoms of the double bond in the resulting alkene. Carbonium ions frequently undergo rearrangement, but essentially the effect of halogenoalkane structure is:

Primary	*Secondary*	*Tertiary*

elimination increases ⟶

⟵ substitution increases

This is illustrated by the data in Table 10.2.

Table 10.2 Reactions of halogenoalkanes with ethanolic potassium hydroxide

Class of halogen compound	Compound	Formula	Percentage elimination reaction
1°	Bromoethane	C_2H_5Br	2
2°	2-Bromopropane	$CH_3CHBrCH_3$	80
3°	2-Bromo-2-methylpropane	$(CH_3)_3CBr$	100

(ii) the use of an alcohol, rather than water, as the reaction medium; and
(iii) an increase in temperature.

Higher secondary and tertiary halogenoalkanes yield a mixture of alkenes on dehydrohalogenation, the composition of which is determined by Saytzeff's Rule (see Unit 12.6(g)).

(c) Other Reactions

(i) **Reduction.** Halogenoalkanes are reduced to alkanes by the action of a dissolving metal or by catalytic hydrogenation (see Unit 5.2(b)).

(ii) **The Wurtz reaction.** See Unit 5.2(b).

(iii) **Formation of Grignard reagents.** Halogenoalkanes react with magnesium turnings in anhydrous, alcohol-free ethoxyethane to yield an alkylmagnesium(II) halide or *Grignard reagent*:

$$RX + Mg \xrightarrow[\text{ether}]{\text{in anhydrous}} RMgX$$

alkylmagnesium(II) halide

A small crystal of iodine is sometimes added as a catalyst. The ease of formation increases: $RCl < RBr < RI$.

Alkylmagnesium(II) halides and their aromatic analogues are important in synthesis as they are readily converted into alkanes, alcohols, carboxylic acids and many other classes of organic compound. The general procedure is to add the second reactant to an anhydrous ethereal solution of the Grignard reagent, forming a magnesium complex which is then hydrolysed with aqueous acid. For example, if dry carbon dioxide is passed into a solution of an alkylmagnesium(II) halide at $0°$ and the product treated with dilute hydrochloric acid, a carboxylic acid is formed:

$$RMgX + CO_2 \longrightarrow R-C\!\!\begin{array}{c} O \\ \diagdown \\ OMgX \end{array} \xrightarrow{HX} RC\!\!\begin{array}{c} O \\ \diagdown \\ OH \end{array} + MgX_2$$

The synthetic uses of Grignard reagents are summarized in Fig. 10.3. The reactions with methanal and epoxyethane make it possible to synthesize primary alcohols containing one and two carbon atoms more than the original halogenoalkane.

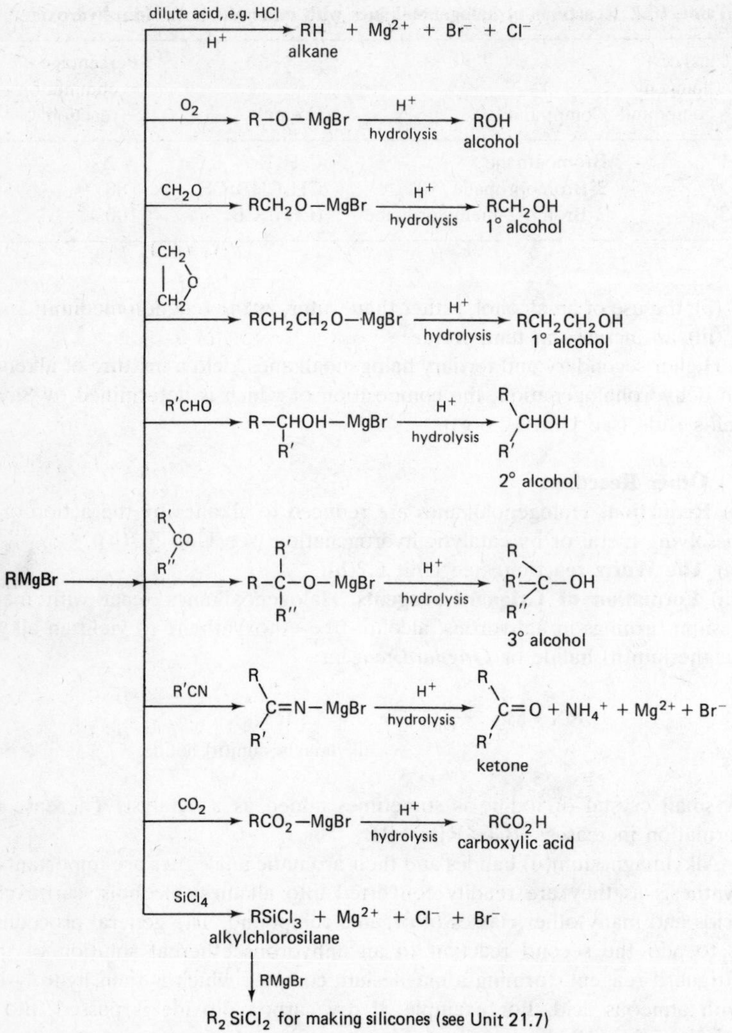

dilute acid, e.g. HCl

H^+ → RH + Mg^{2+} + Br^- + Cl^-
alkane

O_2 → R—O—MgBr $\xrightarrow[\text{hydrolysis}]{H^+}$ ROH
alcohol

CH_2O → RCH_2O—MgBr $\xrightarrow[\text{hydrolysis}]{H^+}$ RCH_2OH
1° alcohol

$\begin{array}{c} CH_2 \\ | \quad O \\ CH_2 \end{array}$ → RCH_2CH_2O—MgBr $\xrightarrow[\text{hydrolysis}]{H^+}$ RCH_2CH_2OH
1° alcohol

R'CHO → R—CHOH—MgBr $\xrightarrow[\text{hydrolysis}]{H^+}$ $\underset{R'}{\overset{R}{\diagdown}}$CHOH
|
R'
2° alcohol

RMgBr

$\underset{R''}{\overset{R'}{\diagdown}}$CO → R—C—O—MgBr $\xrightarrow[\text{hydrolysis}]{H^+}$ R'—C—OH
| R' | R
| | R''
R'' 3° alcohol

R'CN → $\underset{R'}{\overset{R}{\diagdown}}$C=N—MgBr $\xrightarrow[\text{hydrolysis}]{H^+}$ $\underset{R'}{\overset{R}{\diagdown}}$C=O + NH_4^+ + Mg^{2+} + Br^-
ketone

CO_2 → RCO_2—MgBr $\xrightarrow[\text{hydrolysis}]{H^+}$ RCO_2H
carboxylic acid

$SiCl_4$ → $RSiCl_3$ + Mg^{2+} + Cl^- + Br^-
alkylchlorosilane

↓ RMgBr

R_2SiCl_2 for making silicones (see Unit 21.7)

Fig. 10.3 Reactions of Grignard reagents, RMgX (arylmagnesium(II) halides, ArMgX, react similarly)

Grignard reagents are stabilized by complex formation with the ether; tetrahydrofuran, a cyclic ether, is often used instead of ethoxyethane, since it is less volatile and also, being more basic than ethoxyethane, forms more stable complexes with reagents. The carbon–magnesium bond in a Grignard reagent molecule is largely covalent, while the magnesium–halogen bond is mostly ionic.

10.7 Unsaturated Halogenoalkanes

(a) Chloroethene

Chloroethene (vinyl chloride), CH_2=$CHCl$, b.p. $-14°$, is manufactured by passing a mixture of chlorine and ethene over pumice at $600°$ (see Unit 7.6(b)):

$$CH_2{=}CH_2 + Cl_2 \rightarrow CH_2ClCH_2Cl \xrightarrow[\text{pumice}]{600°} CH_2{=}CHCl + HCl$$

1,2-dichloroethane   chloroethene

Alternative methods of preparation are from ethyne (see Unit 8.6(c)) or by heating a mixture of ethene, hydrogen chloride and oxygen:

$$CH_2{=}CH_2 + HCl + \tfrac{1}{2}O_2 \xrightarrow[\text{CuCl}_2 \text{ catalyst}]{250°} CH_2{=}CHCl + H_2O$$

The chloroethene molecule is planar (see Unit 4.4(c)). It is a relatively unreactive compound owing to the delocalization of the unbonded electrons on the chlorine atom with the π orbital of the alkene, but is both flammable and highly toxic, and is known to induce cancer in people who have experienced continued exposure. Chloroethene is used for the manufacture of PVC (see Unit 7.6(j)).

(b) Tetrafluoroethene

Tetrafluoroethene, CF_2=CF_2, b.p. $-76°$, is made by fluorinating trichloromethane with antimony(III) fluoride and then heating the product to $700°$:

$$2CHCl_3 \xrightarrow{\text{SbF}_3} 2CHF_2Cl \xrightarrow{700°} CF_2{=}CF_2 + 2HCl$$

trichloromethane   chlorodifluoromethane   tetrafluoroethene

The product polymerizes by a free-radical mechanism to yield poly(tetrafluoroethene) (PTFE, Teflon or Fluon; see Unit 7.6(j)):

$$nCF_2{=}CF_2 \xrightarrow{\text{(NH}_4)_2\text{S}_2\text{O}_8} {-}[CF_2{-}CF_2]_n$$

Poly(tetrafluoroethene) is an extremely stable solid. It is stable to heat (softening-point $c.$ $320°$) and is unaffected by acids, alkalis and other chemicals. Its coefficient of friction is exceedingly low—about the same as that of one piece of melting ice in contact with another. It is used as a non-stick surface for pans and other cooking utensils and for making low-friction joints and chemical-resistant components.

10.8 Uses of Halogenoalkanes

The halogenoalkanes are important in synthesis because of the wide range of organic compounds which can be made from them. They are used industrially as solvents and for the manufacture of tetraethyl-lead(IV) (see Unit 6.4) and of silicones for silicone rubber and resins and for the methylation of cellulose. Chloroethene is used as a local anaesthetic: the gas liquefies under pressure, but rapidly evaporates when sprayed on the skin and the resulting cooling desensitizes the nerve endings. Dichloro-difluoromethane and other chlorofluoro-derivatives of methane and ethane are used as refrigerants and, under the trade name of Freons, as propellants for aerosols containing paints, hair lacquer, insecticides, shaving cream and so forth. Bromochlorodifluoromethane, $CBrClF_2$, is employed in fire extinguishers. Chloroethene and tetrafluoroethene are both monomers of important plastics (see Unit 7.6(j)). 1-Bromo-1-chloro-2,2,2-trifluoro-ethane, $CHBrClCHF_3$, is used as an anaesthetic (Fluothane).

Questions on the material in Unit 10 are to be found at the end of Unit 11.

Halogen Compounds: Aromatic

11.1 General Formula and Nomenclature

Aromatic halogen compounds are formed by the replacement of one or more of the hydrogen atoms in an aromatic hydrocarbon molecule. The general formula is therefore Ar—X, where Ar represents an aryl group and X a halogen atom. In *halogenoarenes*, the halogen atom is attached to a carbon atom that forms part of the aromatic nucleus.

The compounds are named as derivatives of the parent hydrocarbons; for instance:

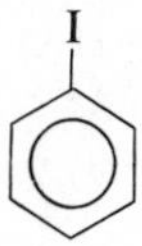

iodobenzene, C_6H_5I 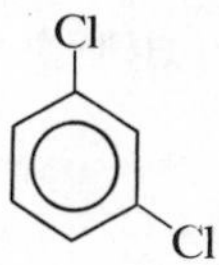   1,3-dichlorobenzene, $C_6H_4Cl_2$

Compounds in which the halogen atom is attached to the side-chain of an aromatic hydrocarbon may be regarded as derivatives of substituted alkanes; for instance:

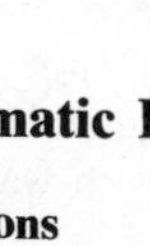

(chloromethyl)benzene, $C_6H_5CH_2Cl$

11.2 Preparation of Aromatic Halogen Compounds

(a) From Aromatic Hydrocarbons

An aromatic hydrocarbon undergoes electrophilic substitution when it is treated with chlorine or bromine in the presence of a halogen carrier. For example, benzene reacts with chlorine in the presence of aluminium chloride to yield first chlorobenzene and then a mixture of the isomeric 1,2- and 1,4-dichlorobenzenes. The monochloro-derivative can be obtained alone by stopping the passage of chlorine into the reaction mixture as soon as the theoretical weight increase has been obtained. Iodination requires the presence of a base or oxidizing agent to remove the hydrogen iodide as it is formed.

Benzene homologues such as methylbenzene may be halogenated by substitution of the hydrogen atoms attached to the nucleus or of those in the side-chain. The site of attack is determined by the reaction conditions.

The mechanisms of these reactions were discussed in Units 9.6(b)(i) and 9.7.

(b) **From Diazonium Salts**
See Unit 18.6.

11.3 Manufacture of Aromatic Halogen Compounds

Chlorobenzene is widely used in industrial syntheses, as it is considerably cheaper than either bromobenzene or iodobenzene. It is manufactured by the *Raschig process*, in which a mixture of benzene vapour, hydrogen chloride and oxygen is passed over copper(II) chloride at 250°:

$$C_6H_6 + HCl + \tfrac{1}{2}O_2 \xrightarrow[\text{CuCl}_2]{250°} \underset{\text{chlorobenzene}}{C_6H_5Cl} + H_2O$$

11.4 Physical Properties of Aromatic Halogen Compounds

Most aromatic halogen compounds are colourless liquids, insoluble in water but readily soluble in organic solvents. They have pleasant 'aromatic' odours; (chloromethyl)benzene, however, like many other compounds containing halogen atoms in the side-chain, has a sharp irritating smell and is lachrymatory (that is, it makes the eyes water).

11.5 Reactivity of Aromatic Halogen Compounds

The halogen atoms in these compounds are unreactive and do not undergo nucleophilic substitution, except where the ring contains strong electron-withdrawing groups, such as —NO$_2$ and —CN; for example, the chlorine atom in 1-chloro-2,4,6-trinitrobenzene is replaced by a hydroxyl group simply by warming the compound with water:

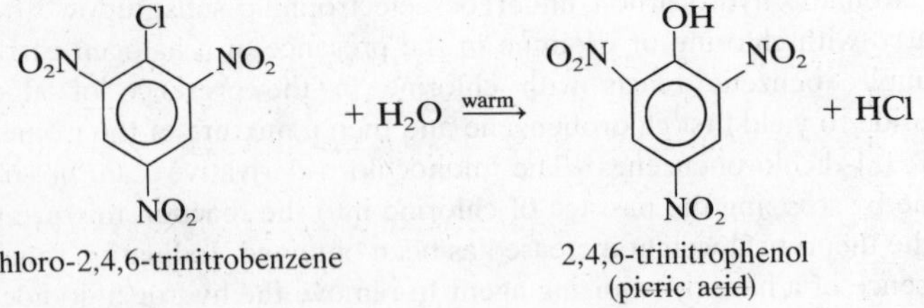

1-chloro-2,4,6-trinitrobenzene   2,4,6-trinitrophenol
                                              (picric acid)

Chlorobenzene does not react under these conditions. This decreased reactivity of the aromatic halogen compared with halogenoalkanes is explained by the reduced polarity of the carbon–halogen bond, which results from the interaction of the p orbitals of the halogen atom with the ring:

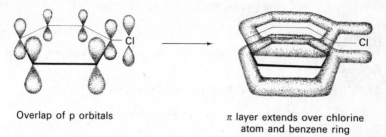

Overlap of p orbitals

π layer extends over chlorine
atom and benzene ring

Fig. 11.1   Structure of the chlorobenzene molecule

The effect of this interaction is to confer some degree of double-bond character to the carbon–halogen bond; in chlorobenzene, for instance, the carbon–chlorine bond is both shorter and stronger than in the chloroalkanes (cf. Table 10.1 in Unit 10.5).

11.6 Reactions of Aromatic Halogen Compounds

(a) Nucleophilic Substitution
As we have seen, halogenoarenes are considerably less reactive than the halogenoalkanes; many nucleophiles, including OH^-, CN^- and NH_3, have no effect on them under ordinary laboratory conditions. Some nucleophilic substitutions can be carried out under extremely vigorous conditions, however; chlorobenzene, for example, is hydrolysed by aqueous sodium hydroxide at 300° under high pressure:

$$C_6H_5Cl + 2NaOH_{(aq)} \xrightarrow{300°/200 \text{ atm}} C_6H_5O^-Na^+ + H_2O + NaCl$$

Phenol is liberated by the action of aqueous acid:

$$C_6H_5O^-Na^+ + H^+_{(aq)} \rightarrow C_6H_5OH + Na^+$$
$$\text{phenol}$$

This reaction is used for the industrial preparation of phenol.

Similarly, the reaction of chlorobenzene with ammonia only occurs at 200° under pressure in the presence of copper(I) oxide:

$$2C_6H_5Cl + 2NH_3 + Cu_2O \xrightarrow{200°/\text{pressure}} 2C_6H_5NH_2 + 2CuCl + H_2O$$
chlorobenzene $\qquad\qquad\qquad\qquad$ phenylamine

(b) Reduction
Chlorobenzene is reduced to benzene by the action of sodium amalgam or

lithium tetrahydridoaluminate(III), or by catalytic hydrogenation:

$$C_6H_5Cl + H_2 \xrightarrow{\text{Raney Ni/KOH}} C_6H_6 + HCl$$

(c) Fittig Reaction

Bromobenzene reacts with sodium in anhydrous ethoxyethane to yield biphenyl:

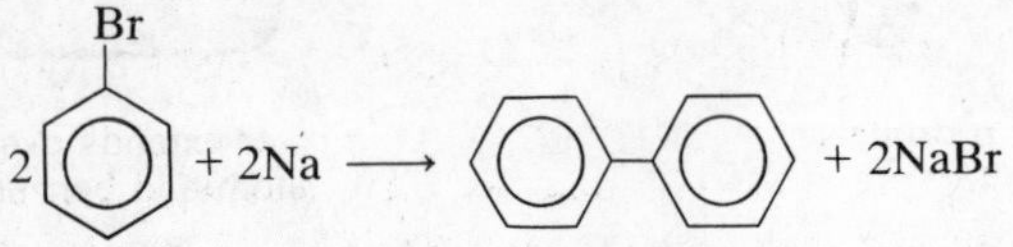

biphenyl

This reaction differs from the Wurtz reaction (see Unit 5.2(b)) in that it involves an aromatic halogen compound rather than a halogenoalkane. The reaction between a halogenoalkane and a halogenoarene with sodium (the *Wurtz–Fittig reaction*) may be used to prepare benzene homologues (see Unit 9.3(d)).

(d) Formation of Grignard Reagents

Bromobenzene and iodobenzene form arylmagnesium(II) halides on treatment with magnesium turnings in anhydrous ethoxyethane (see Unit 10.6(c) (iii) and Fig. 10.3):

$$C_6H_5Br + Mg \xrightarrow{\text{(C}_2\text{H}_5)_2\text{O}} C_6H_5MgBr$$

phenylmagnesium(II) bromide

The reaction of the aromatic Grignard reagents resemble those of their aliphatic analogues.

(e) Electrophilic Substitution

The halogenobenzenes undergo electrophilic substitution in the aromatic nucleus. The halogen atom is *ortho-/para*-directing and attack is more difficult than in benzene itself (see Unit 9.9).

11.7 (Chloromethyl)benzene

(Chloromethyl)benzene (benzyl chloride), $C_6H_5CH_2Cl$, is isomeric with the three chloro(methylbenzenes):

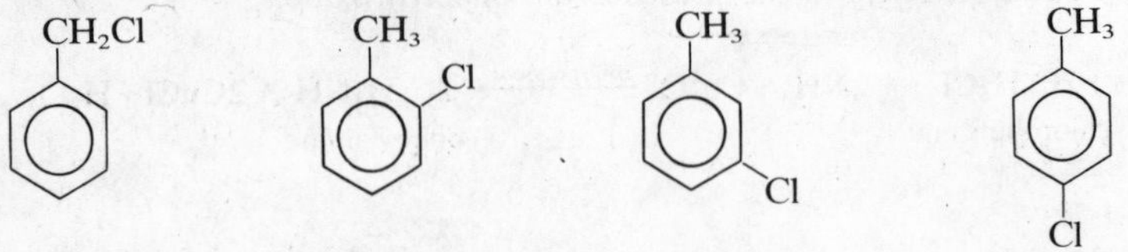

(chloromethyl)-   2-chloro(methyl-   3-chloro(methyl-   4-chloro(methylbenzene   benzene)   benzene)   benzene)

Like other compounds with a halogen atom in the side-chain, (chloromethyl)benzene resembles the halogenoalkanes rather than the halogenoarenes in many of its chemical properties. With the exception of the elimination reaction with ethanolic potassium hydroxide, it readily undergoes the reactions described in Unit 10.6; for example, it is easily hydrolysed by aqueous sodium hydroxide to phenylmethanol (benzyl alcohol):

$$C_6H_5CH_2Cl + OH^-_{(aq)} \xrightarrow{\text{reflux}} C_6H_5CH_2OH + Cl^-_{(aq)}$$

(Chloromethyl)benzene also undergoes electrophilic substitution in the aromatic nucleus: the chloromethyl group is *ortho-/para-*directing.
For instance:

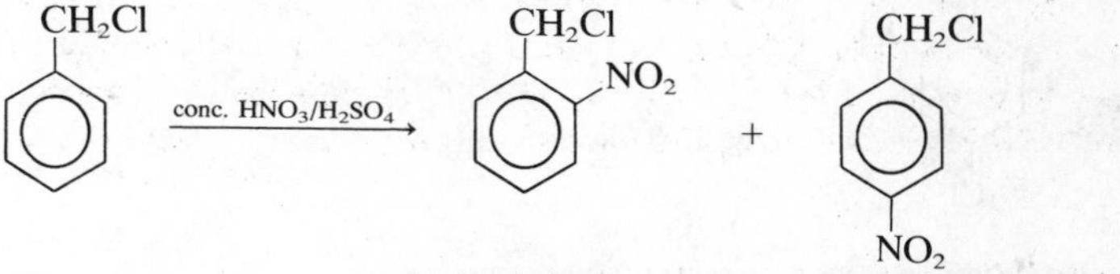

2-nitro(chloromethyl)-   ,4-nitro(chloromethyl)-
benzene   benzene

The side-chain may be oxidized (*cf.* Unit 9.7(c)(i)). Powerful oxidizing agents yield benzoic acid:

$$C_6H_5CH_2Cl \xrightarrow[\text{e.g. alkaline KMnO}_4]{\text{strong oxidizing agent}} C_6H_5CO_2H$$
benzoic acid

while more moderate oxidation gives benzaldehyde:

$$C_6H_5CH_2Cl \xrightarrow[\text{reflux}]{\text{copper(II) nitrate solution}} C_6H_5CHO$$
benzaldehyde

11.8 Uses of Aromatic Halogen Compounds

Chlorobenzene is a starting material for the manufacture of phenol (see Unit 13.3), phenylamine (see Unit 11.6(a)) and the powerful insecticide DDT. DDT is prepared by heating a mixture of chlorobenzene and trichloroethanal (chloral) in the presence of concentrated sulphuric acid:

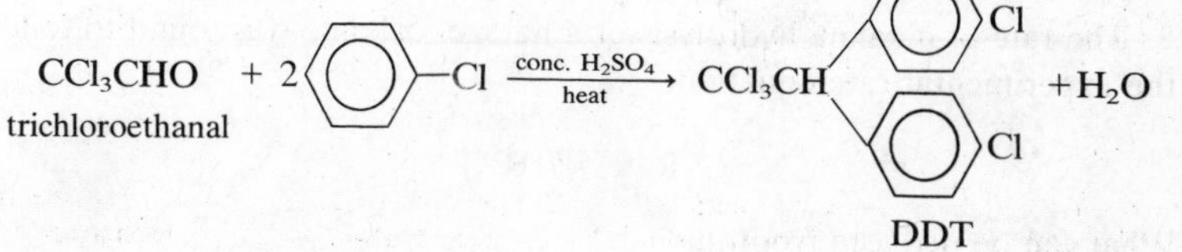

CCl₃CHO
trichloroethanal

DDT

In recent years DDT has increasingly been replaced by other insecticides of lower environmental toxicity.

Test Yourself on Units 10 and 11

1. Name the following compounds:
   (a) $(CH_3)_2CHBr$

   (b) $(CH_3)_3CCl$

   (c) $CH_3CClCH_2C(CH_3)_2CHCl_2$
      |
      CH_3

   (d) CH_2Cl

2. Write structural formulae for the following:
   (a) 3-bromopropene;
   (b) 1,3,5-tribromobenzene;
   (c) 1,1,1-trichloropropane;
   (d) 3-bromo(trichloromethyl)benzene;
   (e) 1,2,3,4,5,6-hexachlorocyclohexane.

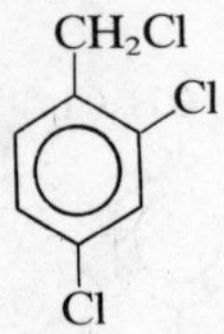

3. How does the molecular orbital theory account for the different reactivities towards nucleophilic substitution of the halogen atoms of bromoethane, (bromomethyl)benzene, bromoethene, 3-bromopropene and bromobenzene?

4. Name the reactants and conditions required to carry out the following changes (in some cases more than one reaction step may be required):
   (a) $C_2H_5Br \rightarrow C_2H_4$
   (b) $C_2H_5Br \rightarrow (C_2H_5)_2O$
   (c) $CH_3I \rightarrow CH_3CO_2H$
   (d) $C_2H_5I \rightarrow C_2H_5CH_2CH_2OH$
   (e) $C_2H_5Br \rightarrow CH_3CHOHC_2H_5$
   (f) benzene $\rightarrow$ 3-chloronitrobenzene
   (g) $C_2H_6 \rightarrow C_2H_5NH_2$
   (h) methylbenzene $\rightarrow$ 2-chloro(dichloromethyl)benzene

5. The rate of alkaline hydrolysis of a halogenoalkane was found to follow the experimental rate equation:

$$Rate = k[RX]$$

What can be deduced from this?

6. Give the names and structural formulae of the organic products (if any) obtained from the following reactions:

   (a) bromobenzene and aqueous sodium hydroxide;

   (b) iodoethane and magnesium;

   (c) chlorobenzene and silver nitrite;

   (d) (chloromethyl)benzene and potassium cyanide;

   (e) bromoethane and ethanolic potassium hydroxide.

7. Discuss the synthetic uses of the halogenoalkanes.

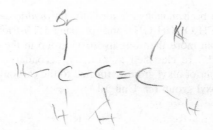

Hydroxy-compounds: Alcohols

12.1 General Formula and Nomenclature

Alcohols, which have the general formula ROH, are compounds in which one or more hydroxyl groups are attached to the saturated carbon of an alkyl or substituted alkyl group; for example:

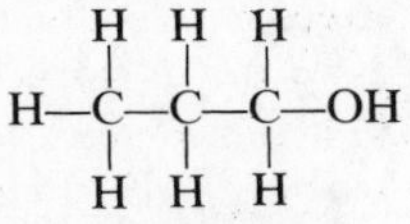

$$
\begin{array}{ccc}
\text{H} & \text{H} & \text{H} \\
| & | & | \\
\text{H—C—C—C—OH} \\
| & | & | \\
\text{H} & \text{H} & \text{H}
\end{array}
$$

propan-1-ol

CH_2OH

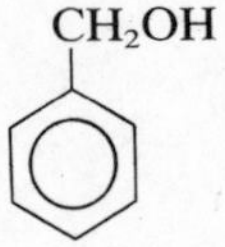

phenylmethanol

These compounds are both *monohydric alcohols*. *Polyhydric alcohols*, such as ethane-1,2-diol, CH_2OHCH_2OH, and propane-1,2,3-triol, $CH_2OH-CHOHCH_2OH$, contain more than one hydroxyl group in the molecule.

Classification. Alcohols are classified as primary, secondary and tertiary according to the number of alkyl groups attached to the carbon atom which is linked to the hydroxyl group (*cf.* Unit 10.1):

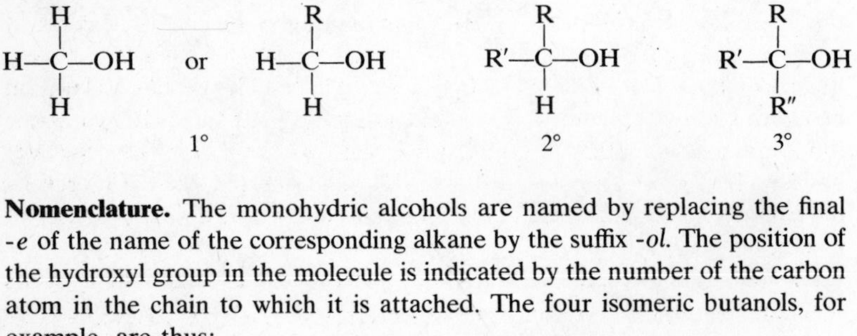

$$
\begin{array}{cccc}
\text{H} & \text{R} & \text{R} & \text{R} \\
| & | & | & | \\
\text{H—C—OH} \quad \text{or} \quad \text{H—C—OH} & \text{R'—C—OH} & \text{R'—C—OH} \\
| & | & | & | \\
\text{H} & \text{H} & \text{H} & \text{R''} \\
& 1° & 2° & 3°
\end{array}
$$

Nomenclature. The monohydric alcohols are named by replacing the final -*e* of the name of the corresponding alkane by the suffix -*ol*. The position of the hydroxyl group in the molecule is indicated by the number of the carbon atom in the chain to which it is attached. The four isomeric butanols, for example, are thus:

$CH_3CH_2CH_2CH_2OH$

butan-1-ol

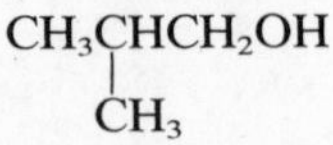

$$
\begin{array}{c}
\text{CH}_3\text{CHCH}_2\text{OH} \\
| \\
\text{CH}_3
\end{array}
$$

2-methylpropan-1-ol

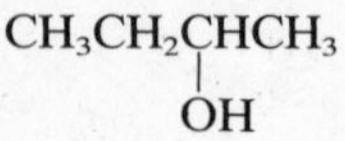

$$
\begin{array}{c}
\text{CH}_3\text{CH}_2\text{CHCH}_3 \\
| \\
\text{OH}
\end{array}
$$

butan-2-ol

$$
\begin{array}{c}
\text{CH}_3 \\
| \\
\text{CH}_3\text{—C—CH}_3 \\
| \\
\text{OH}
\end{array}
$$

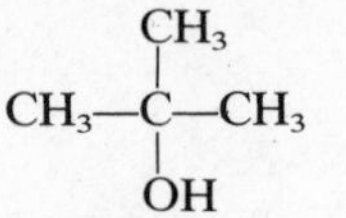

2-methylpropan-2-ol

The first two of these alcohols contain the —CH$_2$OH group and are therefore primary alcohols. The last two isomers are secondary and tertiary alcohols respectively. The saturated aliphatic alcohols are collectively known as *alkanols*.

12.2 Physical Properties of Alcohols

(a) Boiling-points

The first members of the alkanol homologous series are liquids with boiling-points considerably higher than those of alkanes of similar formula weight (see Table 12.1). This greatly decreased volatility is due to hydrogen bonding between the alcohol molecules in the liquid phase. The bond is electrostatic in nature; the proton in the hydroxyl group of the molecule is attracted to the lone pair of electrons on the oxygen atom of the hydroxyl group of another:

$$\underset{\delta-}{\overset{R}{O}}\!\!-\!\!\underset{\delta+}{H}\cdots\underset{\delta-}{\overset{R}{O}}\!\!-\!\!\underset{\delta+}{H}\cdots\underset{\delta-}{\overset{R}{O}}\!\!-\!\!\underset{\delta+}{H}$$

Hydrogen bonding can be detected by infra-red spectroscopy: the characteristic absorption band for the stretching vibrations of the hydroxyl group, which is observed at 3 650–3 590 cm^{-1} in the spectrum of the substance in the gas phase or in dilute solution in an inert solvent, is shifted to approximately 3 550–3 450 cm^{-1} and is considerably broadened by intermolecular hydrogen bonding. The intensity and breadth of this absorption band are strongly dependent on concentration (Fig. 12.1). Hydrogen bonds (bond strength about 20 kJ mol^{-1}) are considerably weaker than covalent bonds (ΔH_{diss} = 464 kJ mol^{-1} for the O—H bond) but the association resulting from such interaction clearly has an enormous effect on the volatility of a compound.

Alcohols with branched carbon chains generally have lower boiling-points than their unbranched-chain isomers (*cf.* the boiling-points of alkanes; see Unit 5.4) and the order of volatility of isomeric alcohols is usually 3° > 2° > 1°. Aliphatic alcohols containing more than twelve carbon atoms and many of the higher aromatic alcohols are waxy solids.

Table 12.1 Comparison of boiling-points of alcohols and alkanes

Alcohol	RMM	b.p. (°C)	Alkane	RMM	b.p. (°C)
Methanol	32	64.5	Ethane	30	−88.6
Ethanol	46	78.5	Propane	44	−42.2
Propan-1-ol	60	97.2	Butane	58	−0.5

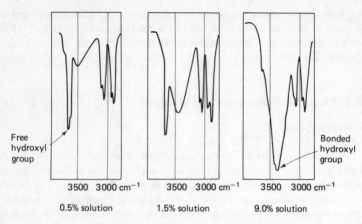

Fig. 12.1   Hydrogen bonding: infra-red spectra of solutions of phenylmethanol in tetrachloromethane

(b) Solubility

The lower alcohols (methanol, ethanol and propanol) are completely miscible with water, largely as a result of hydrogen bonding with the solvent:

$$R \qquad\qquad H$$
$$O\text{—}H\text{---}O$$
$$H$$

but this solubility drops sharply as the number of carbon atoms in the
alcohol molecule increases. The alcohols are completely miscible with
organic solvents.

12.3 Preparation of Alcohols

(a) By Hydrolysis of Esters

The hydrolysis of esters is catalysed by strong acids or bases:

$$RCO_2R' + H_2O \overset{H^+}{\rightleftharpoons} RCO_2H + R'OH$$

$$RCO_2R' + KOH \rightarrow RCO_2^- K^+ + R'OH$$

Alkaline hydrolysis generally gives higher yields than the reversible acid-
catalysed reaction. The process is known as *saponification* and is used in
industry for the manufacture of soaps from naturally occurring fats and oils,
which are esters of long-chain carboxylic acids with polyhydric alcohols,

principally propane-1,2,3-triol (glycerol). For example,

$$
\begin{array}{l}
\text{CH}_2\text{OCO(CH}_2)_{14}\text{CH}_3 \\
| \\
\text{CHOCO(CH}_2)_{14}\text{CH}_3 \quad + \quad 3\text{KOH}_{(aq)} \quad \longrightarrow \\
| \\
\text{CH}_2\text{OCO(CH}_2)_{14}\text{CH}_3
\end{array}
\qquad
\begin{array}{l}
\text{CH}_2\text{OH} \\
| \\
\text{CHOH} \quad + \quad 3\text{CH}_3(\text{CH}_2)_{14}\text{CO}_2\text{K} \\
| \\
\text{CH}_2\text{OH} \qquad \text{potassium hexadecanoate} \\
\text{propane-} \qquad \text{(potassium palmitate)} \\
\text{1,2,3-triol} \qquad \qquad \text{soap}
\end{array}
$$

(b) From Halogenoalkanes

Halogenoalkanes are hydrolysed by boiling under reflux with aqueous alkali or with a suspension of silver(I) oxide in water:

$$ RX + OH^-_{(aq)} \rightarrow ROH + X^-_{(aq)} $$

The mechanism of this nucleophilic substitution was discussed in Unit 10.6(a)(i).

The yield from a tertiary halogenoalkane is low, owing to the ready loss of a proton from the carbonium ion intermediate (see Unit 10.6(b)).

(c) From Aldehydes, Ketones or Esters

Aldehydes and esters yield primary alcohols on reduction:

$$ RCHO \rightarrow RCH_2OH $$
$$ \text{aldehyde} \qquad 1° \text{ alcohol} $$

$$ RCO_2R' \rightarrow RCH_2OH + R'OH $$
$$ \text{ester} \qquad 1° \text{ alcohol} $$

and ketones secondary alcohols:

$$
\begin{array}{c}
R \\
\diagdown \\
C=O \\
\diagup \\
R
\end{array}
\longrightarrow
\begin{array}{c}
R \\
\diagdown \\
CHOH \\
\diagup \\
R'
\end{array}
$$

$$ \text{ketone} \qquad 2° \text{ alcohol} $$

In the *Bouveault–Blanc method* the reducing agent is a mixture of sodium and ethanol. The dissolving metal yields electrons which carry out the reduction:

$$ Na \xrightarrow{\text{ethanol}} Na^+ + e $$

$$
R-\overset{\displaystyle H}{\underset{\displaystyle O^{\delta -}}{\overset{\delta +}{C}}} \xrightarrow{\;e\;}
R-\overset{\displaystyle H}{\underset{\displaystyle O\cdot}{\ddot{C}}} \xrightarrow{C_2H_5OH}
RCH_2O\cdot + C_2H_5O^-
$$

aldehyde

$$ RCH_2O^- \xrightarrow{C_2H_5OH} RCH_2OH + C_2H_5O^- $$

Other reducing agents for this reaction include sodium hydride, lithium tetrahydridoaluminate(III), sodium tetrahydridoborate(III) and aluminium

1-methylethoxide. Reductions with lithium(i) tetrahydridoaluminate(iii) are usually carried out in ethoxyethane solution and the reagent gives good yields of alcohols from aldehydes, ketones, carboxylic acids, esters, acyl halides and acid anhydrides. Sodium tetrahydridoborate(iii) behaves similarly but is less reactive and does not reduce carboxylic acids. It is insoluble in ethoxyethane but, unlike lithium tetrahydridoaluminate(iii), it may be used in aqueous solution.

Catalytic hydrogenation has been used for the preparation of higher alcohols from esters:

$$RCO_2R' + 2H_2 \xrightarrow[\text{Cu catalyst}]{200°/180 \text{ atm}} RCH_2OH + R'OH$$
ester

(d) From Grignard Reagents
This method provides a means of ascending the alcohol homologous series and of synthesizing primary, secondary and tertiary alcohols (see Unit 10.6(c)(iii)).

(e) From Alkenes
The hydration of alkenes to form alcohols is discussed in Unit 7.6(f).

12.4 Manufacture of Alcohols

(a) Methanol
Methanol is prepared industrially by:
(i) The oxidation of methane with a limited amount of oxygen:

$$CH_4 \quad + \quad \tfrac{1}{2}O_2 \xrightarrow{Cu/200°/100 \text{ atm}} CH_3OH$$
(9 volumes)   (1 volume)

(ii) From water gas, a mixture of carbon monoxide and hydrogen obtained by passing steam over white-hot coke:

$$C + H_2O \xrightarrow{1\,300°} CO + H_2$$

The gas is mixed with more hydrogen and passed at a pressure of 200–250 atmospheres over a heated catalyst of zinc and chromium oxides:

$$CO + 2H_2 \rightarrow CH_3OH$$

(b) Ethanol
Ethanol is manufactured by:
(i) **Fermentation.** This was the earliest method of preparing ethanol and is now used principally for the manufacture of beer, wines and spirits. The starting material is a carbohydrate such as starch, which is present in

potatoes and maize, rice and other cereals, or a sugar such as sucrose, $C_{12}H_{22}O_{11}$, or fructose, $C_6H_{12}O_6$, from molasses and grapes respectively. Fermentation is initiated by yeast, which contains a large number of complex organic catalysts or *enzymes*; these convert the starch first into simple sugars such as glucose (see Unit 20.2(b)(i)), and then in the absence of air into ethanol and carbon dioxide:

$$C_6H_{12}O_6 \xrightarrow[\text{approx. 30°/anaerobic conditions}]{\text{yeast enzymes (zymase)}} 2C_2H_5OH + 2CO_2$$
glucose

The liquor obtained by fermentation contains up to 10–15 per cent of ethanol. The alcohol content of whisky, gin and other spirits is increased by distillation and that of fortified wines such as port and sherry by the direct addition of ethanol or spirit. Pure or *absolute* ethanol is far too strong to drink as it rapidly induces unconsciousness and can produce permanent physiological damage.

(ii) **Hydration of ethene.** See Unit 7.6(f).

(c) **Propan-2-ol**
This compound is manufactured by the hydration of propene from cracked petroleum (see Units 7.2 and 7.6(f)).

12.5 Absolute Ethanol

Pure anhydrous ethanol (*absolute alcohol*) cannot be obtained simply by distilling an aqueous solution of ethanol, as it forms a constant-boiling mixture with water (see Unit 2.6(b)). This mixture, which contains about 95.6 per cent of ethanol by weight and boils at 78.1°, is known as *rectified spirit*. Pure ethanol is separated from rectified spirit by fractional distillation after the addition of a small amount of benzene. The first fraction distils over at 64.8° and is a *ternary azeotrope*, that is, a constant-boiling mixture of three components: water (7.4 per cent), ethanol (18.5 per cent) and benzene (74.1 per cent). When all the water has been removed the boiling-point increases and a *binary azeotrope* containing ethanol (32.4 per cent) and benzene (67.6 per cent) distils over at 68.2°. Finally, when all the benzene has been removed, the boiling-point increases to 78.5° and pure ethanol distils over.

Ethanol is strongly *hygroscopic*, that is, it rapidly absorbs moisture from the air. These traces of water can be removed by distillation, first over calcium oxide and then over metallic calcium. Anhydrous calcium chloride cannot be used for this purpose as it forms a compound with ethanol, $CaCl_2 \cdot 3C_2H_5OH$.

Ethanol attracts an enormous duty from almost every government of the world, so most of the duty-free alcohol used in industry is in the form of *methylated spirit*. This is prepared by adding about 5–9 per cent of methanol and sometimes a purple dye, as well as other substances such as petroleum oil and pyridine, to rectified spirit in order to denature it and render it unfit to drink. *Surgical spirit* consists of about 95 per cent rectified spirit and 5 per cent methanol. Methanol is poisonous and causes blindness as it destroys the optic nerve.

12.6 Reactions of Alcohols

(a) Combustion
Alcohols burn rapidly in air to yield a mixture of carbon dioxide and water, for example:

$$C_2H_5OH + 3O_2 \rightarrow 2CO_2 + 3H_2O \; (\Delta H = -1\,367 \text{ kJ mol}^{-1})$$

(b) Reaction with Sodium
Sodium (and other electropositive metals such as potassium and magnesium) liberate hydrogen from alcohols to form *alkoxides*; for example:

$$\underset{\text{ethanol}}{2C_2H_5OH} + 2Na \rightarrow \underset{\text{sodium ethoxide}}{2C_2H_5O^-Na^+} + H_{2(g)}$$

The evolution of hydrogen on addition of metallic sodium is used as a test for the presence of a hydroxyl group in a compound. Alkoxides are white deliquescent solids which dissolve readily in water to yield an alkaline solution:

$$C_2H_5O^-Na^+ + H_2O \rightleftharpoons C_2H_5OH + NaOH$$

(c) Formation of Halogenoalkanes
The evolution of hydrogen chloride by the action of phosphorus pentachloride or sulphur dichloride oxide is indicative of the presence of a hydroxyl group in an organic compound (see Unit 10.2(a)):

$$ROH + SOCl_2 \rightarrow RCl + SO_{2(g)} + HCl_{(g)}$$

(d) Esterification
Alcohols react with carboxylic acids in the presence of a catalyst—usually a strong acid such as sulphuric acid—to form esters (see Unit 17.5):

$$\underset{\text{acid}}{RCO_2H} + \underset{\text{alcohol}}{R'OH} \overset{H^+}{\rightleftharpoons} \underset{\text{ester}}{RCO_2R'} + \underset{\text{water}}{H_2O}$$

The reaction is reversible; the mechanism is discussed in Units 16.5(b) and 17.5(d)(i).

Alcohols may also be converted to esters by the action of acyl chlorides or acid anhydrides. These reactions, in which the hydrogen atom in the hydroxyl group of an alcohol (or in the —NH$_2$ or —NH group of an amine) is replaced by RCO— or ArCO—, are known as *acylations*:

$$RCOCl + C_2H_5OH \rightarrow RCO_2C_2H_5 + HCl$$

acyl chloride   ethanol   ester

$$(CH_3CO)_2O + C_2H_5OH \xrightarrow{pyridine} CH_3CO_2C_2H_5 + CH_3CO_2H$$

ethanoic anhydride   ethanol   ethyl ethanoate   ethanoic acid

Tertiary alcohols give only poor yields of esters with acyl halides, since side-reactions—dehydration to yield alkenes and the formation of tertiary halogenoalkanes—also occur:

$$(CH_3)_3COH \xrightarrow[-H_2O]{H^+} (CH_3)_2C{=}CH_2$$

$$(CH_3)_3COH + CH_3COCl \rightarrow (CH_3)_3CCl + CH_3CO_2H$$

(e) Oxidation

Alcohols may be oxidized with solutions of potassium (or sodium) dichromate(VI) or potassium manganate(VII) acidified with sulphuric acid:

$$Cr_2O_7{}^{2-} + 14H^+ + 6e \rightarrow 2Cr^{3+} + 7H_2O$$

$$MnO_4{}^- + 8H^+ + 5e \rightarrow Mn^{2+} + 4H_2O$$

The product depends on the class of the alcohol undergoing oxidation. A *primary alcohol* yields an aldehyde which can be further oxidized to give a carboxylic acid:

$$RCH_2OH \xrightarrow[oxidation]{[O]} RCHO \xrightarrow[oxidation]{[O]} RCO_2H$$

1° alcohol   aldehyde   carboxylic acid

Secondary alcohols yield ketones:

$$R_2CHOH \xrightarrow[oxidation]{[O]} R_2CO$$

2° alcohol   ketone

Ketones are difficult to oxidize further; powerful oxidizing agents cause the molecule to break up to form a mixture of acids.

Tertiary alcohols resist oxidation, especially in neutral or alkaline solution, but strong oxidizing agents break the molecule into fragments—usually a ketone and a carboxylic acid.

These differences in behaviour towards oxidizing agents may be used to distinguish between primary, secondary and tertiary alcohols.

Oxidation with potassium dichromate(VI) is accompanied by a change in colour from orange-yellow to green with the formation of the chromium(III) ion:

$$3C_2H_5OH + Cr_2O_7{}^{2-} + 8H^+_{(aq)} \rightarrow 3CH_3CHO + 2Cr^{3+} + 7H_2O$$

ethanol   (orange)   ethanal   (green)

This reaction is used in some 'breathalysets' to detect alcohol in motorists whose erratic or dangerous driving is thought to be caused by excessive drinking.

(f) Catalytic Dehydrogenation

Primary and secondary alcohols are dehydrogenated to aldehydes and ketones respectively by the action of copper at 300°:

$$RCH_2OH \xrightarrow[300°]{Cu} RCHO + H_2$$

$$R_2CHOH \xrightarrow[300°]{Cu} R_2CO + H_2$$

These reactions are equivalent to oxidation with the added advantage that the aldehyde does not undergo further oxidation.

Under these conditions tertiary alcohols undergo dehydration; for instance:

$$(CH_3)_3COH \xrightarrow[300°]{Cu} (CH_3)_2C{=}CH_2 + H_2O$$
$$\text{2-methylpropan-2-ol} \qquad \text{2-methylpropene}$$

(g) Dehydration

Alcohols are dehydrated to form alkenes by the action of heated alumina or by heating with sulphuric or phosphoric(v) acid (see Unit 7.3(a)). The ease of dehydration is 3° > 2° > 1°; this is reflected in the temperatures (150°, 250° and 300–350° respectively) required for the vapour-phase reaction with alumina. For example:

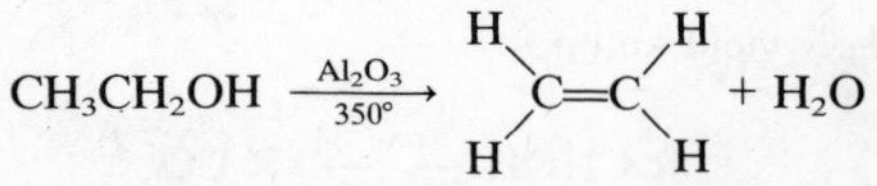

$$CH_3CH_2OH \xrightarrow[350°]{Al_2O_3} \underset{H}{\overset{H}{C}}{=}\underset{H}{\overset{H}{C}} + H_2O$$

Primary alcohols are dehydrated by heating with an excess of concentrated sulphuric acid at temperatures above 170°, while dehydration of secondary and tertiary alcohols takes place on boiling with dilute sulphuric acid. Secondary and tertiary alcohols containing four or more carbon atoms yield a mixture of alkenes; thus, for butan-2-ol:

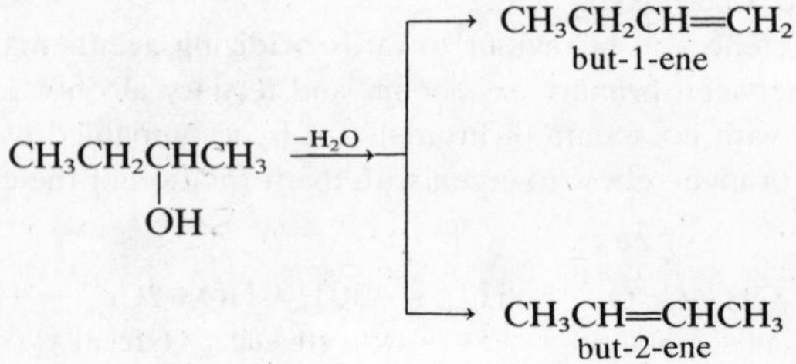

$$CH_3CH_2CHCH_3 \underset{OH}{} \xrightarrow{-H_2O}$$

$$\longrightarrow CH_3CH_2CH{=}CH_2 \quad \text{but-1-ene}$$

$$\longrightarrow CH_3CH{=}CHCH_3 \quad \text{but-2-ene}$$

The identity of the major product may be predicted by *Saytzeff's Rule*. This states that the alkene containing the higher number of alkyl substituents is the predominant product, that is, the hydrogen is preferentially eliminated from the carbon atom linked to the *smaller* number of hydrogen atoms: thus the dehydration of butan-2-ol yields but-2-ene as the main product. Saytzeff's Rule also applies to the elimination of hydrogen halide from halogenoalkanes to yield alkenes (see Unit 10.6(b)).

Phosphoric(v) acid or phosphorus(v) oxide may also be used as dehydrating agents (see Experiment 7.2) with the advantage that formation of ether as a by-product is avoided. All three classes of alcohol give excellent yields of alkene with boric acid as the catalyst:

$$3RCH_2CH_2OH + H_3BO_3 \rightarrow (RCH_2CH_2O)_3B \rightarrow 3RCH{=}CH_2 + H_3BO_3$$

Partial dehydration to form an ether occurs when the alcohol is passed over alumina at a lower temperature than that for alkene formation:

$$2C_2H_5OH \xrightarrow{\text{Al}_2\text{O}_3/260°} (C_2H_5)_2O + H_2O$$
$$\text{ethoxyethane}$$

or when an *excess of alcohol* is treated with concentrated sulphuric acid:

$$2C_2H_5OH \xrightarrow{\text{H}_2\text{SO}_4/140°} (C_2H_5)_2O + H_2O$$

The preparation of ethoxyethane by the latter method is known as *Williamson's continuous ether synthesis*. The reaction is thought to proceed by the mechanism:

$$C_2H_5OH \xrightarrow{H^+} C_2H_5\overset{+}{O}H_2 \xrightarrow{C_2H_5OH} (C_2H_5)_2O + H_3O^+$$

Methanol reacts with concentrated sulphuric acid to yield the toxic ester dimethyl sulphate:

$$2CH_3OH + H_2SO_4 \rightarrow (CH_3)_2SO_4 + 2H_2O$$

(h) Tri-iodomethane (Iodoform) Reaction

Ethanol (and also propan-2-ol, but not methanol or propan-1-ol) forms yellow crystals of tri-iodomethane (iodoform), CHI_3, m.p. 120°, when treated with a mixture of iodine and aqueous sodium hydroxide (see Unit 15.6(c)(iv)):

$$CH_3CH_2OH + 4I_2 + 6NaOH \rightarrow CHI_3 + HCO_2^- Na^+ + 5NaI + 5H_2O$$

Experiment 12.1 *To demonstrate the reactions of alcohols*

1. *Combustion.* Burn a few drops of methanol or ethanol on a spatula or watch-glass and note the colour of the flame.

2. *Reaction with sodium.* Add a small piece of freshly cut sodium to 1 or

Table 12.2 Some differences between primary, secondary and tertiary alcohols

	1° alcohol	2° alcohol	3° alcohol
Functional group	—CH$_2$OH	＞CHOH	—＞COH
Preparation (i)	← ———————— Hydrolysis of esters ————————— →		
(ii)	← ———— Hydrolysis of halogenoalkanes ———— →		Yields are low owing to alkene formation
(iii)	Reduction of aldehydes	Reduction of ketones	—
(iv)	RMgX + CH$_2$O or (CH$_2$)$_2$O	RMgX + aldehydes	RMgX + ketones

Reactions:

	1° alcohol	2° alcohol	3° alcohol
Dehydration	———————— Ease of dehydration increases ————————— →		

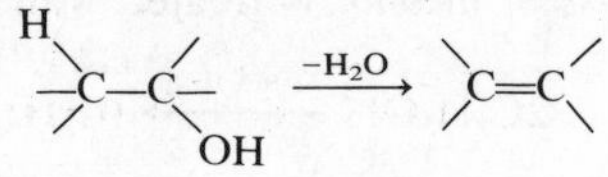

$$\underset{\underset{\displaystyle OH}{|}}{\overset{\overset{\displaystyle H}{|}}{-C-C-}} \xrightarrow{-H_2O} \quad >C=C< $$

	1° alcohol	2° alcohol	3° alcohol
	Al$_2$O$_3$/300–350°	Al$_2$O$_3$/250°	Al$_2$O$_3$/150°
Oxidation	—CHO → —CO$_2$H	＞C=O $\xrightarrow{\text{further oxidation}}$ breaks up	Oxidation difficult, molecule breaks up
Catalytic dehydrogenation e.g. Cu/heat	Yields aldehyde	Yields ketone	Dehydration occurs to yield alkene
Action of HCl/ZnCl$_2$ (Lucas test)	No reaction within 15 min at room temperature	Cloudy solution or separate layer within 5–10 min as ＞CCl slowly forms	Cloudy solution[1] or separate layer obtained at once: immediate ＞CCl formation

[1] Phenylmethanol, C$_6$H$_5$CH$_2$OH, also reacts immediately at room temperature; phenols do not react, even on heating

2 cm^3 of anhydrous methanol in a dry test-tube. Test the gas evolved for hydrogen. Transfer the solution obtained to an evaporating basin and evaporate to dryness on a boiling water bath. Add water to the solid residue and test with litmus or Universal pH paper.

3. *Reaction with phosphorus pentachloride.* Add a small amount of phosphorus pentachloride on a spatula to about 2 cm^3 of the anhydrous alcohol (ethanol or propan-1-ol). Test the gas evolved with moist litmus paper and with gaseous ammonia.

4. *Oxidation.* Add about 1 cm^3 of methanol to 2 cm^3 of potassium dichromate(VI) solution acidified with dilute sulphuric acid. Warm the mixture gently and note any change in odour or colour. Repeat the experiment with ethanol and with samples of secondary and tertiary alcohols such as propan-2-ol, butan-2-ol and 2-methylpropan-2-ol.

5. *Esterification.* (i) Add a few drops of concentrated sulphuric acid to a mixture of 1 cm^3 of glacial ethanoic acid and 2 cm^3 of the alcohol (methanol, ethanol or 2-methylpropan-2-ol). Warm gently for 4 or 5 minutes and then pour into a beaker of water containing an excess of dilute sodium hydroxide solution to neutralize the unreacted acids. Stir well and note the pleasant, 'fruity' odour of the ethanoate ester.
(ii) Gently heat about 1 cm^3 of methanol for 3 or 4 minutes with about 0.5 g of 2-hydroxybenzoic acid (salicylic acid) and a few drops of concentrated sulphuric acid, and then pour into about 20 cm^3 of cold water. Note the odour of methyl 2-hydroxybenzoate (oil of wintergreen).

6. *Tri-iodomethane (iodoform) reaction.* Add dilute aqueous sodium hydroxide to a mixture of iodine solution and 1 cm^3 of ethanol until the iodine colour is discharged. Warm gently and allow to cool. Note the separation of yellow crystals of tri-iodomethane. Repeat with propan-2-ol, and then with methanol.

The differences between primary, secondary and tertiary alcohols are summarized in Table 12.2.

12.7 Uses of Alcohols

(a) Methanol
Most of the methanol produced in the United Kingdom is oxidized to methanal, a starting material for the manufacture of thermosetting plastics such as Bakelite (see Unit 13.7(b)(v)). Other uses are as a solvent for varnishes, polishes and paints, and for the preparation of methyl 2-methylpropenoate (for making Perspex), dimethyl benzene-1,4-dicarboxylate (for making Terylene—see Unit 12.8(a)(iii)) and halogenoalkanes (see Unit 10.2(a)).

(b) **Ethanol**

Ethanol is used as a solvent, for the preparation of ethanal (see Unit 15.3(b)(i)), as a petrol additive to improve octane rating (see Unit 6.4—some methanol is also used for this purpose), as a constituent of spirits, wine, beer and other alcoholic beverages, and as a thermometric liquid—ethanol has a low freezing-point ($-117.6°$) and may therefore be used instead of mercury (m.p. $-39.7°$) for measuring low temperatures.

(c) **Propan-2-ol**

Propan-2-ol is used as a solvent and for the preparation of propanone and hydrogen peroxide:

$$(CH_3)_2CHOH + O_2 \xrightarrow[\text{pressure}]{90-140°} (CH_3)_2CO + H_2O_2$$
$$\text{propanone}$$

12.8 Polyhydric Alcohols

The most important polyhydric alcohols are ethane-1,2-diol (ethylene glycol or 'glycol'), b.p. $197°$, and propane-1,2,3-triol (glycerol), b.p. $289°$:

$$\begin{array}{cc} & CH_2OH \\ & | \\ CH_2OH & CHOH \\ | & | \\ CH_2OH & CH_2OH \\ \text{ethane-1,2-diol} & \text{propane-1,2,3-triol} \end{array}$$

These compounds are both colourless, viscous, high-boiling liquids that are soluble in water. Their low volatility and high viscosity and solubility are a result of intermolecular hydrogen bonding (see Unit 12.2).

(a) **Ethane-1,2-diol**

(i) **Manufacture.** Ethane-1,2-diol is manufactured by the hydration of epoxyethane (see Unit 14.8):

$$\begin{array}{c} CH_2 \\ | \quad\!\!>O + H_2O \xrightarrow[\text{aqueous acid/60°}]{\text{steam/200°/pressure}} \begin{array}{c} CH_2OH \\ | \\ CH_2OH \end{array} \\ CH_2 \\ \text{epoxyethane} \end{array}$$

(ii) **Reactions.** The chemical properties of ethane-1,2-diol are as would be expected for a compound with two primary alcohol groups in the molecule. It reacts with two moles of sodium and forms compounds such as diethers and diesters, although more vigorous conditions are required to make the second hydroxyl group react.

(iii) **Uses.** Ethane-1,2-diol, which melts at $-11.5°$, is used as anti-freeze in cars and for de-icing the wings of aircraft. It is also used in the manufacture of *Terylene*, through reaction with dimethyl benzene-1,4-dicarboxylate (dimethyl terephthalate):

$$HOCH_2CH_2OH \ + \ CH_3OOC-\langle\bigcirc\rangle-COOCH_3 \ + \ HOCH_2CH_2OH$$

heat/catalyst
$(-2CH_3OH)$

$$HOCH_2CH_2OC-\langle\bigcirc\rangle-COCH_2CH_2OH$$
$$\overset{\|}{O} \qquad\qquad \overset{\|}{O}$$

heat,
polymerization

$$HOCH_2\!\left[CH_2OC-\langle\bigcirc\rangle-COCH_2\right]_n\!CH_2OH$$
$$\overset{\qquad\quad\|}{\quad\quad O} \qquad\qquad \overset{\|}{O}$$
Terylene

This is an example of condensation polymerization (see Unit 21.3(*b*)). Terylene is used to make fibres by forcing the molten polymer through fine holes in a metal disc. The filaments are stretched to increase their strength and then, either alone or mixed with wool or cotton, are used to make drip-dry and crease-resistant fabrics.

(*b*) Propane-1,2,3-triol

Propane-1,2,3-triol is a by-product of the manufacture of soap (see Unit 12.3(*a*)). It is also made from propene (from cracked petroleum).

The trinitrate ester (propane-1,2,3-triyl nitrate or nitroglycerine) is obtained by the action of concentrated nitric acid on propane-1,2,3-triol:

$$\begin{array}{l} CH_2OH \\ | \\ CHOH \ + \ 3HNO_3 \ \longrightarrow \\ | \\ CH_2OH \end{array} \qquad \begin{array}{l} CH_2ONO_2 \\ | \\ CHONO_2 \ + 3H_2O \\ | \\ CH_2ONO_2 \end{array}$$

Nitroglycerine is an unstable, colourless oily liquid which explodes violently when subjected to shock. It is a constituent of many explosives; *dynamite*, for example, consists of nitroglycerine absorbed in kieselguhr, and has a disruptive force about eight times that of gunpowder.

Propane-1,2,3-triol is also used to make glyptal resins and plastics (see Unit 21.6(*b*)) and is a starting material for the manufacture of polyurethan foams (for cushions and padding materials) and fibres (for 'stretch fabrics', such as 'Lycra').

12.9 Aromatic Alcohols: Phenylmethanol

In the aromatic alcohols the hydroxyl group is separated from the ring by at least one carbon atom, that is, they are aromatic compounds in which the hydroxyl group is attached to the side-chain. They may be regarded as aryl derivatives of the alkanols, and many of their reactions and the methods used for their preparation are similar to those described for the aliphatic alcohols.

$$CH_2OH$$

phenylmethanol

The simplest aromatic primary alcohol is phenylmethanol (benzyl alcohol), $C_6H_5CH_2OH$. This compound is a colourless liquid, b.p. 205°, sparingly soluble in water. It is used to prepare a number of esters which are employed in perfumery: phenylmethyl ethanoate, $CH_3CO_2CH_2C_6H_5$, for example, occurs in oil of jasmine.

Questions on the material in Unit 12 are to be found at the end of Unit 13.

Hydroxy-compounds: Phenols

13.1 General Formula and Nomenclature

Phenols are hydroxy-compounds in which the hydroxyl group is attached to an unsaturated carbon atom of the aromatic ring; for example:

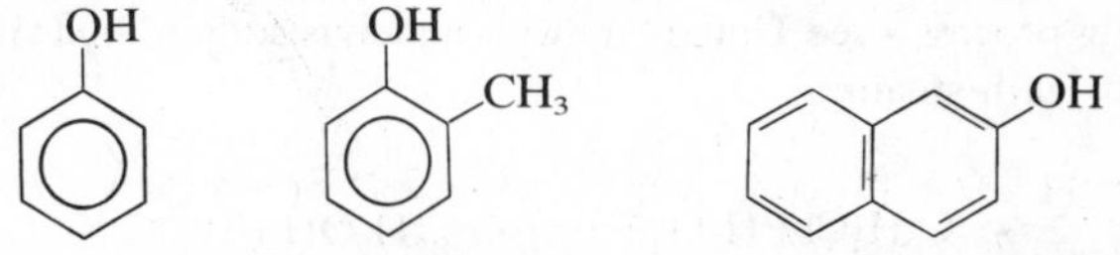

phenol   2-methylphenol   naphthalen-2-ol

The general formula is thus ArOH, which resembles the general formula for alcohols, ROH; but the properties of the hydroxyl group are so strongly modified by the presence of the aromatic ring that many of the reactions of phenols are quite different from the corresponding reactions of alcohols.

13.2 Preparation of Phenol

Phenol, C_6H_5OH, the simplest and most important member of the series, may be prepared in the laboratory either from sodium benzenesulphonate or from benzenediazonium salts.

(a) From Sodium Benzenesulphonate
Sodium benzenesulphonate is fused with sodium (or potassium) hydroxide:

$$C_6H_5SO_3^-Na^+ \quad + 2NaOH \xrightarrow{c.\ 300°} C_6H_5O^-Na^+ \quad +Na_2SO_3+H_2O$$
sodium benzenesulphonate   sodium phenoxide

Phenol is liberated by acidifying the product with dilute hydrochloric acid:

$$C_6H_5O^-Na + HCl_{(aq)} \rightarrow C_6H_5OH + NaCl_{(aq)}$$

and may be separated by ethoxyethane extraction (see Unit 2.4) or by steam-distillation (see Unit 2.1(b)). The process was once used for phenol manufacture but is now obsolete.

(b) From Benzenediazonium Salts
Phenol is liberated when an aqueous solution of a benzenediazonium salt is warmed (see Unit 18.6(c)(i)).

13.3 Manufacture of Phenols

World production of phenol now exceeds one million tonnes per annum, most of which is made by the *cumene process* from (1-methylethyl)benzene (cumene):

$$C_6H_5\underset{\underset{CH_3}{|}}{\overset{\overset{CH_3}{|}}{CH}} \xrightarrow[\text{pH 8.5-10}]{\text{air/c.120°}} C_6H_5\underset{\underset{CCH_3}{|}}{\overset{\overset{CH_3}{|}}{C}}-O-OH \xrightarrow{\text{dil. H}_2\text{SO}_4} C_6H_5OH + CH_3COCH_3$$

cumene   phenol   propanone

Phenol is also manufactured by the hydrolysis of chlorobenzene (made by the Raschig process—see Unit 11.3) with aqueous sodium hydroxide under pressure or with steam:

$$C_6H_5Cl + H_2O \xrightarrow{\text{SiO}_2/500°} C_6H_5OH + HCl$$

The hydrogen chloride formed as a by-product in the reaction is recycled and used for the production of more chlorobenzene.

Some phenol is obtained from the middle oil fraction of coal tar distillation (see Unit 9.2). When the oil is cooled, naphthalene (c. 40 per cent) crystallizes out and is separated, and the remaining liquid is treated with aqueous sodium hydroxide to dissolve the phenols:

$$ArOH + NaOH_{(aq)} \rightarrow ArO^-Na^+_{(aq)} + H_2O$$
phenols   sodium phenoxides

Air is blown through the boiling alkaline solution to remove basic impurities and any remaining naphthalene. Carbon dioxide is then passed into the cooled solution; phenols are weaker acids than carbonic acid and are therefore displaced from the phenoxides:

$$ArO^-Na^+ + CO_2 + H_2O \rightarrow ArOH + HCO_3^- + Na^+$$
phenols

The sodium and hydrogencarbonate ions dissolve in the aqueous layer and are removed. The oily mixture of phenols which remains is fractionally distilled to yield phenol (b.p. 181°), methylphenols (cresols, b.p. 190–203°), and dimethylphenols (xylenols, b.p. 210–225°).

13.4 Properties of Phenol

Phenol is a colourless, crystalline solid (m.p. 42°, b.p. 181°) which slowly turns pink when left exposed to air, owing to the formation of oxidation products. It is moderately soluble in water at 20°, but is completely miscible at temperatures above 65.8°. Phenol has a characteristic disinfectant-like odour: its aqueous solution, under the name of *carbolic acid*, was first used as an antiseptic in surgery by Lister in 1867. It is both caustic and poisonous.

13.5 Structure and Reactivity of Phenol

The difference in reactivity of the hydroxyl group in phenols compared with that in alcohols is due to the delocalization of one of the unbonded pairs of electrons on the oxygen atom of the phenol molecule by interaction with the aromatic nucleus. The molecule is a resonance hybrid of forms such as:

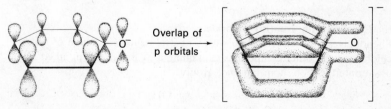

and may be represented as:

This structure is highly susceptible to substitution in the *ortho*- and *para*-positions by electrophiles (see Unit 9.9). The delocalization of the electrons results in a shortening of the carbon–oxygen bond to 0.136 nm (*cf.* the corresponding bond length in ethanol, 0.143 nm). The higher acid strength of phenols compared with that of the alcohols is a result of this delocalization and of the resonance stabilization of the phenoxide ion (*cf.* Unit 16.5(*a*)):

This may be represented in terms of the molecular orbital theory as considerable overlap of the p orbitals on the oxygen atom with the π layer of the ring (see Fig. 13.1). The phenoxide ion is thus more stable than the alkoxide ion, and phenols therefore have a greater tendency to dissociate than alcohols.

Overlap of
p orbitals

Fig. 13.1   Structure of the phenoxide ion

The chemical reactions of phenols may be conveniently sub-divided into (a) the reactions of the hydroxyl group, which may be compared with those of alcohols (see Unit 12.6) and (b) the reactions of the aromatic nucleus.

13.6 Reactions of the Hydroxyl Group

Phenol does not react with hydrogen halides, phosphorus tribromide or with red phosphorus and iodine. Phosphorus pentachloride gives only a very poor yield of chlorobenzene; the principal product is triphenyl phosphate(v), $(C_6H_5O)_3PO$:

$$3C_6H_5OH + PCl_5 \rightarrow (C_6H_5O)_3PO + 3HCl$$

Phenol does not undergo elimination reactions and is not oxidized in the same way as alcohols, but yields a mixture of complex coloured and polymeric materials on oxidation.

(a) Reaction as an Acid
Phenols are stronger acids than alcohols are, owing to resonance stabilization of the phenoxide ion (see Unit 13.5), and form salts such as sodium phenoxide, $C_6H_5O^-Na^+$, with aqueous alkalis. Phenol $(K_a = 1 \times 10^{-10})$ is approximately a million times stronger as an acid than methanol $(K_a = 10^{-16})$. It is a weaker acid than carbonic acid $(K_a = 3 \times 10^{-7})$, and does not liberate carbon dioxide from carbonates; this reaction may therefore be used to distinguish most phenols from carboxylic acids. Phenols containing electron-withdrawing substituents (such as nitro-groups) are stronger acids than phenol itself, however, as these groups facilitate the loss of the proton (see Unit 4.8). 2,4,6-Trinitrophenol (picric acid) is a strong acid $(K_a = 10^{-1}$ approximately) and will liberate carbon dioxide from sodium carbonate solution.

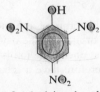

2,4,6-trinitrophenol

(b) Reaction with Iron(III) Chloride
Phenol gives a violet coloration with a neutral aqueous solution of iron(III) chloride, as do other compounds containing a hydroxyl group linked to an unsaturated carbon atom (an *enol* group):

(c) Reaction with Sodium

Phenol reacts with sodium (or potassium) to form a phenoxide (*cf.* Unit 12.6(*b*)):

$$C_6H_5OH + Na \rightarrow C_6H_5O^-Na^+ + \tfrac{1}{2}H_2$$

The product readily forms ethers by Williamson's method (described in Unit 10.6(*a*)(ii)), thus:

$$C_6H_5O^-Na^+ + C_2H_5I \rightarrow C_6H_5OC_2H_5 + NaI$$
ethoxybenzene

Methoxybenzene is synthesized by this method, using the reaction of phenol with dimethyl sulphate, $(CH_3)_2SO_4$, as this compound is considerably cheaper than the halogenomethanes:

$$2C_6H_5O^-Na^+ + (CH_3)_2SO_4 \xrightarrow{NaOH_{(aq)}} 2C_6H_5OCH_3 + Na_2SO_4$$
methoxybenzene

(d) Ester Formation

Phenols form esters, but not by direct reaction with carboxylic acids. Esterification is carried out by the action of acid anhydrides or acid chlorides on the phenol, for example:

$$(CH_3CO)_2O + C_6H_5OH \xrightarrow{H^+} C_6H_5OCOCH_3 + CH_3CO_2H$$
ethanoic anhydride   phenol   phenyl ethanoate   ethanoic acid

$$C_6H_5COCl + C_6H_5OH \xrightarrow{NaOH_{(aq)}} C_6H_5CO_2C_6H_5 + HCl$$
benzoyl chloride   phenol   phenyl benzoate

Acylation reactions (see Unit 12.6(*d*)), involving the use of benzoyl chloride or other aromatic acyl halides in the presence of a base such as aqueous sodium hydroxide or pyridine, are examples of the *Schotten–Baumann* reaction. This reaction is frequently used to prepare solid derivatives of alcohols or phenols for identification purposes. 3,5-Dinitrobenzoyl chloride is particularly useful in this respect as it yields products that melt sharply within a convenient temperature range.

Experiment 13.1 *The Schotten–Baumann reaction*

Dissolve 0.5 g of phenol in about 10 cm^3 of aqueous sodium hydroxide in a small mortar and grind the mixture with about 1.2 g of 3,5-dinitrobenzoyl chloride. Filter off the solid residue, wash well with dilute sodium hydroxide solution and recrystallize from ethanol. Determine the melting-point of the purified product.

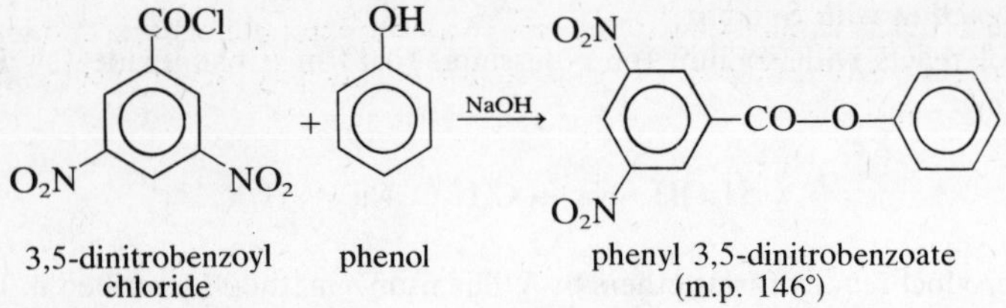

3,5-dinitrobenzoyl   phenol   phenyl 3,5-dinitrobenzoate
chloride   (m.p. 146°)

(e) **Reduction**
Phenol is reduced to benzene by heating with zinc dust (see Unit 9.3(b)).

13.7 Reactions of the Aromatic Nucleus

(a) **Reduction**
Phenol is converted into cyclohexanol by catalytic hydrogenation (cf. the reduction of benzene, Unit 9.6(a)(i)):

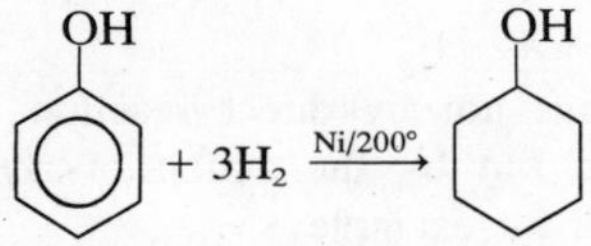

The oxidation of cyclohexanol, $C_6H_{11}OH$, yields hexanedioic acid (adipic acid), an important starting material for the manufacture of nylon (see Unit 21.5):

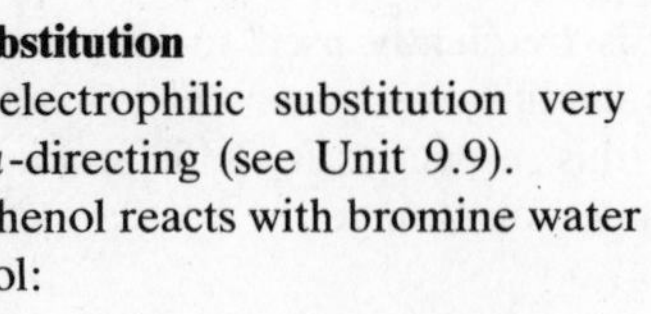

(b) **Electrophilic Substitution**
Phenol undergoes electrophilic substitution very readily. The hydroxyl group is ortho-/para-directing (see Unit 9.9).
(i) **Halogenation.** Phenol reacts with bromine water to yield a precipitate of 2,4,6-tribromophenol:

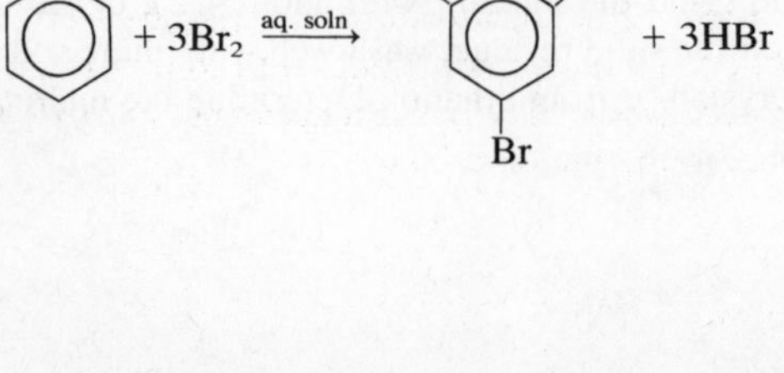

and also reacts similarly with chlorine. Monobromophenols are obtained if the bromine is dissolved in a non-polar solvent such as carbon disulphide or tetrachloromethane:

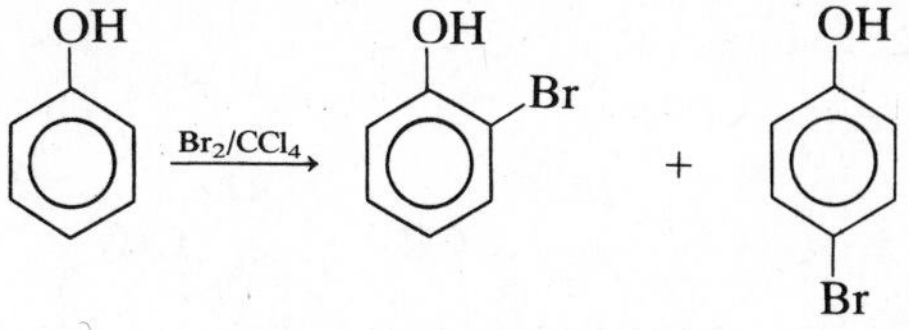

2-bromophenol   4-bromophenol
(major product)

(ii) **Nitration.** Phenol is nitrated by dilute nitric acid to yield a mixture of 2- and 4-nitrophenol:

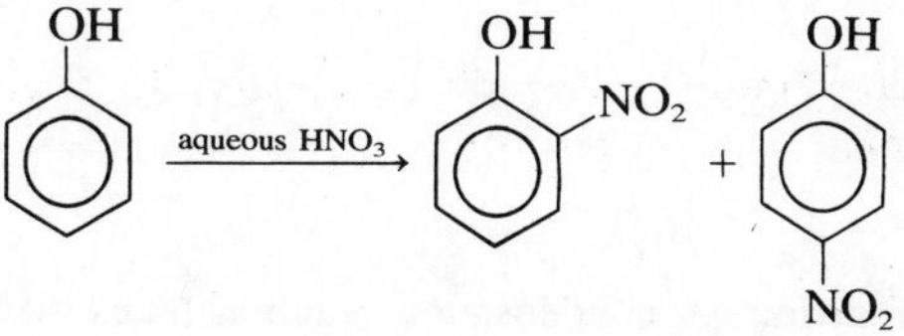

Sulphuric acid is not required (*cf.* benzene, Unit 9.6(*b*)(ii)); the two isomers may be separated by steam-distillation. Both compounds exhibit hydrogen bonding, but in 2-nitrophenol this occurs *intramolecularly* (within the molecule):

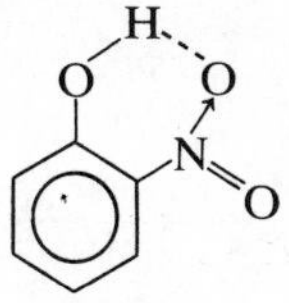

This makes the compound more volatile (b.p. 216°) than its 4-isomer (b.p. 279°), in which the hydrogen bonding occurs *intermolecularly* between the hydrogen atom of the hydroxyl group of one molecule and the nitro-group of another:

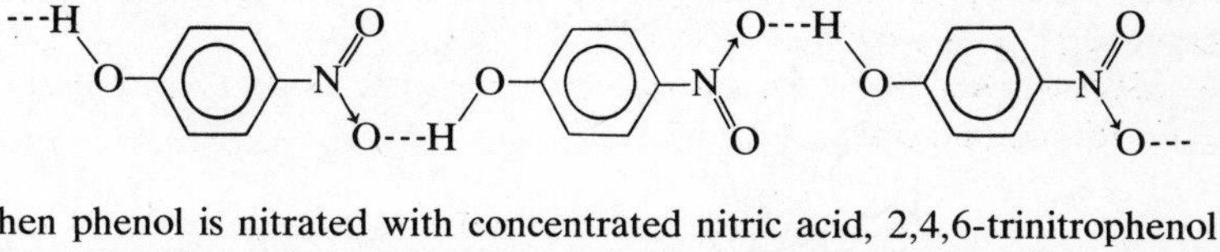

When phenol is nitrated with concentrated nitric acid, 2,4,6-trinitrophenol is formed. It is a yellow, crystalline solid, m.p. 122°, which is also known as *picric acid*. It is used in the manufacture of explosives.

(iii) **Sulphonation.** Sulphonation of phenol with concentrated sulphuric acid at room temperature yields mainly 2-phenolsulphonic acid. At 100°, however, the 4-isomer is the major product.

(iv) **Coupling with diazonium salts.** See Unit 18.6(c)(iii).

(v) **Condensation with aldehydes.** Phenol condenses with aldehydes, forming 2- and 4-substituted derivatives. The most important of these reactions is with an excess of methanal: a complex three-dimensional, cross-linked polymer (Bakelite) is obtained:

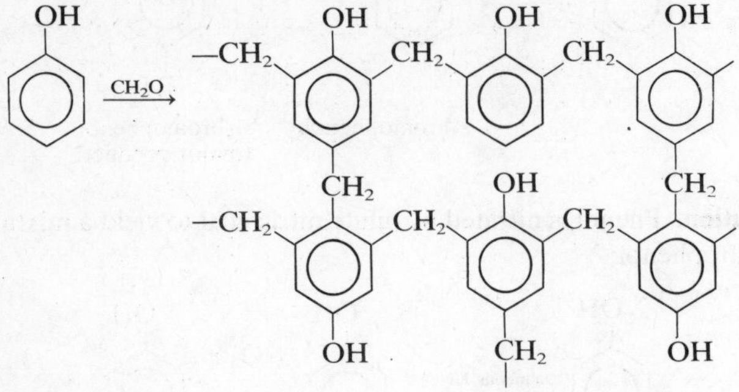

Bakelite

(vi) **Phthalein reaction.** A condensation reaction takes place when phenol is warmed gently with benzene-1,2-dicarboxylic anhydride (phthalic anhydride) in the presence of concentrated sulphuric acid:

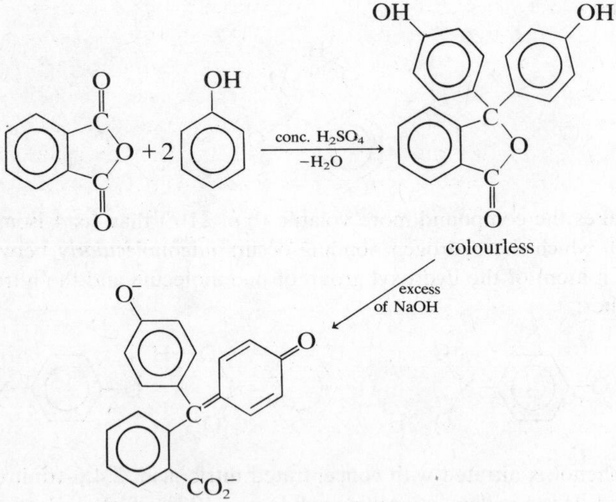

The product is the indicator *phenolphthalein*, which changes from colourless to pink on the addition of an excess of sodium hydroxide. The colour is a result of the extended conjugated system in the alkaline form.

Experiment 13.2 *To demonstrate the reactions of phenols*
Care: Phenol is caustic and poisonous.

1. *Solubility.* Test the solubility of approximately 0.5 g of phenol in (i)
water—determine the pH of the solution with Universal indicator paper, (ii)
aqueous sodium hydroxide and (iii) aqueous sodium carbonate solution.
Note the odour of phenol.

2. *Action of iron(III) chloride.* First prepare a neutral solution of iron(III)
chloride (see Appendix II). Test for the presence of an enol group in phenol
by adding 2 or 3 drops of this solution to a very dilute solution of phenol in
water. Note the characteristic violet-blue coloration.

3. *Action of bromine water.* Add bromine water gradually to a concentrated solution of phenol in water (approximately 2 cm³) and note whether
the bromine colour is discharged. Add an excess of bromine and note the
formation of a white precipitate of 2,4,6-tribromophenol (m.p. 95°).

4. *Coupling with diazonium salts.* Prepare a solution of benzenediazonium chloride (see Unit 18.6(*a*)) by adding a few drops of
aqueous 20 per cent sodium nitrite to a solution of 3 or 4 drops of
phenylamine (aniline) in 2 cm³ of concentrated hydrochloric acid and 4 cm³
of water cooled in ice. Add this cold solution to a cold solution of phenol in
an excess of aqueous sodium hydroxide. Note the colour of the azo-dye
produced. Naphthalen-2-ol (2-naphthol) gives a scarlet precipitate (see Unit
18.6(*c*)(iii)).

5. *Phthalein reaction. Gently* warm a mixture of approximately 0.2 g each
of phenol and benzene-1,2-dicarboxylic anhydride (phthalic anhydride) with
two drops of concentrated sulphuric acid in a clean, dry test-tube for about
two minutes. Allow the products to cool thoroughly, and then add an excess
of dilute sodium hydroxide. Note the characteristic colour of phenolphthalein. Add a little dilute hydrochloric acid and then again make the
solution alkaline by adding an excess of sodium hydroxide solution. Different colours are obtained with other phenols; benzene-1,3-diol (resorcinol),
for instance, gives a green fluorescent solution (fluorescein).

13.8 Uses of Phenol

Phenol is used for the manufacture of plastics such as Bakelite, and as a
starting material for the production of antiseptics, such as 2,4-dichloro-3,5-
dimethylphenol, the active constituent of 'Dettol',

and also the synthesis of hexanedioic acid (adipic acid) for the manufacture of nylon (see Unit 21.5), and of selective weedkillers such as 2,4-dichlorophenoxyethanoic acid, sold commercially as '2,4-D':

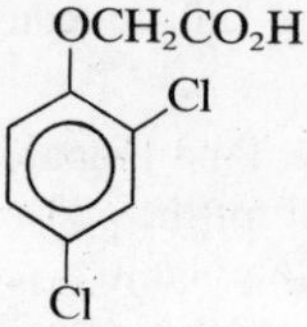

$$OCH_2CO_2H$$

Cl

Cl

Test Yourself on Units 12 and 13

1. Name the following compounds:
   (a) $C_6H_5CHOHCH_3$
   (b) $CH_2OHCH_2CH_2OH$
   (c) $CH_3CH(CH_3)CHOHCH_3$

   (d) $C_2H_5-\overset{\overset{\displaystyle CH_3}{|}}{\underset{\underset{\displaystyle OH}{|}}{C}}-CH_3$

   (e) OH OH

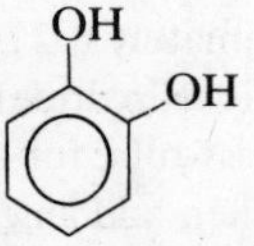

2. Suggest one chemical test to distinguish between each of the following pairs of compounds:
   (a) ethanol and methanol;
   (b) 2-methylphenol and phenylmethanol;
   (c) 2-methylpropan-1-ol and 2-methylpropan-2-ol;
   (d) phenol and ethanoic acid;
   (e) ethanol and ethoxyethane.

3. Explain the following:
   (a) 2-nitrophenol may be separated from its isomer, 4-nitrophenol, by steam-distillation;
   (b) phenol is a stronger acid than ethanol;
   (c) bromine water is decolorized by the addition of phenol but, except for dissolving the bromine from the aqueous layer, benzene does not appear to react;
   (d) the carbon–oxygen bond length is considerably shorter in phenol than in ethanol.

4. Suggest syntheses for the following compounds using ethanol as the sole organic starting material:
   (a) ethanal;
   (b) butan-2-ol;
   (c) ethyl ethanoate;
   (d) ethoxyethane.

5. Discuss Saytzeff's Rule and Markownikoff's Rule with particular reference to the dehydration of alcohols and the hydration of alkenes.

6. Name the secondary and tertiary alcohols of formula $C_5H_{11}OH$.

7. Compare and contrast the structures and reactions of primary, secondary and tertiary alcohols.

8. Name the reagents and reaction conditions for carrying out the following changes:
   (a) phenol → 4-bromophenol;
   (b) benzene → phenol;
   (c) glucose → ethanol;
   (d) ethanol → ethanoic acid;
   (e) phenol → 2,4,6-trichlorophenol.

9. Compare and contrast the preparation, properties and reactions of ethanol and phenol.

10. Outline the methods used for the large-scale preparation of alcohols and phenol.

11. How and under what conditions does sulphuric acid react with (a) ethanol, (b) phenol and (c) methanol?

12. Two liquids, A and B, have the same molecular formula, $C_4H_{10}O$, and both effervesce with sodium. Treatment with acidified potassium dichromate(VI) has no effect on A, but B yields a volatile liquid, C. C does not react with sodium carbonate solution, but is readily oxidized to D, $C_4H_8O_2$, which dissolves in sodium carbonate solution with effervescence. A forms an oily liquid, E, on treatment with concentrated hydrochloric acid. A pleasant-smelling liquid, F, $C_8H_{16}O_2$, is obtained when B is treated with D in the presence of sulphuric acid; the major volatile product from a similar reaction with A is a colourless gas which rapidly decolorized bromine to form a dense oil, G.

Suggest possible structures for the compounds A to G and elucidate the reactions. A complete identification may not be possible.

Ethers

14.1 General Formula and Nomenclature

The general formula of the ethers is:

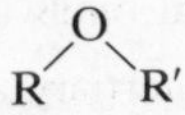

$$R \overset{\displaystyle O}{\diagdown \diagup} R'$$

Compounds in which R and R' are identical are described as *symmetrical* or *simple ethers*, while compounds in which these groups are different are *unsymmetrical* or *mixed ethers*. *Aromatic ethers* contain at least one aryl group:

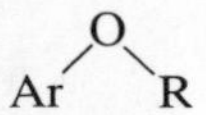

$$Ar \overset{\displaystyle O}{\diagdown \diagup} R \quad \text{or} \quad Ar \overset{\displaystyle O}{\diagdown \diagup} Ar$$

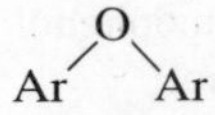

According to the IUPAC system the ethers are named as alkoxy- or aryloxy-derivatives of the corresponding alkane or aromatic hydrocarbon, that is, as alkoxyalkanes, alkoxyarenes or aryloxyarenes. The older (and equally systematic) nomenclature, based on the alkyl or aryl groups attached to the oxygen atom in the ether molecule, is still widely used, however. The formulae and names—based on the two systems of nomenclature—of a number of ethers are listed in Table 14.1. Ethoxyethane, the most important member of the series, is frequently referred to as 'ether'.

Table 14.1 Nomenclature and physical properties of ethers

IUPAC name	Trivial name	Formula	m.p. (°C)	b.p. (°C)	d (g cm^{-3})
Methoxymethane	dimethyl ether	CH_3OCH_3	−138.5	−24	—
Methoxyethane	ethyl methyl ether	$CH_3OC_2H_5$	—	10.8	0.725
Ethoxyethane	diethyl ether ('ether')	$C_2H_5OC_2H_5$	−116	34.5	0.714
Methoxybenzene	methyl phenyl ether ('anisole')	$C_6H_5OCH_3$	−37.5	155	0.996
Ethoxybenzene	ethyl phenyl ether ('phenetole')	$C_6H_5OC_2H_5$	−29.5	170	0.967

14.2 Physical Properties of Ethers

The ethers are isomeric with the alcohols but are considerably more volatile, since their molecules cannot associate by hydrogen bonding (*cf.*

alcohols, Unit 12.2(a)); for example, methoxyethane is a gas (b.p. $-24°$) but the alcohol with which it is isomeric, ethanol, is a liquid boiling at $78.5°$. The boiling-points and melting-points of a number of common ethers are listed in Table 14.1. The lower alkoxyalkanes are gases or volatile liquids with a sweet, sickly, characteristic 'ether' smell. They are highly flammable and form explosive mixtures with air. Ethoxyethane is particularly dangerous in this respect owing to its high volatility (b.p. $35°$) and its tendency to form a dense vapour which collects in sinks or drains.

Ethoxyethane (density $0.71 \, \mathrm{g \, cm^{-3}}$) is partially miscible with water. Two layers are obtained: the upper is a solution of water (approximately 1 per cent) in ether, the lower a solution of ether (approximately 7 per cent) in water. The ethoxyethane layer dissolves readily on the addition of acid owing to protonation of the unbonded pair of electrons on the oxygen atom to form an oxonium ion:

$$C_2H_5-\overset{..}{O}-C_2H_5 + H^+_{(aq)} \rightleftharpoons C_2H_5-\overset{\overset{H}{|}}{\overset{..}{O}^+}-C_2H_5$$

and this reaction may be used to separate ethers from other organic compounds such as hydrocarbons and halogen compounds. Like other ethers, ethoxyethane is soluble in most organic solvents. Reference was made in Unit 2.4 to its use in solvent extraction.

The ready co-ordination of the unbonded electron pairs on the oxygen atom of the ether molecule stabilizes Grignard reagents in solution (see Unit 10.6(c)(iii)):

$$
\begin{array}{c}
C_2H_5 \qquad C_2H_5 \\
\diagdown \quad \diagup \\
O \\
\overset{..}{\downarrow} \\
R-Mg-Br \\
\uparrow \\
\overset{..}{O} \\
\diagup \quad \diagdown \\
C_2H_5 \qquad C_2H_5
\end{array}
$$

Tetrahydrofuran (see Unit 14.7) is more effective than ethoxyethane in this respect, however, owing to its greater basicity.

14.3 Preparation of Ethers

(a) Partial Dehydration of Alcohols
This reaction is discussed in Unit 12.6(g). It is applicable to the preparation of symmetrical ethers only; the preparation of ethoxyethane by this method is not recommended as a laboratory experiment, however, owing to the flammability of this compound and its formation of explosive mixtures with air.

(b) Williamson's Ether Synthesis
This reaction is discussed in Unit 10.6(a)(ii).

If the ether to be synthesized contains a secondary or a tertiary alkyl group, the alkoxide starting material should incorporate this group rather than the halogenoalkane; this avoids the formation of appreciable amounts of alkene as a by-product. Methyl and ethyl ethers may be prepared using the cheaper methyl or ethyl sulphate as starting material, rather than the halogenoalkane.

(c) From Halogenoalkanes

Ethers are produced when halogenoalkanes are heated with dry silver(I) oxide:

$$2RI + Ag_2O \rightarrow R_2O + 2AgI$$

14.4 Manufacture of Ethoxyethane

The major industrial source of ethoxyethane is the hydration of ethene with sulphuric acid to form ethanol, in which it is obtained as a by-product.

14.5 Reactions of Ethers

Ethers are fairly unreactive compounds: they have no effect on sodium and other metals, strong bases or the phosphorus trihalides, nor will they react with phosphorus pentachloride in the cold.

(a) Combustion

Ethoxyethane burns readily in air or oxygen to yield a mixture of carbon dioxide and water:

$$(C_2H_5)_2O + 6O_2 \rightarrow 4CO_2 + 5H_2O \quad (\Delta H = -2\,761 \text{ kJ mol}^{-1})$$

(b) Reaction with Hydriodic Acid

Fission of the carbon–oxygen bond occurs when an ether is treated with aqueous hydrogen iodide. At room temperature the reaction is:

$$R_2O + HI \rightarrow RI + ROH$$
$$\text{ether} \qquad\qquad \text{alcohol}$$

If the ether is refluxed with aqueous hydriodic acid, however, the alcohol reacts further, and is converted to the iodoalkane:

$$ROH + HI \rightarrow RI + H_2O$$

The other halogen acids (except hydrofluoric acid) behave similarly. The order of reactivity is $HI > HBr > HCl$.

(c) Peroxide Formation

Ethoxyethane slowly undergoes *autoxidation* in sunlight on standing in contact with oxygen from the air to yield a peroxide:

$$(CH_3CH_2)_2O + O_2 \xrightarrow{h\nu} CH_3CH_2O\underset{\underset{OOH}{|}}{C}HCH_3$$

a peroxide

These peroxides are unstable compounds and explode violently on heating. Their formation is reduced by storing ether in dark-glass bottles and their presence may be detected by adding an acidified solution of potassium iodide; peroxides oxidize the iodide ion to iodine which gives a blue coloration with starch. Peroxides may be removed from ethoxyethane by adding a solution of an iron(II) salt; for safety's sake, however, ethoxyethane for distillation should always be taken from bottles which have been kept virtually full. The violent reaction of ethoxyethane with concentrated nitric acid is due to peroxide formation.

(d) Hydrolysis

Ethoxyethane is slowly converted into ethyl hydrogen sulphate by the action of warm concentrated sulphuric acid. The product yields ethanol on diluting with water:

$$(C_2H_5)_2O + H_2SO_4 \xrightarrow{warm} 2C_2H_5HSO_4 + H_2O$$

$$C_2H_5HSO_4 + H_2O \xrightarrow{warm} C_2H_5OH + H_2SO_4$$

This process is the reverse of Williamson's continuous ether synthesis (see Unit 12.6(g)) and occurs by an analogous reaction mechanism.

(e) Electrophilic Substitution (aromatic ethers only)

Aromatic ethers undergo electrophilic substitution. The alkoxy-group activates the ring and is *ortho*- and *para*-directing.

14.6 Uses of Ethers

Ethers (especially ethoxyethane) are mainly used as solvents for fats, oils and resins. Ethoxyethane is employed to separate and purify compounds by solvent extraction (see Unit 2.4) and as a solvent in syntheses involving Grignard reagents (see Unit 10.6(c)(iii)).

Ethoxyethane vapour depresses the activity of the central nervous system if inhaled and is used as an anaesthetic.

14.7 Cyclic Ethers

Some cyclic ethers are used in synthesis or as solvents; for instance:

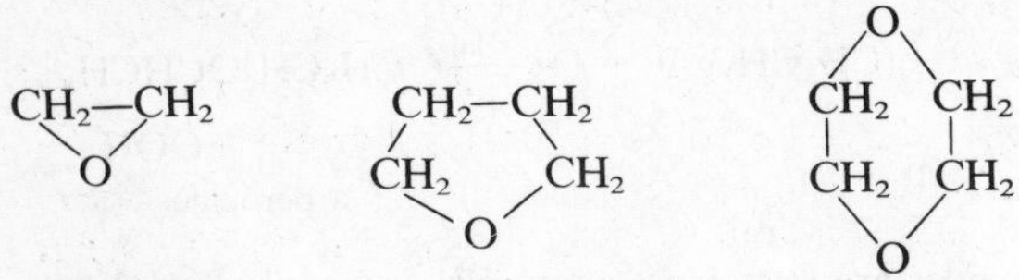

epoxyethane
(ethylene oxide)
b.p. 13°

tetrahydrofuran
b.p. 65°

1,4-dioxan
b.p. 101°

The most important of these is epoxyethane. The carbon and oxygen atoms in the three-membered ring are sp^3 hybridized, so there is considerable strain in the molecule (cf. Unit 4.4(f)); this is reflected in the high reactivity of the compound, particularly in reactions in which the ring is opened.

14.8 Epoxyethane

Epoxyethane is manufactured by the oxidation of ethene (see Unit 7.6(h)). It is a colourless, very volatile liquid (b.p. 13°) which is soluble in water and in most organic solvents. Its principal use is as a source material for the manufacture of a number of important organic compounds, such as *ethane-1,2-diol* (see Unit 12.8(a)(i)) and the *diol ethers*. These compounds, which contain an alkoxy-group and a primary alcohol group, are manufactured by the action of epoxyethane on alcohols:

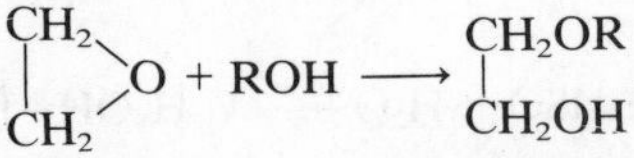

$$\begin{array}{c}CH_2\\ | \quad \rangle O + ROH \longrightarrow \\ CH_2\end{array} \quad \begin{array}{c} CH_2OR \\ | \\ CH_2OH \end{array}$$

Diol ethers are used as solvents, in particular for cellulose ethanoate.

Test Yourself on Unit 14

1. Draw the structural (or displayed) formulae and name the ethers of molecular formula $C_4H_{10}O$.

2. Outline the hazards associated with the distillation of ethoxyethane solutions and describe how these dangers may be avoided.

3. Methoxybenzene and 3-methylphenol are isomeric. Describe three chemical tests to distinguish between these two compounds.

4. Explain the following:
   (a) Two layers are formed when ethoxyethane is added to water but only one layer is obtained when ethoxyethane is added to aqueous hydrochloric acid.

(b) Methoxymethane (b.p. −24°) is considerably more volatile than ethanol (b.p. 78.5°).

(c) Better yields of Grignard reagents are often obtained when tetrahydrofuran is used as a solvent instead of ethoxyethane.

5. 0.025 52 g of a volatile organic liquid Q produced 0.063 81 g of carbon dioxide and 0.031 32 g of water on combustion. Q does not react with sodium at room temperature, nor does it yield hydrogen chloride with phosphorus pentachloride. Q was synthesized by the action of an iodoalkane, R, on a solution of sodium in propan-2-ol. What are compounds Q and R?

6. The alkanols and ethers (alkoxyalkanes) are isomeric. Compare and contrast the structures and chemical properties of methoxymethane and ethanol.

7. Describe the manufacture, structure and synthetic uses of epoxyethane in organic chemistry.

Unit Fifteen

Aldehydes and Ketones

15.1 General Formula and Nomenclature

The aldehydes and ketones are isomeric, and are known as *carbonyl compounds* as both classes contain the carbonyl group, $\diagup C{=}O$. In aldehydes this group is linked to a hydrogen atom (to two hydrogen atoms in the simplest member of the series, methanal) whereas in ketones the carbonyl carbon atom is always linked to two hydrocarbon groups. The general formulae are thus:

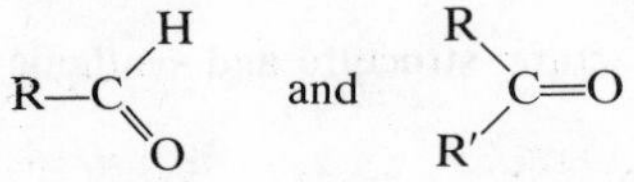

$$R-C\underset{O}{\overset{H}{\diagup}} \quad \text{and} \quad \underset{R'}{\overset{R}{\diagdown}}C{=}O$$

$$\text{aldehydes} \qquad\qquad \text{ketones}$$

where R and R' are either alkyl or aryl groups.

Ketones are said to be *simple* or *symmetrical* if the two substituent groups R and R' are the same, and as *mixed* or *unsymmetrical* if the groups are different (*cf.* ethers, Unit 14.1).

The aliphatic aldehydes or *alkanals* are named by replacing the final *-e* of the name of the corresponding alkane with the suffix *-al*. The first members of the homologous series, RCHO (where $R = C_nH_{2n+1}$), are thus:

n	formula		IUPAC name	trivial name
0	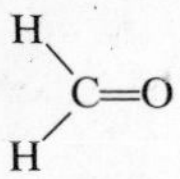 $\underset{H}{\overset{H}{\diagdown}}C{=}O$	CH_2O	methanal	formaldehyde
1	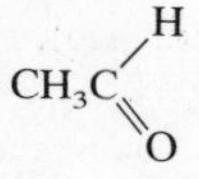 $CH_3C\underset{O}{\overset{H}{\diagup}}$	CH_3CHO	ethanal	acetaldehyde
2	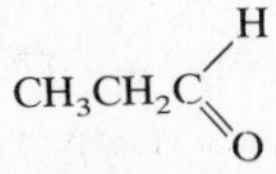 $CH_3CH_2C\underset{O}{\overset{H}{\diagup}}$	C_2H_5CHO	propanal	propionaldehyde

Complex and branched-chain aldehydes are named as derivatives of the aldehyde with the *longest* possible carbon chain. The carbon atom of the carbonyl group is counted as the first of the chain and the position of the substituents is indicated by numbering; for instance,

$$CH_3CHCH_2CHO \qquad\qquad CH_3CH_2CHCH(CH_3)CH(CH_3)CH_3$$
$$\quad\;|\qquad\qquad\qquad\qquad\qquad\;\;|$$
$$\;\,CH_3 \qquad\qquad\qquad\qquad\qquad CHO$$

3-methylbutanal   2-ethyl-3,4-dimethylpentanal

Aromatic aldehydes are named by adding the suffix *carbaldehyde* to the name of the corresponding hydrocarbon, although compounds in which the aldehyde group is attached directly to the benzene ring are more commonly referred to as *benzaldehyde derivatives*:

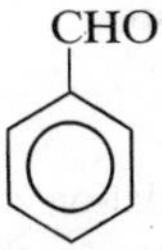

benzenecarbaldehyde   3-nitrobenzenecarbaldehyde
or benzaldehyde   or 3-nitrobenzaldehyde

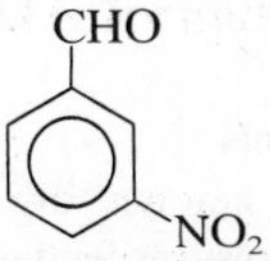

Compounds in which the aldehyde group is attached to the side-chain of an aromatic hydrocarbon are named as aryl-substituted alkane, alkene or alkyne derivatives; for example:

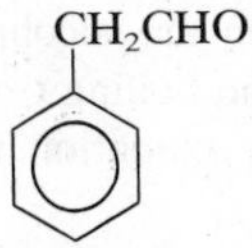

phenylethanal 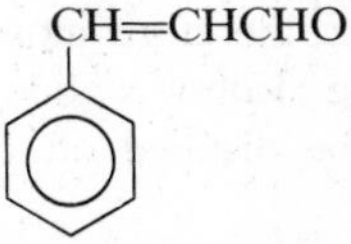   3-phenylpropenal

The aliphatic ketones or *alkanones* are named by dropping the final *-e* of the name of the alkane with the same number of carbon atoms and adding the suffix *-one*; the position of the carbonyl group in ketones containing more than four carbon atoms is indicated by numbering:

CH_3COCH_3	propanone (dimethyl ketone or acetone)
$CH_3CH_2COCH_3$	butanone (methyl ethyl ketone)
$CH_3CH_2COCH_2CH_3$	pentan-3-one (diethyl ketone)
$CH_3CH_2CH_2COCH_3$	pentan-2-one (methyl n-propyl ketone)

Substituted or branched-chain ketones are named as derivatives of the compound with the longest hydrocarbon chain; for instance,

$$CH_3CH_2CHCOCHCH_3$$
$$\qquad\quad|\qquad\;\;|$$
$$\quad\;\;CH_3\quad\;CH_3$$

2,4-dimethylhexan-3-one

Similar rules apply to the nomenclature of the aromatic ketones, which are named as aryl-substituted alkanones; for instance:

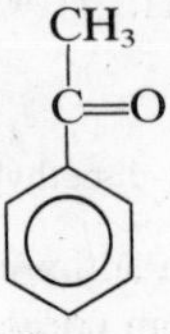

phenylethanone 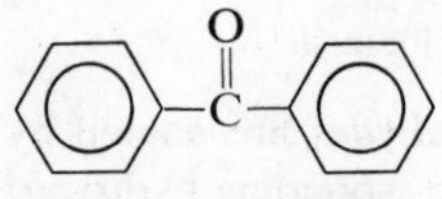   diphenylmethanone

15.2 Preparation of Aldehydes and Ketones

(a) From Alcohols

Aldehydes and ketones are formed by the oxidation of primary and secondary alcohols respectively (see Unit 12.6(e)). In the oxidation of primary alcohols with a mixture of sodium dichromate(VI) and sulphuric acid the aldehyde must be removed as soon as it is formed, as otherwise it will be oxidized further to the carboxylic acid:

$$3RCHO + Cr_2O_7^{2-} + 8H^+ \rightarrow 3RCO_2H + 2Cr^{3+} + 4H_2O$$

Aldehydes are unable to form intermolecular hydrogen bonds (cf. Unit 12.2(a)) and are therefore more volatile than are alcohols or carboxylic acids; thus if the alcohol is added slowly to the boiling oxidizing agent the aldehyde may be distilled off before further oxidation takes place. For example:

$$CH_3CH_2OH \rightarrow CH_3CHO \rightarrow CH_3CO_2H$$
b.p. 78°   b.p. 21°   b.p. 118°

Oxidation of primary alcohols can lead to ester formation as a by-product by the action of the unreacted alcohol on the carboxylic acid.

Alternatively, primary and secondary alcohols may be oxidized by passing the alcohol vapour mixed with air over a heated copper or platinum catalyst; or they may be dehydrogenated under similar conditions in the absence of air (see Unit 12.6(f)).

Aromatic alcohols may be oxidized with alkaline potassium manganate(VII), with aqueous nitric acid or with cerium(IV) oxide in the presence of sulphuric acid—this last is a particularly valuable oxidizing agent as the reaction does not pass beyond the aldehyde stage. For instance:

$$C_6H_5CH_2OH \xrightarrow{[O]} C_6H_5CHO$$
phenylmethanol   benzaldehyde

Secondary alcohols may be oxidized to ketones by refluxing with aluminium 2-methylpropan-2-oxide (aluminium t-butoxide) in presence of a large excess of propanone (the *Oppenauer oxidation*).

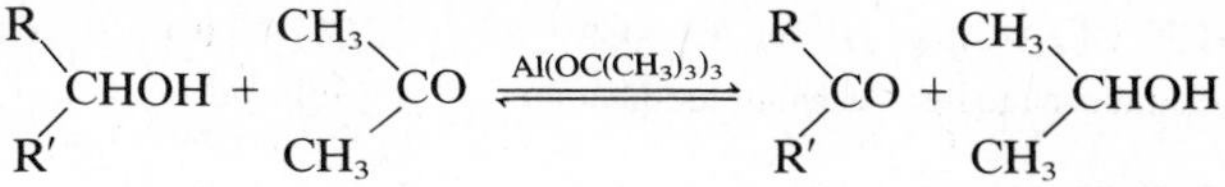

2° alcohol	propanone		ketone	propan-2-ol

The large excess of propanone displaces the equilibrium to the right. The Oppenauer oxidation does not affect carbon–carbon double bonds and may therefore be used to oxidize unsaturated secondary alcohols.

(b) From gem-Dihalogenoalkanes
A carbonyl group is obtained when two halogen atoms attached to the same carbon atom are hydrolysed:

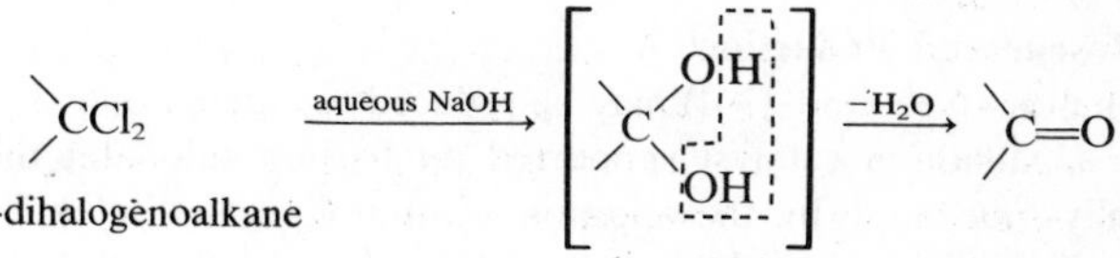

a *gem*-dihalogenoalkane

(unstable)

The synthetic value of these reactions is limited by the difficulty of preparing the *gem*-dihalogenoalkanes. In practice these compounds are usually themselves obtained from the corresponding aldehyde or ketone, by treating it with phosphorus pentachloride:

$$RCHO + PCl_5 \rightarrow RCHCl_2 + POCl_3$$
$$R_2CO + PCl_5 \rightarrow R_2CCl_2 + POCl_3$$

Aromatic aldehydes are frequently prepared by this method, however, as the corresponding dihalogeno-compound can readily be obtained by the photochemical chlorination of a methyl group attached to the benzene nucleus (see Unit 11.2(*a*)). For example, (dichloromethyl)benzene is hydrolysed to benzaldehyde by the action of boiling water at 100° in the presence of iron filings which act as a catalyst:

$$C_6H_5CHCl_2 + H_2O \xrightarrow{100°/\text{iron filings}} C_6H_5CHO + 2HCl$$

(c) From Carboxylates
Aldehydes and ketones are formed by the action of heat on anhydrous calcium or barium salts of carboxylic acids, or on mixtures of these salts. For example, calcium and barium ethanoate both yield propanone:

$$(CH_3CO_2)_2Ca \xrightarrow{\text{heat}} CH_3COCH_3 + CaCO_3$$

while a mixture of calcium methanoate with the calcium salt of a higher carboxylic acid yields an aldehyde; thus

$$(CH_3CO_2)_2Ca \ + \ (HCO_2)_2Ca \ \xrightarrow{\text{heat}} \ 2CH_3CHO + 2CaCO_3$$

calcium ethanoate   calcium methanoate   ethanal

Yields are usually poor owing to the formation of many by-products; symmetrical ketones may be obtained in high yield, however, by the pyrolysis of iron(II) salts:

$$(RCO_2)_2Fe \ \xrightarrow{\text{heat}} \ RCOR + FeCO_3$$

$$\downarrow$$

$$FeO + CO_2$$

(d) Rosenmund Reduction

Acyl halides (see Unit 17.4) may be reduced to aldehydes by hydrogenation using a palladium catalyst supported on barium sulphate; the catalyst is partially 'poisoned' by the addition of quinoline and sulphur in order to reduce its efficiency and prevent further reduction of the aldehyde to a primary alcohol. For instance:

$$C_6H_5COCl \ \xrightarrow[\text{quinoline–sulphur}]{H_2/Pd–BaSO_4} \ C_6H_5CHO \ + HCl$$

benzoyl chloride   benzaldehyde

Ketones cannot be prepared by this method.

(e) Friedel–Crafts Reaction

Aromatic hydrocarbons react with acyl halides in the presence of anhydrous aluminium chloride to give aromatic ketones (see Unit 9.6(b)(iv)).

15.3 Manufacture of Aldehydes and Ketones

(a) Methanal

Methanal is manufactured by passing methanol vapour mixed with air over a silver or copper catalyst at about 500°:

$$CH_3OH + \tfrac{1}{2}O_2 \ \xrightarrow[500°]{\text{Ag catalyst}} CH_2O + H_2O \quad (\Delta H = -155 \text{ kJ mol}^{-1})$$

The reaction is exothermic and no external source of heat is required once the oxidation has started. The endothermic dehydrogenation

$$CH_3OH \ \xrightarrow{\text{Ag catalyst}} \ CH_2O + H_2 \quad (\Delta H = +120 \text{ kJ mol}^{-1})$$

also occurs to some extent.

(b) **Ethanal**

Three methods are available for the manufacture of ethanal.

(i) **From ethanol.** Ethanol is oxidized or dehydrogenated in the gas phase; a silver or copper catalyst is used. Ethanol vapour, alone or mixed with air, is passed over the heated catalyst:

$$CH_3CH_2OH + \tfrac{1}{2}O_2 \xrightarrow[500°]{Ag} CH_3CHO + H_2O \text{ (exothermic)}$$

$$CH_3CH_2OH \xrightarrow[500°]{Cu} CH_3CHO + H_2 \text{ (endothermic)}$$

(ii) **Wacker process.** A mixture of ethene and oxygen is passed under pressure into an acidified solution of palladium(II) chloride and copper(II) chloride at 30–60°:

$$CH_2{=}CH_2 + H_2O + PdCl_2 \rightarrow CH_3CHO + 2HCl + Pd$$

$$Pd + 2HCl + \tfrac{1}{2}O_2 \rightarrow PdCl_2 + H_2O$$

The palladium(II) chloride thus acts as an oxygen carrier. The copper(II) chloride promotes the second reaction above, which proceeds much more slowly than the first:

$$Pd + 2CuCl_2 \rightarrow 2CuCl + PdCl_2$$

$$2CuCl + 2HCl + \tfrac{1}{2}O_2 \rightarrow 2CuCl_2 + H_2O$$

Since the palladium(II) and copper(II) chlorides are both regenerated, only catalytic amounts are required. This method, using ethene obtained directly from cracked petroleum (see Unit 7.2) is now the most important process for ethanal manufacture.

(c) **Propanone**

(i) **Wacker process.** The starting material is propene from cracked petroleum (see Unit 7.2):

$$CH_3CH{=}CH_2 + H_2O + PdCl_2 \xrightarrow{CuCl_2} CH_3COCH_3 + 2HCl + Pd$$

(ii) **The cumene process** for the manufacture of phenol (see Unit 13.3) yields propanone as a by-product.

(iii) **The dehydrogenation of propan-2-ol.** Propan-2-ol vapour is passed over a heated copper catalyst:

$$CH_3CHOHCH_3 \xrightarrow[400°]{Cu} CH_3COCH_3 + H_2$$

15.4 Properties of Aldehydes and Ketones

The first member of the aldehyde homologous series, methanal, CH_2O, is a colourless gas, b.p. −21°. It is readily soluble in water and its aqueous solution, known as *formalin*, has a characteristic, pungent odour and is used as a disinfectant and antiseptic. The other aldehydes and ketones are generally colourless, volatile liquids whose solubility in water decreases with increasing formula weight. The solubility of the lower aliphatic aldehydes and ketones in water is due mainly to the ability of the carbonyl group to form hydrogen bonds with water:

$$\overset{\delta+}{\diagdown}\underset{\diagup}{C}=\overset{\delta-}{O}\cdots\overset{\delta+}{H}-\overset{\delta-}{O}\diagdown\underset{H}{\overset{\delta+}{}}$$

Methanal and ethanal are also largely hydrated in aqueous solution:

$$\diagdown C=O + H_2O \rightleftharpoons \diagup{C}\diagdown\overset{OH}{\underset{OH}{}}$$

The hydration is virtually complete in aqueous solutions of methanal, compared with about 58 per cent and 0 per cent for ethanal and propanone respectively. As a general rule, any compound with two or more hydroxyl groups attached to a single carbon atom is too unstable to be isolated from solution and tends to lose water to form a carbonyl or carboxyl group:

$$\diagup C \diagdown \overset{O H}{\underset{OH}{}} \longrightarrow \diagdown C=O + H_2O$$

$$-C \diagdown \overset{OH}{\underset{OH}{\overset{|}{O H}}} \longrightarrow -C \overset{\diagup O}{\diagdown OH} + H_2O$$

Hydration is decreased by the presence of electron-donating (+I) groups, such as alkyl groups:

$$\overset{H}{\underset{H}{\diagdown}}\overset{\delta+}{C}=\overset{\delta-}{O} > \overset{CH_3}{\underset{H}{\diagdown}}C=O > \overset{CH_3}{\underset{CH_3}{\diagdown}}C=O$$

In trichloroethanal (chloral), CCl_3CHO, however, the powerful electron-withdrawing effect of the three chlorine atoms confers an appreciable positive charge on the central carbon atom and stabilizes the hydrate to such an extent that 2,2,2-trichloroethane-1,1-diol (chloral hydrate), $CCl_3CH(OH)_2$, m.p. 57°, may be isolated in the crystalline state.

Ethanal has a sharp, unpleasant odour, while propanone and butanone are pleasant-smelling liquids which are used as solvents. Benzaldehyde has a strong, pleasant smell of almonds. It is a colourless, steam-volatile liquid, only slightly soluble in water but dissolving readily in ethanol, ethoxyethane and other organic solvents.

Both aldehydes and ketones are polar compounds, because of the presence of the $\overset{\delta+}{\diagup}\overset{\delta-}{C=O}$ group, and although the resulting intermolecular attraction makes the compounds of both series less volatile than non-polar compounds of similar molecular mass such as the hydrocarbons and ethers, they have considerably lower boiling-points than those of the corresponding alcohols or carboxylic acids.

15.5 Structure and Reactivity of Aldehydes and Ketones

The carbon atom of the carbonyl group is sp^2 hybridized (see Unit 4.4(c)) and its three σ bonds are therefore co-planar. The remaining p orbitals of the carbon and oxygen atoms overlap to form a π bond:

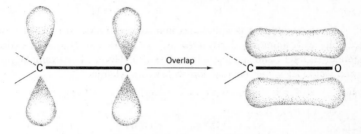

Fig. 15.1   Structure of the carbonyl group

Many of the important reactions of aldehydes and ketones involve addition to the double bond of the carbonyl group (*cf.* alkenes and alkynes, see Units 7.5 and 8.5 respectively).

The carbonyl group is polarized as a result of the mesomeric effect:

$$\overset{\diagup}{C=O} \longleftrightarrow \overset{(+)}{\underset{\diagup}{C}}\overset{(-)}{-O}$$

This increases the electron density on the oxygen atom and the carbonyl group may therefore be represented as:

$$\overset{\delta+}{\underset{\diagup}{C}}\overset{\delta-}{=\!=\!=O}$$

Aldehydes and ketones are thus susceptible to attack both by nucleophiles at the carbon atom and by electrophiles at the oxygen atom:

$$\overset{\delta+}{\underset{\diagup}{C}}\overset{\delta-}{-O}$$

nucleophiles   electrophiles

Except for protonation, which can increase the positivity of the carbon atom and hence its susceptibility to a nucleophile, electrophilic attack on the oxygen atom is the less significant. Protonation does, however, account for the catalytic effect of acids on the addition reactions of the carbonyl group:

$$\overset{\delta+}{\underset{}{C}}\!\!=\!\!\overset{\delta+}{O} \underset{}{\overset{H^+}{\rightleftharpoons}} \;\; C\!\!=\!\!\overset{+}{O}H \longleftrightarrow \;\; \overset{+}{C}\!\!-\!\!OH$$

rate-determining attack by
nucleophile

The order of reactivity—the increasing ease of nucleophilic attack on the carbonyl carbon atom of aldehydes and ketones—is:

$$\underset{Ar}{\overset{Ar}{C}}\!\!=\!\!O < \underset{R}{\overset{Ar}{C}}\!\!=\!\!O < \underset{H}{\overset{Ar}{C}}\!\!=\!\!O < \underset{R'}{\overset{R}{C}}\!\!=\!\!O < \underset{H}{\overset{R}{C}}\!\!=\!\!O < \underset{H}{\overset{H}{C}}\!\!=\!\!O$$

Nucleophilic addition is sometimes immediately followed by elimination, especially with ammonia derivatives such as hydrazine, NH_2NH_2, hydroxylamine, $HONH_2$, and semicarbazide, $NH_2CONHNH_2$. For example, propanone yields an *oxime* on reaction with hydroxylamine:

$$\underset{CH_3}{\overset{CH_3}{C}}\!\!=\!\!O + H_2NOH \longrightarrow \left[\underset{CH_3}{\overset{CH_3}{C}}\!\!\underset{NHOH}{\overset{OH}{}}\right] \xrightarrow{-H_2O} \underset{CH_3}{\overset{CH_3}{C}}\!\!=\!\!\underset{OH}{\overset{}{N}}$$

intermediate $\qquad$ propanone
oxime

Addition–elimination processes of this type are known as *condensation reactions*. The condensation reactions of aldehydes and ketones are described in Unit 15.6(*b*).

15.6 Reactions of Aldehydes and Ketones

(*a*) Addition Reactions
(i) **Addition of sodium hydrogensulphite.** Sodium hydrogensulphite (sodium bisulphite) forms an addition compound with aldehydes and with many ketones:

$$\overset{\delta+}{\underset{}{C}}\!\!=\!\!\overset{\delta-}{O} + Na^+SO_3H^- \rightleftharpoons \underset{SO_3H}{\overset{O^-Na^+}{C}} \rightleftharpoons \underset{SO_3{}^-Na^+}{\overset{OH}{C}}$$

If a saturated solution of sodium hydrogensulphite is added to propanone or benzaldehyde, for example, the mixture becomes warm and then almost solid as the crystalline adduct separates out on cooling:

$$(CH_3)_2CO + NaHSO_3 \longrightarrow (CH_3)_2C\underset{SO_3{}^-Na^+}{\overset{OH}{}}$$

Sodium disulphate(IV) (sodium metabisulphite), $Na_2S_2O_5$, is often used instead of sodium hydrogensulphite, as it is less susceptible to atmospheric oxidation. It is hydrolysed in solution to yield hydrogensulphite ions:

$$S_2O_5^{2-} + H_2O \rightarrow 2HSO_3^-$$

(ii) **Addition of hydrogen cyanide.** Aldehydes and ketones add hydrogen cyanide to the carbonyl group to yield a 2-hydroxynitrile (*cyanohydrin*):

$$\text{C=O} + HCN \longrightarrow \text{C}\begin{smallmatrix}OH\\CN\end{smallmatrix}$$

The reaction proceeds via nucleophilic attack on the carbonyl carbon atom by the cyanide anion, followed by protonation by the solvent:

$$\begin{array}{c} \overset{\delta+}{C} \overset{\delta-}{=} O \\ N \equiv C^- \end{array} \longrightarrow \begin{array}{c} C \\ O^- \\ CN \end{array} \xrightarrow{H_2O} \begin{array}{c} C \\ OH \\ CN \end{array}$$

The cyano-group is hydrolysed if the 2-hydroxynitrile is refluxed with concentrated hydrochloric acid; cyanohydrin synthesis thus provides a route to 2-hydroxycarboxylic acids. For example:

$$CH_3C\overset{H}{\underset{O}{}} \xrightarrow{HCN} CH_3-\underset{OH}{\overset{H}{C}}-CN \xrightarrow{hydrolysis} CH_3-\underset{OH}{\overset{H}{C}}-CO_2H$$

| ethanal | 2-hydroxypropanonitrile | 2-hydroxypropanoic acid |

Propanone cyanohydrin, $CH_3C(CN)(OH)CH_3$, is used in Perspex manufacture.

(iii) **Addition of ammonia.** A white, unstable addition compound is formed when gaseous ammonia is passed through a solution of an alkanal (except methanal) in anhydrous ethoxyethane:

$$R-C\overset{H}{\underset{O}{}} + NH_3 \xrightarrow[0°]{anhyd. (C_2H_5)_2O} R-\underset{OH}{\overset{H}{C}}-NH_2$$

aldehyde-ammonia

The product readily undergoes polymerization. Propanone reacts with ammonia according to this equation only at $-65°$; at room temperature a complex mixture of condensation products is obtained. Condensation reactions also occur when methanal, ketones and aromatic aldehydes are treated with ammonia, and the nature of the product is determined by the structure of the carbonyl compound.

Hexamethylenetetramine, $(CH_2)_6N_4$, is obtained as a white crystalline solid when an aqueous solution of methanal and ammonia is evaporated to dryness:

$$6HCHO + 4NH_3 \longrightarrow$$

hexamethylenetetramine

Hexamethylenetetramine is used in medicine under the name of *hexamine* in the treatment of gout and rheumatism and as a urinary antiseptic.

(iv) **Addition of alcohols.** Aldehydes react slowly with anhydrous alcohols in the presence of gaseous hydrogen chloride to yield first *hemiacetals* and then *acetals*:

a hemiacetal   an acetal

The reaction may be reversed by the addition of dilute acid. Acetals, such as 1,1-diethoxyethane, $CH_3CH(OC_2H_5)_2$, are diethers of the unstable 1,1-dihydroxyalkanes. They are stable in alkaline solution, so that acetal formation may be used to protect the aldehyde group against alkaline oxidizing agents. The aldehyde can be regenerated by the action of acid after carrying out an oxidation in alkaline solution on some other part of the molecule.

Ketals, $R_2C(OR')_2$, are difficult to prepare directly by the action of an alcohol on a ketone.

(v) **Reaction with Grignard reagents.** Primary, secondary and tertiary alcohols are obtained when a Grignard reagent is treated with methanal, aldehydes and ketones respectively (see Unit 10.6(*c*)(iii)).

(vi) **Polymerization reactions.** 1. *Methanal*. Methanal readily polymerizes on treatment with concentrated sulphuric acid or when gaseous methanal is passed into an inert hydrocarbon containing an amine as a catalyst. *Polyoxymethylenes*, of general formula $HOCH_2(CH_2O)_nCH_2OH$ where $n > 100$, are obtained as a white, insoluble solid that is a useful plastic, being easily moulded, very hard and resistant to abrasion or the action of chemicals.

Poly(methanal) (paraformaldehyde), m.p. 121–3°, is formed when an aqueous solution of methanal is evaporated to dryness. It has a structure similar to that of the polyoxymethylenes, with $n < 50$. If, however, methanal is distilled from a solution acidified with dilute sulphuric acid, a cyclic trimer, $(CH_2O)_3$ is obtained. This compound shows few of the reactions typical of an aldehyde; for example, it does not react with Fehling's solution or with ammoniacal silver nitrate (*cf.* Unit 15.6(*c*)(i)). Its properties are consistent with the cyclic structure

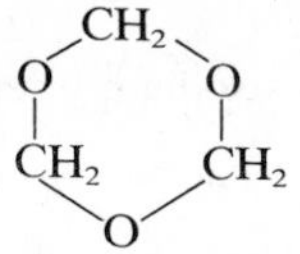

$$\begin{array}{c} CH_2 \\ O \qquad O \\ CH_2 \qquad CH_2 \\ O \end{array}$$

Methanal trimer, poly(methanal) and the polyoxymethylenes all yield methanal on heating and are sometimes used as a convenient source of this gas.

Methanal polymerizes in the presence of calcium hydroxide to yield a mixture of hexose sugars known as *formose*:

$$6CH_2O \xrightarrow{Ca(OH)_2} C_6H_{12}O_6$$
formose

2. *Ethanal.* Ethanal forms a trimer on treatment with a few drops of concentrated sulphuric acid. It is a pleasant-smelling liquid, b.p. 128°, with a structure similar to that of methanal trimer:

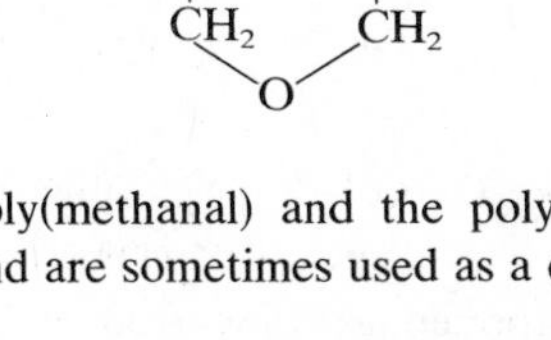

$$\begin{array}{c} CH_3 \\ CH \\ O \qquad O \\ CH_3-CH \qquad CH-CH_3 \\ O \end{array}$$

It is used in medicine as a hypnotic under the name of *paraldehyde*. Other polymers of ethanal include the tetramer $(CH_3CHO)_4$ (*metaldehyde*), m.p. 246°, which is formed by the action of sulphur dioxide or a few drops of concentrated sulphuric acid on ethanal at 0°, and the yellow-brown resin of high relative molecular mass which is obtained when ethanal is treated with aqueous sodium hydroxide.

Aldehydes dimerize in the presence of an aluminium alkoxide to yield esters. For example, ethyl ethanoate is obtained when ethanal is treated with aluminium ethoxide:

$$2CH_3CHO \xrightarrow{Al(OC_2H_5)_3} CH_3CO_2C_2H_5$$

or, in general,

$$2RCHO \rightarrow RCOOCH_2R$$

This is known as the *Tischenko reaction.*

3. *Ketones and aromatic aldehydes.* Most ketones and aromatic aldehydes do not polymerize.

(vii) **Reduction.** Aldehydes and ketones are reduced to primary and secondary alcohols respectively by several reducing agents, either:

1. hydrogen, using a nickel, platinum or palladium catalyst (*cf.* Unit 5.2(*a*)); or

2. dissolving metals, such as sodium in ethanol:

$$Na \xrightarrow{C_2H_5OH} Na^+ + e$$

$$\underset{}{\overset{}{>}}C=O + e \longrightarrow \underset{}{\overset{}{>}}\dot{C}-O^- \xrightarrow{H^+} \underset{}{\overset{}{>}}\dot{C}-OH \xrightarrow[\text{(ii) } H^+]{\text{(i) } e} \underset{}{\overset{}{>}}CHOH$$

Some diol is generally formed as a by-product by dimerization of the radicals, especially in the reduction of ketones in acid solution—that of propanone yields some $(CH_3)_2C(OH)C(OH)(CH_3)_2$, for instance; or

3. lithium tetrahydridoaluminate(III) in anhydrous ethoxyethane, sodium tetrahydridoborate(III) in aqueous solution or in methanol, or sodium hydride.

(b) Condensation Reactions

A condensation reaction involves the combination of two or more molecules (which may be the same or of different substances) to yield a single molecule of higher relative molecular mass, often with the elimination of a simple molecule such as water or ammonia. For example, propanone undergoes a condensation reaction to yield 1,3,5-trimethylbenzene (mesitylene) when it is distilled from 70 per cent sulphuric acid:

$$3CH_3COCH_3 \xrightarrow[\text{distil}]{70\% \ H_2SO_4} \text{[mesitylene structure]} + 3H_2O$$

The condensation of aldehydes or ketones with hydroxylamine, H_2NOH, hydrazine, NH_2NH_2, and other ammonia derivatives is also important as many of the products obtained are crystalline solids whose melting-point may be used to identify the original carbonyl compound. A molecule of water is eliminated in these condensations:

$$\underset{}{\overset{}{>}}C=O + \underset{\text{hydroxylamine}}{H_2NOH} \longrightarrow \underset{\text{an oxime}}{\overset{}{>}C=NOH} + H_2O$$

$$\underset{}{\overset{}{>}}C=O + \underset{\text{hydrazine}}{H_2NNH_2} \longrightarrow \underset{\text{a hydrazone}}{\overset{}{>}C=NNH_2} + H_2O$$

The hydrazine molecule contains two amino-groups. If the carbonyl compound is present in an excess two molecules of the aldehyde or ketone condense with a single molecule of hydrazine to yield an *azine*; for example,

$$2CH_3CHO + H_2NNH_2 \xrightarrow{-2H_2O} CH_3CH{=}NN{=}CHCH_3$$

Azines are crystalline solids with sharp melting-points which are also used for identification purposes.

Substituted hydrazines are frequently employed in practice, as many of these yield crystalline solids with high melting-points. Phenylhydrazine and (especially) 2,4-dinitrophenylhydrazine ('DNPH') are most commonly used:

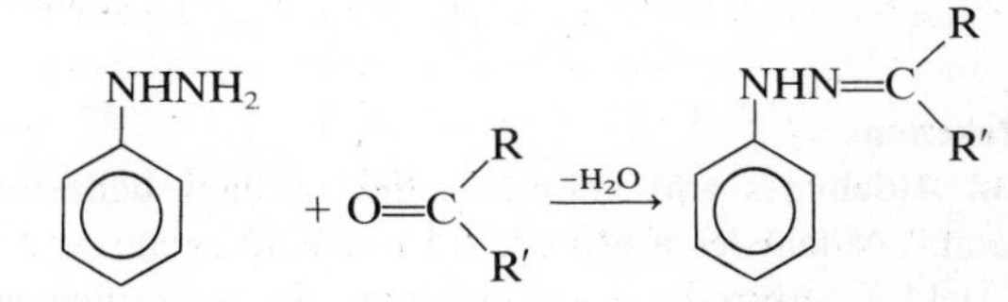

phenylhydrazine · · · · · · · · · · · · · · a phenylhydrazone

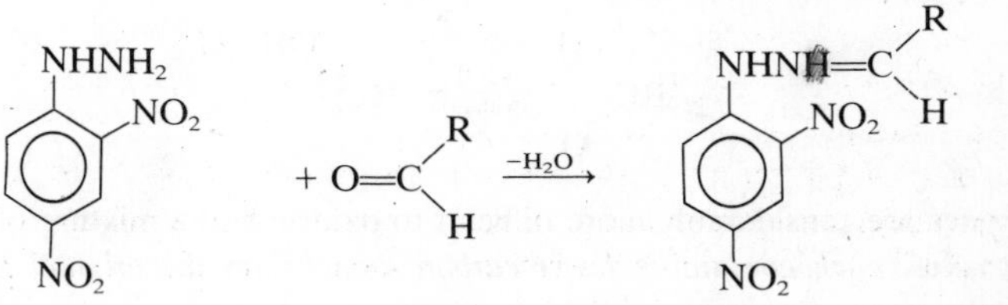

2,4-dinitrophenylhydrazine · · · · · · · · a 2,4-dinitrophenylhydrazone

A solution of 2,4-dinitrophenylhydrazine in aqueous methanol containing sulphuric acid is known as *Brady's reagent*. The formation of a yellow precipitate on the addition of Brady's reagent is used as a test for an aldehyde or ketone. The melting-point of the derivative may be used to identify the carbonyl compound. For example,

benzaldehyde

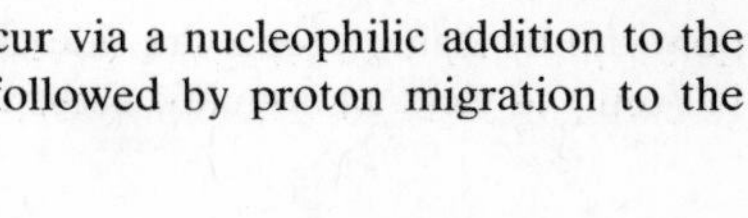

benzaldehyde 2,4-dinitrophenylhydrazone
m.p. 237°

All these condensation reactions occur via a nucleophilic addition to the carbon atom of the carbonyl group, followed by proton migration to the oxygen atom prior to the elimination of a molecule of water; for example:

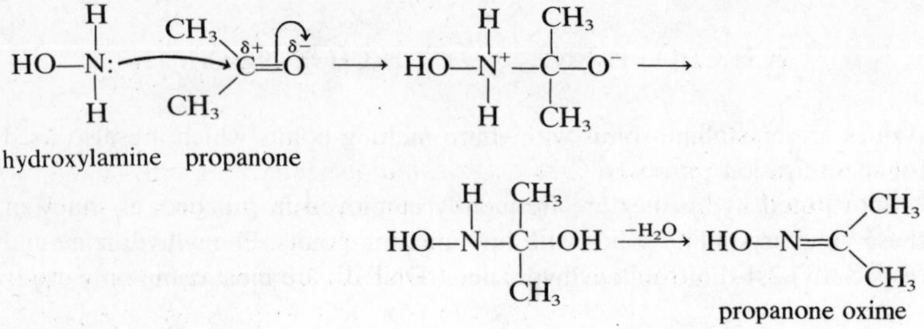

hydroxylamine   propanone

propanone oxime

(c) Other Reactions

(i) **Oxidation.** Aldehydes and ketones differ in their behaviour towards oxidizing agents. Aldehydes are powerful reducing agents and are readily oxidized to yield a carboxylic acid *containing the same number of carbon atoms as the original aldehyde:*

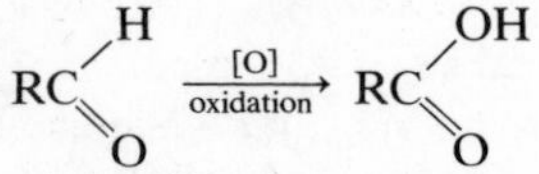

Ketones are considerably more difficult to oxidize and a mixture of carboxylic acids, *each containing fewer carbon atoms than the original ketone,* is obtained.

Aldehydes reduce Tollen's reagent (an ammoniacal solution of silver nitrate) to metallic silver, thus forming a silver mirror on the inner wall of the test-tube or other containing vessel. They will also reduce Fehling's solution (a mixture of aqueous copper(II) sulphate and an alkaline solution of a salt of 2,3-dihydroxybutanedioic acid (tartaric acid)) to red or orange copper(I) oxide (see Experiment 15.1.4).

Ammoniacal silver nitrate and Fehling's solution are both weak oxidizing agents and have no effect on ketones: acidified potassium (or sodium) dichromate(VI), nitric acid or other powerful oxidizing agents are required. Generally only the carbon atoms attached to the carbonyl group are attacked and the carbon atom joined to the *smaller* number of hydrogen atoms is oxidized preferentially; thus butanone, for instance, yields ethanoic acid as the major oxidation product:

$$CH_3COCH_2CH_3 \xrightarrow[Cr_2O_7^{2-}/H^+]{oxidation\cdot} 2CH_3CO_2H$$

preferential oxidation

Aromatic aldehydes and ketones behave similarly, except that with powerful oxidizing agents the side-chain tends to be oxidized too (*cf.* Unit 9.7(c)(i)) to yield an aromatic carboxylic acid in which the carboxy-group is attached directly to the ring:

$CH_2CH_2COCH_3$

CO_2H

$\xrightarrow[\text{Cr}_2\text{O}_7{}^{2-}/\text{H}^+]{\text{oxidation}}$

$+ CH_3CO_2H + CO_2$ etc.

Benzaldehyde reduces Tollen's reagent, but does not react with Fehling's solution. It slowly oxidizes in air at room temperature to form crystals of benzoic acid.

Aldehydes restore the magenta-pink colour to *Schiff's reagent* (see Appendix II). Ketones either have no effect on this solution or, like propanone, react only extremely slowly or on warming.

(ii) **Clemmensen reduction.** Ketones are reduced to alkanes by the action of zinc amalgam and concentrated hydrochloric acid (see Unit 5.2(e)); aldehydes react only with difficulty.

(iii) **Action of phosphorus pentachloride.** Aldehydes and ketones react with phosphorus pentachloride to form *gem*-dichloro-compounds (see Unit 15.2(b)).

(iv) **Trihalomethane (haloform) reaction.** Aldehydes and ketones that contain the CH_3COC- or the CH_3CHOH- group yield pale-yellow crystals of tri-iodomethane (iodoform) on treatment with iodine and aqueous alkali (see Unit 12.6(h)) or trichloromethane (chloroform) on warming with sodium chlorate(I) or bleaching powder. Tribromomethane may be obtained from such compounds under similar conditions by the action of a mixture of aqueous sodium chlorate(I) and potassium bromide.

Propanone, butanone, pentan-2-one and phenylethanone all give a positive result in these tests, but methanal, diphenylmethanone (($C_6H_5)_2CO$) and pentan-3-one do not. Ethanal does react, because in aqueous solution it exists in the hydrated form $CH_3CH(OH)_2$ (see Unit 15.4).

(v) **Reaction with halogens.** When aldehydes and ketones react with chlorine or bromine, the hydrogen atoms attached to the carbon atom that is linked to the carbonyl group are successively replaced by halogen atoms. For example, if chlorine is passed into propanone the hydrogen atoms first in one and then in the second methyl group are substituted:

$$CH_3COCH_3 + Cl_2 \longrightarrow CH_3COCH_2Cl + HCl$$

$$\downarrow Cl_2$$

$$CH_3COCHCl_2 + HCl$$

$$\downarrow \text{continued substitution}$$

$$CH_3COCCl_3 \longrightarrow CCl_3COCCl_3$$
hexachloropropanone

Similarly, with ethanal:

$$CH_3CHO + 3Cl_2 \rightarrow CCl_3CHO + 3HCl$$
trichloroethanal

Benzaldehyde has no hydrogen atoms attached to the carbon atom linked to the carbonyl group, and chlorination of benzaldehyde in the absence of a halogen carrier yields benzoyl chloride:

$$C_6H_5C\overset{O}{\underset{H}{\diagdown}} + Cl_2 \longrightarrow C_6H_5C\overset{O}{\underset{Cl}{\diagdown}} + HCl$$

(vi) **The Cannizzaro reaction.** Aldehydes which do not possess at least one α-hydrogen atom (that is, a hydrogen atom on the carbon atom linked to the carbonyl group)—$(CH_3)_3CCHO$, for instance—disproportionate when they are treated with aqueous alkali; for example, methanal yields a mixture of sodium methanoate (the oxidation product) and methanol (the reduction product) with 50 per cent aqueous sodium hydroxide:

$$2CH_2O + NaOH_{(aq)} \rightarrow HCO_2^-Na^+ + CH_3OH$$

Similarly benzaldehyde yields a mixture of sodium benzoate and phenylmethanol (benzyl alcohol):

$$2C_6H_5CHO + NaOH_{(aq)} \rightarrow C_6H_5CO_2^-Na^+ + C_6H_5CH_2OH$$

These are examples of the *Cannizzaro reaction*: half the aldehyde molecules undergo oxidation while the other half are reduced.

Aldehydes with α-hydrogen atoms, such as ethanal, do not undergo the Cannizzaro reaction on treatment with alkalis but form a yellow resin.

(vii) **Electrophilic substitution** (aromatic aldehydes and ketones only). The carbonyl group is *meta*-directing and deactivates the benzene nucleus with respect to electrophilic substitution (see Unit 9.9).

Experiment 15.1 *To demonstrate the reactions of aldehydes and ketones*

1. *Preparation of propanone hydrogensulphite.* Shake 1 cm³ of propanone with an equal volume of a saturated solution of sodium disulphate(IV) (sodium metabisulphite) and allow the mixture to stand. Note the formation of a white precipitate of the addition compound.

This reaction may be repeated with samples of other aldehydes or ketones, such as benzaldehyde and ethanal. Aqueous solutions of methanal or ethanal do not give precipitates owing to the solubility of the adducts. Phenylethanone and diphenylmethanone do not react.

2. *Action of Schiff's reagent.* Add 1 cm³ of Schiff's reagent (see Appendix II) to an equal volume of (*a*) aqueous methanal and (*b*) ethanal. Note the rapid change in colour. Repeat this test with benzaldehyde or propanone. Compare the rates of reaction.

3. *Action of ammoniacal silver nitrate.* Prepare the ammoniacal silver nitrate solution (Tollen's reagent) as instructed in Appendix II. Add about 5 drops of ethanal to 3 or 4 cm³ of the reagent in a test-tube and place the tube in a beaker of water; gradually heat the water to boiling-point and note the formation of a silver mirror on the test-tube wall. Repeat with

benzaldehyde, propanone and an aqueous solution of methanal. **Care:** Wash all the ammoniacal silver nitrate solution down the sink with plenty of water *immediately* after the experiment as the reagent can become explosively unstable on standing.

4. *Action of Fehling's solution.* Add 6 drops of ethanal to a mixture of equal amounts (approximately $1 \, cm^3$) of Fehling's solutions I and II (see Appendix II). Warm the mixture gently and note the formation of a red precipitate of copper(I) oxide as the deep-blue colour of the Fehling's solution is discharged.

Repeat with an aqueous solution of methanal and with benzaldehyde and propanone. (Methanal reduces Fehling's reagent to metallic copper.)

5. *Action of acidified potassium manganate(VII).* Add a few drops of benzaldehyde to $1 \, cm^3$ of 1 per cent aqueous potassium manganate(VII) solution and acidify the mixture by the addition of about $1 \, cm^3$ of dilute sulphuric acid. Warm the solution gently and note any changes that occur. Repeat this test, first with aqueous methanal and then with aqueous ethanal, and compare the results with propanone under the same conditions.

6. *Resin formation.* **Cautiously** add concentrated sodium hydroxide solution drop by drop to about $1 \, cm^3$ of ethanal in a test-tube. Note the characteristic odour (similar to bad apples) of the yellow-brown resin which is formed.

7. *Cannizzaro reaction.* Add $0.5 \, cm^3$ of benzaldehyde to $2 \, cm^3$ of 30 per cent aqueous sodium hydroxide in a test-tube and stir the mixture well with a glass rod while warming it gently for 4 or 5 minutes. Add sufficient water to dissolve the sodium benzoate which is formed and decant the aqueous layer into a second test-tube. Add concentrated hydrochloric acid to this solution and note the precipitation of benzoic acid (m.p. 121°).

8. *Tri-iodomethane (iodoform) reaction* (see Experiment 12.1.6). Carry out this reaction on (*a*) ethanal and (*b*) propanone.

9. *Condensation with 2,4-dinitrophenylhydrazine.* Add a few drops of propanone or ethanal to about $1 \, cm^3$ of Brady's reagent (see Appendix II). Note the formation of the yellow-orange 2,4-dinitrophenylhydrazone. Filter off the derivative, recrystallize from ethanol and determine the melting-point. The melting-points of the 2,4-dinitrophenylhydrazones of a number of common aldehydes and ketones are listed in Appendix I.

10. *Colour test for ethanal or propanone.* Add $1 \, cm^3$ of freshly prepared sodium pentacyanonitrosylferrate(II) (sodium nitroprusside) solution to $0.5 \, cm^3$ of ethanal or propanone. A red coloration is produced on the addition of an excess of dilute sodium hydroxide.

This reaction is also given by phenylethanone and other ketones that contain the —CH_2CO— group, which can yield the —$CH{=}C(OH)$— by enolization.

11. *Preparation of Bakelite.* Add 6 drops of concentrated sulphuric acid to a mixture of 2 g of phenol and $5 \, cm^3$ of 40 per cent aqueous methanal in an old test-tube. Stir well and leave the mixture for several days to allow the

polymer to form. (Alternatively the supernatant liquid can be decanted and the residue heated in a warm oven at 50–60°.) The solid resin is difficult to remove and it is best to throw the tube away after use.

15.7 Uses of Aldehydes and Ketones

(a) Methanal
Methanal is used in solution as a disinfectant and as a preservative for anatomical specimens. Its major industrial use is as a starting material for the manufacture of Bakelite (see Unit 13.7(b)(v)), carbamide–methanal (urea–formaldehyde) resins and polyoxymethylene (see Unit 15.6(a)(vi)).

(b) Ethanal
Ethanal is used for the production of ethanoic acid and hence of ethanoic anhydride, cellulose ethanoate, ethenyl ethanoate and poly(ethenyl ethanoate) (poly(vinyl acetate)).

(c) Propanone
Propanone is used as a solvent for lacquer, grease, varnish and plastics and for making photographic film. It is also a starting material for the manufacture of Perspex (see Unit 7.6(j)) and ethenone (ketene), $CH_2{=}C{=}O$ (see Unit 17.6(b)(i)).

(d) Benzaldehyde
Benzaldehyde smells of almonds and is used for flavouring foods and scenting soaps. It is also used for the preparation of dyestuffs, such as malachite green, and for the synthesis of antibiotics.

Test Yourself on Unit 15

1. Name the following compounds:
   (a) $(CH_3)_3CCHO$;
   (b) $CH_3COCH_2COCH_3$;
   (c) $C_6H_5CH_2COCH_3$;
   (d) $CH_3CH(C_2H_5)CH_2CHCH_3$;

   (e) $(CH_3)_3CCOC_2H_5$.

2. An organic liquid, A, gives a yellow precipitate with a solution of 2,4-dinitrophenylhydrazine. Describe the tests you would carry out to identify A, assuming that it contains only one functional group.

3. How do you account for the differences in the chemical properties of methanal, propanone and diphenylmethanone?

4. Explain, with reference to suitable examples from the chemistry of methanal and ethanal, what is meant by the terms *addition, condensation* and *polymerization*.

5. An organic liquid, B, (RMM = about 60) contains C, 62.1 per cent; H, 10.3 per cent. Suggest possible structural formulae for B and describe chemical tests you would carry out to distinguish the different isomers.

6. Suggest syntheses for the following compounds: (a) 2-nitrobenzaldehyde (from (chloromethyl)benzene); (b) 1-phenylethanol (from benzene); (c) $(CH_3)_2C(OH)CO_2H$ (from $(CH_3)_2CO$); (d) cyclohexanone (from cyclohexene).

7. How and under what conditions does methanal react with (a) sodium hydroxide, (b) oxygen, (c) ammonia, (d) silver nitrate, (e) phenol?

8. Describe one chemical test to distinguish between the following pairs of compounds: (a) methanal and ethanal; (b) propanal and ethanal; (c) propanal and propanone; (d) benzaldehyde and ethanal.

9. Describe the laboratory preparation of propanone. What are the reactions (if any) between propanone and (a) sulphuric acid, (b) magnesium and hydrochloric acid, (c) iodine and sodium hydroxide, (d) ethylmagnesium bromide, (e) Tollen's reagent (ammoniacal silver nitrate)?

10. A solution of the hydrocarbon C_6H_{12} in trichloromethane was treated with ozonized oxygen. When the resulting ozonide was broken down with zinc dust and water a mixture of two compounds, X and Y, was obtained. X, but not Y, was oxidized by Fehling's solution; both X and Y formed cyanohydrins with hydrogen cyanide. The cyanohydrin obtained from X yielded 2-hydroxypropanoic acid on hydrolysis with hot aqueous hydrochloric acid. Which of the following is the formula of the hydrocarbon?

A: $(CH_3)_2C$=$CHCH_2CH_3$
B: $CH_3CH_2CH_2CH_2CH$=CH_2
C: $CH_3CH_2CH_2CH$=$CHCH_3$
D: $CH_3(C_2H_5)C$=$CHCH_3$
E: $(CH_3)_2CHCH$=$CHCH_3$

11. (a) The alcohol A, $C_4H_{10}O$, may be oxidized with sodium dichromate(VI) and sulphuric acid to yield a compound B which contains the same number of carbon atoms as A.
(b) B effervesces with sodium carbonate solution.
(c) On passing the vapour of A over alumina heated to 350° C, C_4H_8, is obtained. C reacts with hydrogen iodide to yield D, C_4H_9I, which may be hydrolysed to give a compound E which is isomeric with A.
(d) On oxidation E yields a mixture of products, each of which contains fewer carbon atoms than E.

From the information in (a), state whether A is:
    a primary alcohol;
    a secondary alcohol;
    a tertiary alcohol;
    a primary *or* secondary alcohol;
    a secondary *or* tertiary alcohol.

Using all the information provided, state the most probable structural formulae which may be deduced for A and C, respectively:
    (i) $CH_3CH_2CH_2CH_2OH$ and $CH_3CH_2CH=CH_2$;
    (ii) $(CH_3)_2CHCH_2OH$ and $(CH_3)_2C=CH_2$,
    (iii) $CH_3CH_2CH(OH)OH$ and $CH_3CH_2CH=CH_2$,
    (iv) $(CH_3)_3COH$ and $(CH_3)_2C=CH_2$,
    (v) $CH_3CH_2CH(OH)CH_3$ and $CH_3CH=CHCH_3$.

12. A compound A, $C_3H_6Cl_2$, is formed by the action of phosphorus pentachloride on an organic liquid, B. When treated with ethanolic potassium hydroxide A yields a colourless gas C which gives a red precipitate with an ammoniacal solution of copper(I) chloride. On treatment with hydrogen chloride in the presence of a catalyst, compound C yields a liquid D which is isomeric with A. D is hydrolysed by boiling aqueous sodium hydroxide solution to yield E. E has the same molecular formula as B. Identify the compounds A to E, and explain the reactions.

Unit Sixteen

Carboxylic Acids

16.1 General Formula and Nomenclature

(*a*) **Alkanoic Acids**
The aliphatic carboxylic or *alkanoic* acids have the general formula:

$$R-C{\overset{\displaystyle O}{\underset{\displaystyle OH}{<}}}$$

where R is C_nH_{2n+1}. They may be regarded as derivatives of the alkanes, and are named by deleting the final -*e* of the name of the alkane having the same number of carbon atoms and adding the suffix -*oic* followed by the word *acid*. The names of the first members of the homologous series, together with their trivial names, are listed in Table 16.1. Acids with

Table 16.1 Nomenclature of alkanoic acids

IUPAC name	Trivial name	Formula
Methanoic acid	Formic acid	HCO_2H
Ethanoic acid	Acetic acid	CH_3CO_2H
Propanoic acid	Propionic acid	$CH_3CH_2CO_2H$
Butanoic acid	Butyric acid	$CH_3CH_2CH_2CO_2H$
Pentanoic acid	Valeric acid	$CH_3CH_2CH_2CH_2CO_2H$

branched carbon chains are named as derivatives of the alkanoic acid with the longest carbon skeleton. Substituents are, as usual, listed in alphabetical order and their position is indicated by numbering: the carbon atom of the carbonyl group is counted as the first in the carbon chain. For example:

$$\overset{\displaystyle CH_3}{\underset{}{|}}$$
$$CH_3CHCH_2CO_2H \qquad\qquad CH_3CCO_2H$$
$$\underset{\displaystyle Cl}{|}$$

3-methylbutanoic acid   2-chloro-2-methylpropanoic acid

The alkanoic acids were once known as the *fatty acids* because of their occurrence in many fats and oils (see Unit 12.3(*a*)). The common names for many of these compounds were derived from the Latin or Greek name of the source from which they were first obtained; formic (methanoic) acid, for example, is present in the 'stings' of stinging-nettles and many insects, and was first isolated by distilling crushed ants (Latin, *formica*, ant). Similarly, the name of acetic (ethanoic) acid is derived from the Latin *acetum*, meaning vinegar, of which ethanoic acid is the active constituent. Butyric (butanoic) acid is found in rancid butter (Latin, *butyrum*, butter).

The alkanoic acids are isomeric with esters: CH_3CO_2H (ethanoic acid), for instance, is isomeric with HCO_2CH_3 (methyl methanoate). Similarly, ethyl methanoate, $HCO_2C_2H_5$, and methyl ethanoate, $CH_3CO_2CH_3$, are both isomeric with propanoic acid, $CH_3CH_2CO_2H$.

(b) Aromatic Carboxylic Acids

The general formula of the aromatic carboxylic acids is $ArCO_2H$. The simplest representative of this series is benzoic acid, $C_6H_5CO_2H$, m.p. 121°. Other important aromatic acids are:

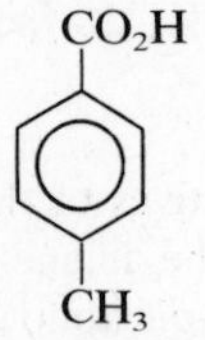

4-methylbenzoic acid 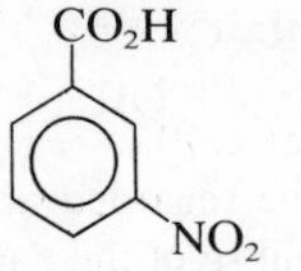   3-nitrobenzoic acid 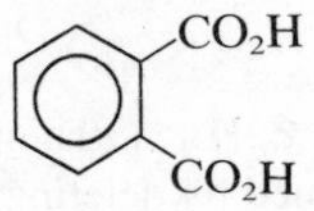   benzene-1,2-dicarboxylic acid

16.2 Preparation of Carboxylic Acids

(a) From Primary Alcohols or Aldehydes
See Units 12.6(e) and 15.6(c)(i).

(b) From Nitriles or Amides
See Units 17.7(d)(i) and 17.8(d)(i).

(c) From Grignard Reagents
See Unit 10.6(c)(iii).

(d) From Esters
Esters may be hydrolysed by refluxing with aqueous alkali, a process called *saponification*:

$$RCO_2R' + NaOH \longrightarrow RCO_2^-Na^+ + R'OH$$
$$\downarrow {\scriptstyle H^+/H_2O}$$
$$RCO_2H$$

The hydrolysis is also catalysed by strong acids, such as sulphuric acid:

$$RCO_2R' + H_2O \underset{}{\overset{H^+}{\rightleftharpoons}} RCO_2H + R'OH$$

The mechanism of this reaction is discussed in Unit 17.5(d)(i). Acids are also obtained by the hydrolysis of acyl halides, anhydrides and the like (see Units 17.4(d)(i) and 17.6(d)(i)).

(e) Other Methods

Sodium methanoate and sodium benzoate are formed from the corresponding aldehydes, methanal and benzaldehyde respectively, by the Cannizzaro
reaction (see Unit 15.6(c)(vi)). Benzoic acid is also formed by the hydrolysis
of (trichloromethyl)benzene:

$$C_6H_5CCl_3 + 4NaOH_{(aq)} \xrightarrow{\text{reflux}} C_6H_5CO_2^-Na^+ + 3NaCl$$

or the oxidation of (chloromethyl)benzene (see Unit 11.7) or of methylbenzene and other aromatic compounds with a hydrocarbon side-chain (see
Unit 9.7(c)(i)).

Methanoic acid may be prepared in the laboratory by heating a mixture
of ethanedioic (oxalic) acid and propane-1,2,3-triol (glycerol) at 140°:

$$\underset{CO_2H}{\overset{CO_2H}{|}} \xrightarrow[140°]{\text{propane-1,2,3-triol}} HCO_2H + CO_2$$

16.3 Manufacture of Carboxylic Acids

(a) Air-oxidation of Alkanes

The C_4–C_7 alkanes from the naphtha fraction of petroleum distillation are
oxidized at a high temperature and pressure to yield a mixture of the lower
carboxylic acids. For example:

$$CH_3CH_2CH_2CH_3 \xrightarrow[\text{cobalt ethanoate catalyst}]{\text{air/200°/pressure}} C_2H_5CO_2H + CH_3CO_2H + HCO_2H \text{ etc.}$$

The individual acids are separated from the reaction products by fractional
distillation.

(b) Methanoic Acid

Methanoic acid is obtained as its sodium salt by the action of carbon
monoxide under pressure on sodium hydroxide at 200°:

$$NaOH + CO \xrightarrow{200°/pressure} HCO_2^-Na^+ \xrightarrow{H^+} HCO_2H$$

(c) Ethanoic Acid

Ethanoic acid may be obtained by the action of carbon monoxide on
methanol at high temperature and pressure.

Vinegar. Vinegar is an aqueous solution containing up to 10 per cent of
ethanoic acid in addition to caramel colouring matter and flavouring material. It is formed by the oxidation of a 6–10 per cent ethanol solution from
beer or wine by *Mycoderma aceti* or other micro-organisms. The process
requires air and the presence of phosphates and other inorganic salts.

(d) Ethanedioic Acid

Ethanedioic acid is obtained in the form of its sodium salt by the rapid heating of sodium methanoate:

$$2HCO_2^-Na^+ \xrightarrow{360°} \begin{array}{c} CO_2^-Na^+ \\ | \\ CO_2^-Na^+ \end{array} + H_2$$

(e) Benzoic Acid

Benzoic acid is manufactured by the air-oxidation of methylbenzene:

$$C_6H_5CH_3 \xrightarrow[\text{Sn(IV) vanadate(V) catalyst}]{O_2/\text{heat/pressure}} C_6H_5CO_2H$$

16.4 Physical Properties of Carboxylic Acids

Simple alkanoic acids containing less than 10 carbon atoms are liquids at room temperature. Anhydrous ethanoic acid melts at 16.7° and is known as *glacial* ethanoic acid as it freezes to a colourless, ice-like solid in a cold room. Carboxylic acids tend to associate, and the lower members of the series exist as dimers in solution in benzene and other solvents. The pairs of molecules are linked by hydrogen bonding; for example,

$$CH_3-C \begin{array}{c} O\text{---}H-O \\ \\ O-H\text{---}O \end{array} C-CH_3$$

The energy required to separate these associated molecules when the liquid vaporizes is reflected in the higher boiling-points of the acids. For example, ethanoic acid (RMM = 60) boils at 118°, over 100° higher than does butane (RMM = 58, b.p. −0.5°) which has a similar relative molecular mass, and is considerably less volatile than methyl methanoate, b.p. 32°, the ester with - which it is isomeric.

Alkanoic acids with an even number of carbon atoms have appreciably higher melting-points than their neighbours in the series with odd numbers; X-ray diffraction studies have shown that this is due to differences in the packing of the molecules in the crystal. Aromatic carboxylic acids are crystalline solids, again with melting-points and boiling-points considerably higher than those of the corresponding hydrocarbons or esters.

The lower alkanoic acids have a sharp, vinegar-like odour, while the higher members of the series smell of rancid butter. The C_1–C_4 acids are completely miscible with water, owing to the ability of the carboxy-group to form hydrogen bonds with the solvent, but the solubility of the rest of the series decreases with increasing molecular mass. Benzoic acid is slightly soluble in cold water, but dissolves readily in hot. All the carboxylic acids are soluble in organic solvents.

16.5 Reactions of Carboxylic Acids

(a) As Acids

The carboxylic acids react with sodium carbonate with effervescence (liberating carbon dioxide) and with alkalis to form salts; for example,

$$2CH_3CO_2H + Na_2CO_3 \rightarrow 2CH_3CO_2{}^-Na^+ + H_2O + CO_2$$

sodium ethanoate

$$C_6H_5CO_2H + NaOH \rightarrow C_6H_5CO_2{}^-Na^+ + H_2O$$

sodium benzoate

The reaction with sodium carbonate may be used to distinguish carboxylic acids from phenols, as many of the latter are weaker acids than carbonic acid and do not liberate carbon dioxide (see Unit 13.6(a)). The unsubstituted alkanoic and aromatic acids are weak acids and are only slightly ionized (1 to 4 per cent) in solution. Their strengths are determined by the readiness with which they will donate a proton (see Unit 4.8):

$$HY_{(aq)} \rightleftharpoons H^+_{(aq)} + Y^-_{(aq)}$$

acid   proton   conjugate base

Acid strength will be increased by any factor which increases the stability of the conjugate base relative to the undissociated acid or which promotes proton loss. Thus ethanoic acid is a stronger acid than either ethanol or phenol, partly because the powerful electron-withdrawing effect of the carbonyl oxygen atom facilitates the loss of the proton:

$$CH_3-C\overset{\displaystyle O}{\underset{\displaystyle O\leftarrow H}{}}$$

and partly because the ethanoate anion is stabilized relative to the acid by resonance or delocalization (see Unit 4.6(c)) to a far greater extent than either the corresponding ethoxide or phenoxide ions:

$$CH_3-C\overset{O}{\underset{O^-}{}} \longleftrightarrow CH_3-C\overset{O^-}{\underset{O}{}}$$

The high acidic strength of phenol compared with ethanol is again largely a result of resonance stabilization of the phenoxide ion which is not possible in the ethoxide ion (see Unit 13.5 and Table 16.2).

The introduction of electron-withdrawing substituents into the carboxylic acid molecule has the expected effect on acid strength (see Table 16.3) as the $-I$ inductive effect of the substituent promotes the loss of the proton; for example,

$$\overset{\delta-}{Cl}\leftarrow\overset{\delta+}{CH_2}\leftarrow C\overset{\displaystyle O}{\underset{\displaystyle O\leftarrow H}{}}$$

Table 16.2 Relative acid strengths of ethanol, phenol and ethanoic acid

	Ethanol	Phenol	Ethanoic acid
Structure:	$CH_3 \rightarrow CH_2 \rightarrow OH$	 (phenol structure)	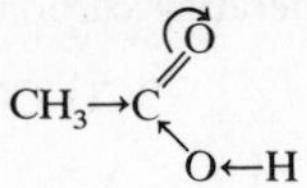 (ethanoic acid structure)
K_a:	10^{-16}	10^{-10}	1.8×10^{-5}
Relative strengths:	1 :	10^6 :	1.8×10^{11}
Explanation:	+I effect of CH_3 group inhibits proton loss	−I effect of benzene ring promotes proton loss	Electron-withdrawing effect of carbonyl group promotes proton loss
	Alkoxide ion not resonance-stabilized	Phenoxide ion resonance-stabilized	Carboxylate anion stabilized by resonance and by hydration

Similarly the presence of electron-donating (+ I) groups makes proton loss more difficult and thus decreases acid strength (see Table 16.4). The inductive effect may be transmitted along a saturated hydrocarbon chain; it decreases rapidly, however, as the distance between the substituent (halogen atom, alkyl group or other functional group) and the carboxy-group increases and is negligible after the second carbon atom (Table 16.5).

Aromatic acids and acids in which the carboxy-group is attached to an unsaturated carbon atom are stronger than their saturated analogues owing to the electron-withdrawing effect of the aromatic nucleus or multiple bond. The presence of electron-withdrawing and electron-donating substituents in

Table 16.3 Effect of electron-withdrawing groups on acid strength

Formula	pK_a	Formula	pK_a
CH_3CO_2H	4.74	CH_3CO_2H	4.74
$I \leftarrow CH_2CO_2H$	3.12	$Cl \leftarrow CH_2CO_2H$	2.86
$Br \leftarrow CH_2CO_2H$	2.90		
$Cl \leftarrow CH_2CO_2H$	2.86	Cl_2CHCO_2H	1.29
$F \leftarrow CH_2CO_2H$	2.66		
$O_2N \leftarrow CH_2CO_2H$	1.67	Cl_3CCO_2H	0.65

Acid strength increases (↓ arrow indicates direction for left column)

Table 16.4 Effect of electron-donating groups on acid strength

Formula	pK_a
$H—CO_2H$	3.77
$CH_3 \rightarrow CO_2H$	4.74
$CH_3 \rightarrow CH_2 \rightarrow CO_2H$	4.88
$CH_3 \diagdown$ $\quad CH \rightarrow CO_2H$ $CH_3 \diagup$	4.85
$CH_3 \diagdown$ $CH_3 \rightarrow C \rightarrow CO_2H$ $CH_3 \diagup$	5.07

the nucleus of aromatic carboxylic acids has the expected effect on acid strength (see Table 16.6). This influence is particularly marked in the *ortho*-isomer, where the substituent is nearest to the carboxy-group.

The higher acidic strength of *cis*-butenedioic acid ($pK_a = 1.92$) compared with its *trans*-isomer ($pK_a = 3.02$) is due to the stabilization of the *cis*-butenedioate anion by *intramolecular* hydrogen bonding:

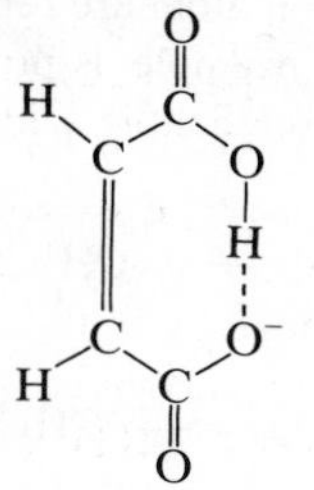

Table 16.5 The inductive effect and acid strength

Structure	pK_a
$\overset{Cl}{\underset{\uparrow}{CH_3CH_2CH}} \leftarrow CO_2H$	2.84
$\overset{Cl}{\underset{\uparrow}{CH_3CH}} \leftarrow CH_2 \leftarrow CO_2H$	4.06
$\overset{Cl}{\underset{\uparrow}{CH_2}} \leftarrow CH_2 \leftarrow CH_2 \leftarrow CO_2H$	4.52
(*cf.* $CH_3CH_2CH_2CO_2H$	4.82)

Table 16.6 pK_a values of substituted benzoic acids

Position of substituent	Substituent						
	—H	—NO$_2$	—Cl	—Br	—CH$_3$	—OCH$_3$	—CO$_2$H
2	4.20	2.17	2.92	2.84	3.91	4.09	(i) 2.89 (ii) 5.51
3	4.20	3.45	3.83	3.86	4.27	4.09	(i) 3.54 (ii) 4.60
4	4.20	3.43	3.99	4.00	4.36	4.47	(i) 3.51 (ii) 4.82

(b) Esterification

Carboxylic acids react with alcohols in the presence of a mineral acid catalyst to yield esters and water. The use of alcohols labelled with the oxygen-18 isotope has shown that the oxygen atom in the water molecule is generally derived from the carboxylic acid and not from the alcohol (cf. Unit 17.5(d)(i)):

$$RCO_2H + R'^{18}OH \rightleftharpoons RCO^{18}OR' + H_2O$$

(c) Chlorination

When an alkanoic acid is treated with chlorine in the presence of a halogen carrier such as red phosphorus, sulphur or iodine, the hydrogen atoms attached to the α- (or 2-) carbon atom are replaced one by one by chlorine atoms. Thus ethanoic acid, for example, is progressively substituted to give mono-, di- and finally tri-chloroethanoic acids:

$$CH_3CO_2H + Cl_2 \xrightarrow{\text{red P}} CH_2ClCO_2H + HCl$$

$$CH_2ClCO_2H + Cl_2 \xrightarrow{\text{red P}} CHCl_2CO_2H + HCl$$

$$CHCl_2CO_2H + Cl_2 \xrightarrow{\text{red P}} CCl_3CO_2H + HCl$$

The products are obtained as substituted acyl chlorides, such as RCHClCOCl. This reaction also occurs in the presence of ultra-violet light, without the halogen carrier. Bromine reacts in the same way and the chlorination or bromination can be stopped at any stage when the weight increase calculated for the required degree of substitution has been obtained.

Benzoic acid and other aromatic carboxylic acids undergo electrophilic substitution by chlorine or bromine in the presence of a halogen carrier. The carboxy-group is *meta*-directing (see Unit 9.9).

(d) Formation of Acyl Halides

Carboxylic acids react with phosphorus halides such as phosphorus pentachloride, or with sulphur dichloride oxide, to yield acyl chlorides:

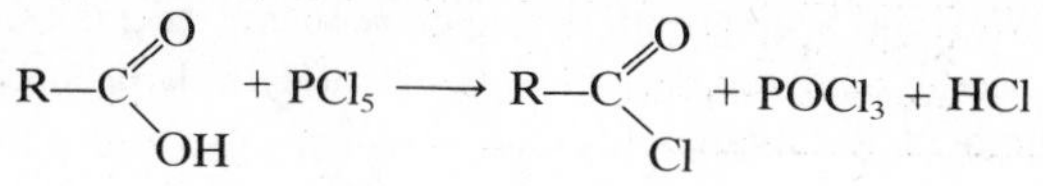

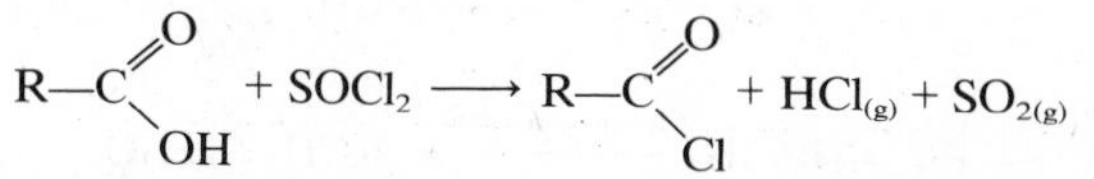

$$R-C \overset{O}{\underset{OH}{\diagdown}} + PCl_5 \longrightarrow R-C \overset{O}{\underset{Cl}{\diagdown}} + POCl_3 + HCl$$

$$R-C \overset{O}{\underset{OH}{\diagdown}} + SOCl_2 \longrightarrow R-C \overset{O}{\underset{Cl}{\diagdown}} + HCl_{(g)} + SO_{2(g)}$$

The evolution of hydrogen chloride in these reactions is evidence for the presence of a hydroxyl group in the carboxylic acid molecule (*cf.* Unit 12.6(*c*)). Acyl bromides may be similarly obtained, by treating the carboxylic acid with a mixture of red phosphorus and bromine:

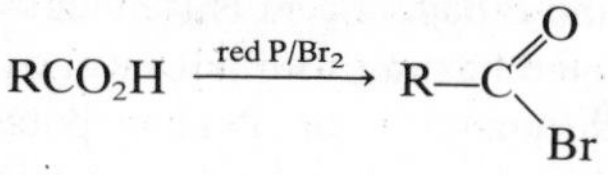

$$RCO_2H \xrightarrow{\text{red P/Br}_2} R-C \overset{O}{\underset{Br}{\diagdown}}$$

(*e*) Anhydride Formation

Alkanoic acids are dehydrated by heating with phosphorus(v) oxide (or, better, by the action of zinc oxide at 250°) to form carboxylic acid anhydrides. For example,

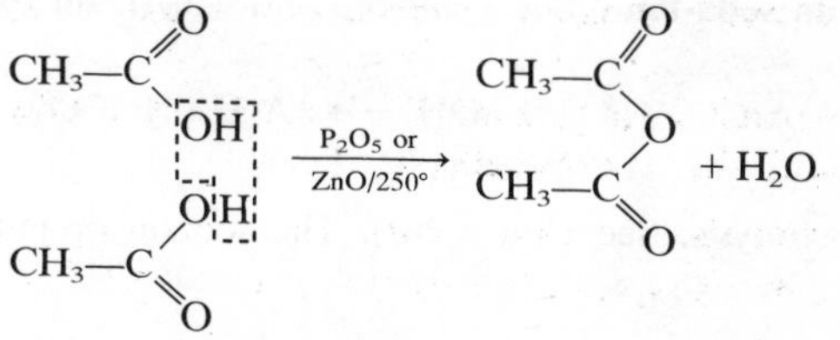

A carboxylic anhydride may also be obtained by the action of an acyl halide on the sodium salt of a carboxylic acid (see Unit 17.4(*d*)(iv)). This reaction is particularly useful for the synthesis of mixed anhydrides, RCOOCOR'.

(*f*) Reduction

Carboxylic acids are resistant to reduction and only powerful reducing agents have any effect. Both lithium tetrahydridoaluminate(iii), $LiAlH_4$, and diborane, B_2H_6, reduce a carboxylic acid to the primary alcohol:

$$RCO_2H \xrightarrow{\text{LiAlH}_4} (RCH_2O)_4Al^-Li^+ \xrightarrow{\text{H}_2O} 4RCH_2OH + Al(OH)_3 + LiOH$$

Diborane is a selective reducing agent and may be used to reduce carboxylic acid groups in the presence of other unsaturated groups; for example,

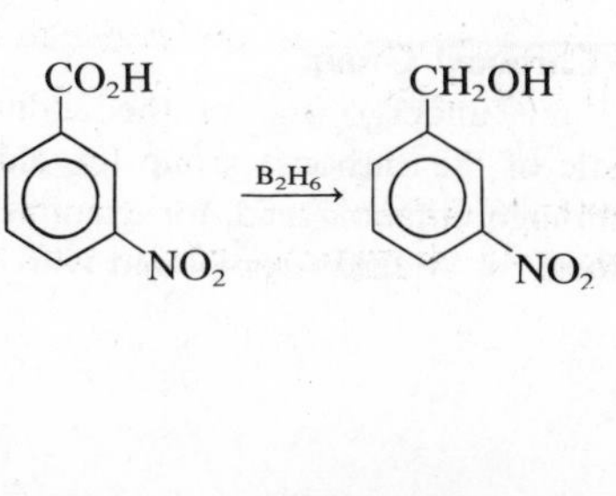

Sodium tetrahydridoborate(III), Na_3BH_4, is not sufficiently powerful to reduce the carboxylic acid group. Stronger reducing agents, such as concentrated hydriodic acid–red phosphorus or catalytic hydrogenation, convert carboxylic acids to alkanes:

$$RCO_2H \xrightarrow{\text{red P/HI}} RCH_3$$

$$RCO_2H + 3H_2 \xrightarrow{\text{Ni/pressure/heat}} RCH_3 + 2H_2O$$

(g) Oxidation
The carboxylic acids (except methanoic acid, see Unit 16.6) are extremely resistant to oxidation, and ethanoic acid is frequently used as a solvent for oxidizing agents. Prolonged heating with powerful oxidizing agents, such as acidified potassium dichromate(VI) or alkaline potassium manganate(VII), eventually converts carboxylic acids to carbon dioxide and water.

(h) Decarboxylation
The salts of carboxylic acids undergo a number of decarboxylation reactions:
(i) **Heating with soda-lime.** See Units 5.3 and 9.3(a); for example:

$$ArCO_2^- Na^+ + \text{'NaOH'} \xrightarrow{\text{heat}} ArH + Na_2CO_3$$
$$\text{soda-lime}$$

(ii) **Kolbe electrolysis.** See Unit 5.2(d). The sodium or potassium salt is electrolysed:

$$2RCO_2^- \xrightarrow{\text{at anode}} R\text{—}R + 2CO_2 + 2e$$

The salts of aromatic acids in which the carboxy-group is attached directly to the ring, such as benzoic acid, do not give hydrocarbons on electrolysis.
(iii) **Formation of aldehydes or ketones.** See Unit 15.2(c).

(i) Amide Formation
The ammonium salts of carboxylic acids undergo dehydration on heating in the presence of excess free acid to yield amides (see Unit 17.7(b)(i)):

$$RCO_2^- NH_4^+ \xrightarrow[\text{RCO}_2\text{H}]{\text{heat}} RCONH_2 + H_2O$$

(j) Reactions of the Carbonyl Group
Carboxylic acids do not undergo any of the addition or condensation reactions characteristic of the carbonyl group (cf. aldehydes and ketones, Unit 15.6). Thus, although ethanoic acid, for example, contains a carbonyl group, it does not form an addition compound with sodium hydrogensul-

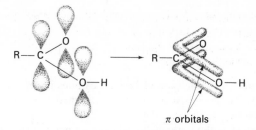

Fig. 16.1   Structure of the carboxylic acid group

phite, nor does it react with hydrogen cyanide or undergo condensation reactions with hydroxylamine or hydrazine. The carbonyl group in carboxylic acids is resistant to addition reactions because of the interaction of the unbonded pair of electrons on the oxygen atom of the hydroxyl group with the p orbital of the carbonyl carbon atom (see Fig. 16.1 and Unit 17.2).

16.6 Methanoic Acid

The chemical properties of methanoic acid—the first member of the alkanoic acid homologous series—are different from those of the other carboxylic acids. This is principally a result of the compound's structure:

$$\text{aldehyde group} \underbrace{\overbrace{\text{H—C}}^{}_{\substack{\\ \text{OH}}}^{\displaystyle O}}$$

Methanoic acid contains an aldehyde group and the compound is therefore able to act as a reducing agent. It reduces ammoniacal silver nitrate to metallic silver and decolorizes both alkaline and acidic solutions of potassium manganate(vii). Methanoic acid and its salts are also able to reduce mercury(ii) chloride solution to mercury(i) chloride and metallic mercury. It has little or no effect on Fehling's solution, however. Other important differences between methanoic acid and other members of the homologous series include:

(i) **Acid strength.** Methanoic acid ($pK_a = 3.77$) is a stronger acid than any other unsubstituted carboxylic acid (pK_a for ethanoic acid $= 4.74$; see Unit 16.5(a)).

(ii) **Action of sulphuric acid.** Methanoic acid is dehydrated by the action of concentrated sulphuric acid to yield carbon monoxide:

$$HCO_2H \xrightarrow[-H_2O]{conc.\ H_2SO_4} H_2O + CO$$

Except for protonation, ethanoic acid and other alkanoic acids do not react with sulphuric acid.

(iii) **Action of soda-lime.** Hydrogen is evolved when sodium methanoate is heated with soda-lime:

$$HCO_2^-Na^+ + \text{'NaOH'} \xrightarrow{\text{heat}} Na_2CO_3 + H_2$$

$$\underset{\text{soda-lime}}{}$$

The salts of other alkanoic acids yield hydrocarbons under these conditions (see Unit 5.3). Sodium methanoate does not yield a hydrocarbon in the Kolbe electrolysis (*cf.* Unit 5.2(*d*)).

(iv) **Formation of sodium ethanedioate.** Sodium methanoate yields sodium ethanedioate and hydrogen on heating:

$$2HCO_2^-Na^+ \xrightarrow{350°} \begin{array}{c} CO_2^-Na^+ \\ | \\ CO_2^-Na^+ \end{array} + H_2$$

(v) **Anhydride formation.** Methanoic acid does not form a simple anhydride, $(HCO)_2O$. Mixed anhydrides may be synthesized, however; methanoyl ethanoate, $HCOOCOCH_3$, for instance, is produced by the action of ethanoyl chloride on sodium methanoate:

$$CH_3COCl + HCO_2Na \rightarrow HCOOCOCH_3 + NaCl$$

16.7 Dicarboxylic Acids

The most important dicarboxylic acids are:

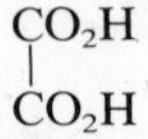

ethanedioic acid
(oxalic acid)

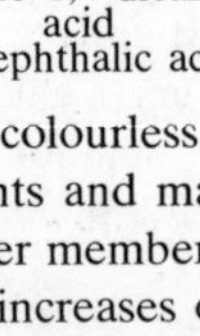

benzene-1,4-dicarboxylic
acid
(terephthalic acid)

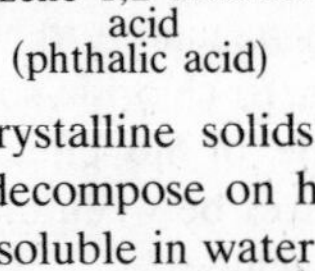

benzene-1,2-dicarboxylic
acid
(phthalic acid)

The dicarboxylic acids are colourless, odourless crystalline solids. They have fairly high melting-points and many of them decompose on heating, yielding anhydrides. The lower members are slightly soluble in water and in ethanol, and their solubility increases on warming.

Ethanedioic acid is manufactured by heating sodium methanoate (see Unit 16.3(*d*)). It can be prepared in the laboratory by oxidizing sucrose or some other carbohydrate, such as starch, with concentrated nitric acid in the presence of vanadium(v) oxide as a catalyst:

$$\underset{\text{sucrose}}{C_{12}H_{22}O_{11}} + [O] \xrightarrow[\text{heat}]{HNO_3/V_2O_5} (CO_2H)_2 + H_2O$$

Ethanedioates are poisonous and about 1 g is fatal. The antidote is calcium hydroxide (slaked lime), which precipitates ethanedioic acid as the insoluble calcium salt. Ethanedioic acid occurs in nature in many plants, including rhubarb leaves. It is a moderately strong dibasic acid ($K_a' = 5.37 \times 10^{-2}$, $K_a'' = 5.42 \times 10^{-5}$). It reacts with alkalis and alcohols to yield salts and esters respectively. Concentrated sulphuric acid dehydrates it to yield carbon monoxide and carbon dioxide:

$$\begin{array}{c} CO_2H \\ | \\ CO_2H \end{array} \xrightarrow{\text{conc. } H_2SO_4} CO_2 + CO + H_2O$$

It decolorizes warm acidified potassium manganate(VII) solution. The purple manganate(VII) ion is reduced to manganese(II):

$$MnO_4^- + 8H^+ + 5e \rightarrow Mn^{2+} + 4H_2O$$

and the ethanedioate ion is oxidized to carbon dioxide:

$$\begin{array}{c} CO_2^- \\ | \\ CO_2^- \end{array} \longrightarrow 2CO_2 + 2e$$

Sodium ethanedioate is used in volumetric analysis for the standardization of solutions of potassium manganate(VII):

$$2MnO_4^- + 5(CO_2^-)_2 + 16H^+ \xrightarrow{\text{warm}} 2Mn^{2+} + 8H_2O + 10CO_2$$

It yields methanoic acid on heating with propane-1,2,3-triol at 140° (see Unit 16.2(e)).

Experiment 16.1 *To demonstrate the reactions of carboxylic acids*

1. *Solubility.* Test the solubility in water of a number of carboxylic acids, such as methanoic, ethanoic, ethanedioic, benzoic and benzene-1,2-dicarboxylic acids. Determine the pH of each solution with Universal indicator paper. Add sodium hydroxide solution to those acids which are only slightly soluble in water, followed by an excess of concentrated hydrochloric acid. Boil the mixture and allow it to cool, noting any changes in appearance.

2. *Action of sodium carbonate solution.* Add 2 or 3 cm³ of aqueous sodium carbonate to about 0.3 g of the carboxylic acid. Note the evolution of carbon dioxide.

3. *Action of soda-lime.* In a dry test-tube, heat approximately 1 g of the anhydrous carboxylic acid (or, preferably, its sodium salt) well mixed with two or three times its volume of powdered soda-lime. Note the odour of the gas or vapour evolved and test it with a lighted splint. Repeat the experiment with (a) methanoic acid, (b) ethanoic acid and (c) benzoic acid.

4. *Ester formation.* Warm a mixture of about 1 cm³ of ethanol, 0.5 g of ethanoic acid and 2 or 3 drops of concentrated sulphuric acid for two or three minutes. Cool, and then pour the mixture into a boiling-tube containing about 10 cm³ of distilled water. Neutralize the unreacted ethanoic acid

with an excess of aqueous sodium carbonate solution, and note the pleasant odour of the ester, ethyl ethanoate.

Repeat this test using about $1\,cm^3$ of methanol, $0.5\,g$ of 2-hydroxybenzoic acid (salicylic acid) and a few drops of concentrated sulphuric acid. The product is oil of wintergreen (methyl salicylate); note its characteristic smell.

5. *Action of iron*(III) *chloride.* Prepare a neutral solution of ethanoic acid by adding aqueous ammonia to about $0.5\,cm^3$ of the acid until the solution is just alkaline (test with litmus). Boil off the excess of ammonia, allow the solution to cool and then add a few drops of neutral iron(III) chloride solution (see Appendix II). Note the formation of a deep-red coloration.

Repeat this test with other carboxylic acids. Methanoic acid also yields a red colour, while benzoic and benzene-1,2-dicarboxylic acids give a buff or brownish precipitate. 2-Hydroxybenzoic acid gives a violet colour, indicating the presence of a phenol group.

6. *Phenolphthalein formation.* Benzene-1,2-dicarboxylic acid gives the phthalein test (see Experiment 13.2.5).

Experiment 16.2 *Comparison of the reactions of methanoic, ethanoic and ethanedioic acids and of their sodium salts*

1. *Odour.* Note the odour of aqueous solutions of the acids.

2. *Action of concentrated sulphuric acid.* Warm $0.5\,cm^3$ of methanoic acid (or about $0.5\,g$ of sodium methanoate) with $1\,cm^3$ of concentrated sulphuric acid (**Care!**). Test the gas evolved (*a*) with lime-water and then (*b*) with a lighted splint. Carbon monoxide burns with a pale-blue flame which slowly travels back down the tube. Repeat this test with disodium ethanedioate or ethanedioic acid and then, for comparison, with sodium ethanoate. How does this single test distinguish between the three acids?

3. *Action of ammoniacal silver nitrate.* Warm a few drops of a neutral solution of methanoic acid with about $2\,cm^3$ of ammoniacal silver nitrate solution (Tollen's reagent—see Appendix II). Note the formation of a grey precipitate or mirror of metallic silver. Ethanoic and ethanedioic acids do not reduce ammoniacal silver nitrate.

4. *Action of mercury*(II) *chloride.* Add a little mercury(II) chloride solution to a solution of methanoic acid or sodium methanoate in water. Note the formation of a grey-white precipitate of mercury(I) chloride which is insoluble in dilute hydrochloric acid.

5. *Action of potassium manganate*(VII). Add $1\,cm^3$ of dilute sulphuric acid to about $0.5\,g$ of methanoic acid (or sodium methanoate) in a test-tube. Warm the solution and then add 1 per cent aqueous potassium manganate(VII) solution drop by drop and observe the immediate decolorization. Repeat this test with (*a*) ethanedioic acid and (*b*) ethanoic acid, and compare the results.

Repeat with alkaline potassium manganate(VII) solution by adding 1 per cent potassium manganate(VII) drop by drop to a cold solution of about $0.5\,g$ of methanoic acid (or sodium methanoate) in $5\,cm^3$ of 10 per cent sodium carbonate solution. Warm the mixture gently. Ethanoic acid is unaffected by alkaline potassium manganate(vII) solution and ethanedioic acid is only oxidized extremely slowly on heating.

6. *Action of calcium chloride solution.* Prepare a neutral solution of ethanedioic acid or disodium ethanedioate in water by adding a slight excess of aqueous ammonia to the solution (test with litmus) and then boiling off the excess of ammonia. Add a few drops of 5 per cent aqueous calcium chloride solution, and note the immediate formation of a white precipitate. Write an equation for this reaction and test the solubility of the solid in (*a*) aqueous ethanoic acid, (*b*) dilute hydrochloric acid.

7. *Action of heat on sodium methanoate.* Heat about 1 g of sodium methanoate in a dry test-tube. Identify the gas evolved. Repeat the experiment with sodium ethanoate.

16.8 Uses of Carboxylic Acids

Methanoic acid and ethanoic acid are used to coagulate rubber latex and their salts have many applications in the dye industry and the manufacture of paints. Ethanoic acid is used in aqueous solution as vinegar. It is a useful solvent (for instance, for oxidation reactions) and is used for the preparation of poly(ethenyl ethanoate) (see Unit 7.6(*j*)) and of cellulose ethanoate (for artificial fibres such as Celanese rayon, films, varnish and lacquer) (see Unit 20.8(*b*)(ii)).

Benzoic acid is employed for the preparation of medicines and as a preservative in foodstuffs. Hexanedioic acid (see Unit 13.7(*a*)) and benzene-1,4-dicarboxylic acid are used in the manufacture of nylon-6,6 (see Unit 21.5) and Terylene (see Unit 12.8(*a*)(iii)), respectively.

Test Yourself on Unit 16

1. Name the following compounds:
   (*a*) $CH_3CCl_2CO_2H$;
   (*b*) $(CH_3)_3CCO_2H$;
   (*c*) $(CH_2)_3(CO_2H)_2$;
   (*d*) $C_6H_5CH_2CO_2H$.

2. Give TWO tests in each case to distinguish between the following pairs of compounds:
   (*a*) sodium carbonate and sodium ethanoate;
   (*b*) methanoic acid and ethanoic acid;
   (*c*) methanoic acid and ethanedioic acid;
   (*d*) benzoic acid and phenol.

3. State how the following changes may be carried out:
   (*a*) methanal → disodium ethanedioate;
   (*b*) benzene → benzoic acid.
   (*c*) ethanol → ethyl ethanoate;
   (*d*) bromoethane → propanoic acid;
   (*e*) ethanal → ethanoyl chloride.

4. Without reference to tables, arrange the following groups of compounds in order of increasing acidic strength:

(a) methanoic acid, ethanoic acid, phenol, carbonic acid;

(b) ethanoic acid, fluoroethanoic acid, iodoethanoic acid, bromoethanoic acid;

(c) benzoic acid, 2-nitrobenzoic acid, 4-methylbenzoic acid.

5. The esters and carboxylic acids are isomeric. Name the esters and acids of molecular formula $C_3H_6O_2$ and describe chemical tests to distinguish between them.

6. How and under what conditions does ethanedioic acid react with (a) sulphuric acid, (b) sodium carbonate, (c) phosphorus pentachloride, (d) potassium manganate(vII) and (e) propane-1,2,3-triol?

7. Discuss, with reference to suitable examples, the factors that determine the relative strengths of carboxylic acids.

8. Compare and contrast the structures, preparations and reactions of methanoic and ethanoic acid.

Multiple completion questions (Attempt these questions after studying Unit 17)

In Questions 9–16 ONE OR MORE of the five stated responses may be correct. Consider all the responses and answer

A if 1, 3 and 4 are correct;

B if 1 and 3 are correct;

C if 2 and 3 are correct;

D if 2 and 4 are correct;

E if some other response or combination of responses is correct.

9. Ethanoic acid reacts with chlorine in the presence of red phosphorus. Which of the following are possible products of this reaction?

1. CH_3Cl, CO_2 and HCl;
2. CH_3COCl;
3. $CH_2ClCOCl$;
4. $CHCl_2COCl$;
5. CCl_3COCl.

10. Sodium ethanoate is one of the products obtained by boiling the following compounds with aqueous sodium hydroxide:

1. ethanamide;
2. ethanal;
3. 1,1-dichloroethane;
4. monochloroethanoic acid;
5. 1,1,1-trichloroethane.

11. Methanoic acid may be prepared by:

1. refluxing isocyanoethane with dilute sulphuric acid;
2. boiling trichloromethane with aqueous sodium hydroxide and acidifying the product;

3. heating a mixture of propane-1,2,3-triol and ethanedioic acid;

4. refluxing cyanoethane with dilute sulphuric acid;

5. strongly heating sodium ethanedioate and acidifying the product.

12. Sodium ethanedioate is formed by:

1. strongly heating sodium hydroxide with carbon monoxide;

2. heating sodium methanoate;

3. strongly heating sodium hydroxide with carbon dioxide;

4. the reaction of sodium methanoate with warm alkaline potassium manganate(VII) solution.

13. Ethanoic anhydride is formed by:

1. the reaction of anhydrous sodium ethanoate with sulphur dichloride oxide;

2. heating calcium ethanoate;

3. the reaction between anhydrous sodium ethanoate and ethanoyl chloride;

4. the reaction of ethyne with ethanoic acid in the presence of mercury(II) sulphate;

5. the reaction between ethanal and phosphorus pentachloride.

14. Ethanoic acid is obtained as a product of:

1. the oxidation of propanone with hot chromic acid;

2. the hydrolysis of ethanal oxime;

3. the hydrolysis of ethanonitrile with boiling hydrochloric acid;

4. the reaction of ethanamide with nitrous acid;

5. the reaction of ethanedioic acid with acidified potassium manganate(VII).

15. Methanoic acid may be distinguished from ethanoic acid by its effect on the following reagents:

1. acidified potassium manganate(VII);

2. sodium hydrogencarbonate solution;

3. alkaline potassium manganate(VII) solution;

4. aqueous ammonia;

5. mercury(II) chloride solution.

16. The sodium salt of a carboxylic acid P was electrolysed. $6.8 \, cm^3$ of the gas evolved at the anode yielded $13.6 \, cm^3$ of carbon dioxide on combustion. Which of the following are possible formulae for P?

1. CH_3CO_2H;

2. HCO_2H;

3. $(CH_2CO_2H)_2$;

4. $HO_2CCH{=}CHCO_2H$;

5. $CH_3CH_2CO_2H$.

Carboxylic Acid Derivatives

17.1 Introduction

The carboxylic acid derivatives may be regarded as compounds in which the hydroxyl group of a carboxylic acid has been replaced by another functional group, such as an amino- ($-NH_2$) or alkoxy- ($-OR$) group or a halogen atom. The compounds in these different homologous series all contain an *acyl group*, RCO— or ArCO—, and as they have a number of reactions in common, it is convenient to discuss them in a single Unit.

Functional group	Class of compound	General formula (R = alkyl or aryl)
—OH	carboxylic acid	RCO_2H
—X (X = halogen)	acyl halide	$RC\overset{\displaystyle O}{\underset{X}{\big\langle}}$
—OR'	ester	$RC\overset{\displaystyle O}{\underset{OR'}{\big\langle}}$
—NH₂	amide	$RC\overset{\displaystyle O}{\underset{NH_2}{\big\langle}}$
—OCOR	acid anhydride	RCOOCOR'

17.2 Structure and Reactivity of Carboxylic Acid Derivatives

The planar carbonyl group, containing the sp^2 hybridized carbon atom, is present in all the carboxylic acid derivatives. Its properties are so modified by the presence of the $-\ddot{O}H$, $-\ddot{C}l$, $-\ddot{N}H_2$, $-\ddot{O}R'$ and $-\ddot{O}COR'$ groups, however, that carboxylic acids, acyl chlorides, amides, esters and acid anhydrides have few reactions in common with the other main classes of carbonyl compounds, the aldehydes and ketones. The principal reactions of the carboxylic acid derivatives are *nucleophilic substitutions*. These occur by an addition–elimination reaction via an unstable tetrahedral intermediate:

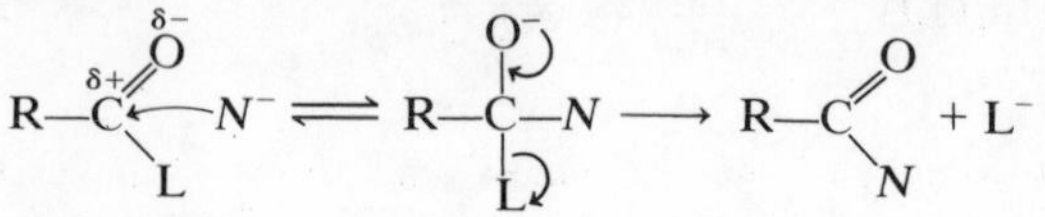

$$R-\overset{\overset{\displaystyle \delta-}{\displaystyle \overset{\|}{O}}}{\underset{L}{C}}\overset{\delta+}{\longleftarrow}N^- \;\rightleftharpoons\; R-\overset{O^-}{\underset{L}{\overset{|}{C}}}-N \;\longrightarrow\; R-\overset{O}{\overset{\|}{C}}\diagdown_N + L^-$$

nucleophile

where N^- (or N:) is the attacking nucleophile (such as (OH^-, :NH_3, RCO_2^- or H_2O:) and L is the *leaving group*, the functional group (such as —Cl, —NH_2 or —OR) in the original carboxylic acid derivative. By contrast, the principal reactions of the aldehydes and ketones involve *addition* to the carbonyl group or *condensation* via an addition–elimination mechanism in which the carbonyl oxygen atom is lost (see Unit 15.5).

Carboxylic acids and their derivatives do not undergo the condensation and addition reactions of the free carbonyl group; for example, unlike aldehydes and ketones, they do not yield oximes with hydroxylamine, nor do they form cyanohydrins or hydrogensulphite addition compounds (see Units 15.6(*a*) and (*b*)). The relatively high reactivity of the carboxylic acid derivatives is determined by the electron distribution in the carbonyl group and is largely a result of inductive and mesomeric (or resonance) effects. Other factors, such as the nature of the leaving group and steric hindrance to the approach of the nucleophile, are important, but the approximate order of reactivity towards nucleophilic attack is:

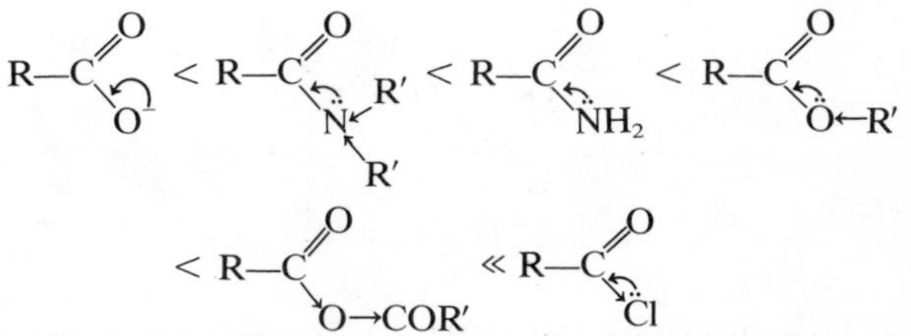

The acyl halides are the most reactive of the carboxylic acid derivatives as the strong inductive effect of the halogen atom decreases the electron density on the carbon atom, making it susceptible to nucleophilic attack even by such weak nucleophiles as water, H_2O:, and thus facilitating loss of the halide ion. The highly reactive acylium ion, $R—\overset{+}{C}{=}O$, formed by heterolytic fission of the carbon–halogen bond, is involved in some acyl halide reactions.

Aromatic carboxylic acid derivatives are less reactive than the corresponding aliphatic compounds owing to the reduction in the position nature of the carbonyl carbon atom because of resonance:

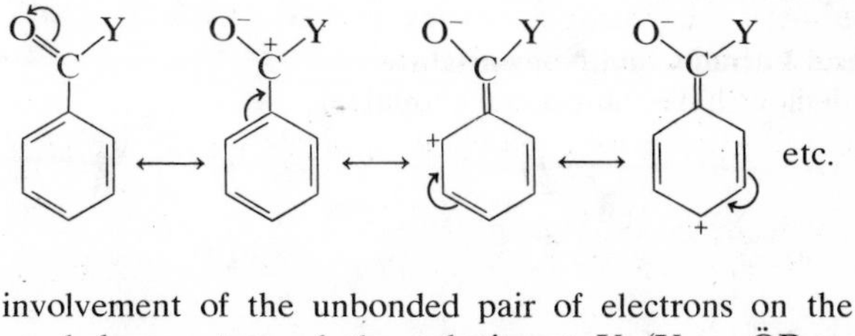

and the involvement of the unbonded pair of electrons on the oxygen, nitrogen or halogen atom of the substituent Y (Y = —ÖR, —ÖCOR,

—N̈H$_2$, —C̈l, etc.):

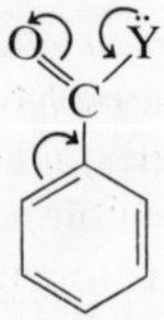

These p electrons are thus partially delocalized by participation in a π orbital extending over the whole molecule (*cf.* Fig. 16.1), thus decreasing the susceptibility of the carbonyl carbon atom to nucleophilic attack.

17.3 Physical Properties of Carboxylic Acid Derivatives

The acyl halides, esters and carboxylic acid anhydrides have similar boiling-points to those of aldehydes and ketones of comparable relative molecular mass. The amides are much less volatile because of intermolecular hydrogen bonding:

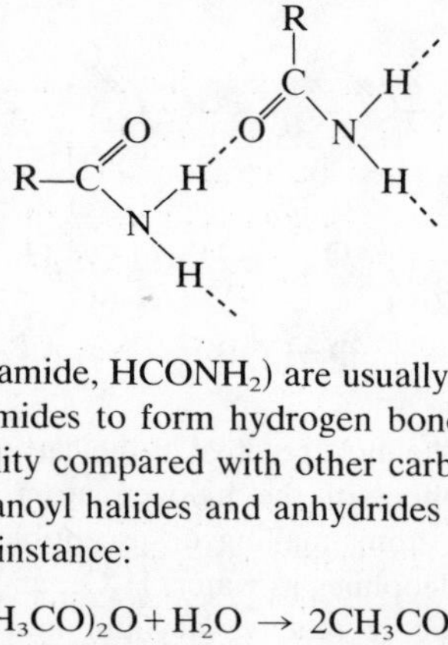

and (except for methanamide, HCONH$_2$) are usually solids at room temperature. The ability of amides to form hydrogen bonds with water accounts for their greater solubility compared with other carboxylic acid derivatives. Many of the lower alkanoyl halides and anhydrides react with (rather than dissolve in) water; for instance:

$$(CH_3CO)_2O + H_2O \rightarrow 2CH_3CO_2H$$

ethanoic anhydride   ethanoic acid
(sparingly soluble)   (soluble)

The properties of the different classes of carboxylic acid derivatives are described separately below.

17.4 Acyl Halides

(a) General Formula and Nomenclature
The acyl halides have the general formula

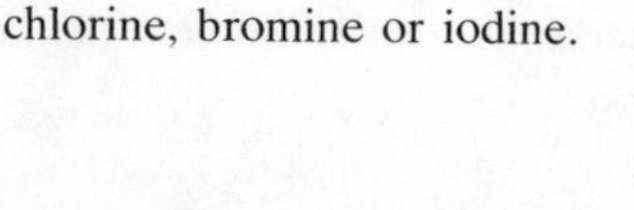

where X is fluorine, chlorine, bromine or iodine.

The acyl halides are named by changing the suffix -*ic* of the corresponding alkanoic or aromatic acid name to -*yl* and then adding the name of the halide. For example, CH_3COCl is *ethanoyl chloride*. The chlorides are typical of the series and are the most commonly used acyl halides, principally because of their ready availability.

(b) Preparation

The acyl chlorides are prepared by the action of phosphorus trichloride, phosphorus pentachloride or sulphur dichloride oxide on a carboxylic acid RCO_2H, where R is an alkyl or aryl group:

$$3RCO_2H + PCl_3 \rightarrow 3RCOCl + H_3PO_3$$
$$\text{b.p. } 76° \qquad\qquad\qquad (\text{decomposes } 200°)$$

$$RCO_2H + PCl_5 \rightarrow RCOCl + POCl_3 + HCl_{(g)}$$
$$\text{(sublimes)} \qquad\qquad \text{b.p. } 107°$$

$$RCO_2H + SOCl_2 \rightarrow RCOCl + SO_{2(g)} + HCl_{(g)}$$
$$\text{b.p. } 78°$$

The choice of phosphorus or sulphur halide used is determined by the relative boiling-points of the acyl chloride and of the other components of the reaction mixture. Sulphur dichloride oxide is particularly useful, as the by-products of the reaction (sulphur dioxide and hydrogen chloride) are both gases, so that separation and purification of the acyl halide is generally easy.

Benzoyl chloride is made by treating benzoic acid with phosphorus pentachloride:

$$C_6H_5CO_2H + PCl_5 \rightarrow C_6H_5COCl + POCl_3 + HCl$$

The reaction mixture is fractionally distilled and phosphorus trichloride oxide (b.p. 107°) distils over first to leave benzoyl chloride (b.p. 197°) which is then purified by distillation. Aromatic sulphonyl chlorides are made from the corresponding sulphonic acid (or its sodium salt, $ArSO_2O^-Na^+$) by the same route:

$$ArSO_2OH + PCl_5 \rightarrow ArSO_2Cl + POCl_3 + HCl$$

Benzoyl chloride may also be prepared by the chlorination of benzaldehyde in the absence of a halogen carrier (see Unit 15.6(c)(v)).

Acyl bromides and iodides are prepared by treating the carboxylic acid with the appropriate phosphorus trihalide or, alternatively, with a mixture of red phosphorus and bromine or iodine.

(c) Physical Properties

The lower acyl halides are colourless liquids with a sharp, irritating odour. They fume in moist air owing to their hydrolysis with release of hydrogen halide. The first member of the chloride series, methanoyl chloride, HCOCl, has not been isolated and methanoyl fluoride is only stable at very low temperatures.

(d) Reactions

Benzoyl chloride and the other aromatic acyl halides are considerably less reactive than ethanoyl chloride (see Unit 17.2).

(i) **Hydrolysis.** Alkanoyl chlorides are rapidly hydrolysed in water to yield the parent carboxylic acid and hydrogen chloride:

$$RCOCl + H_2O \longrightarrow RCO_2H + HCl_{(aq)}$$

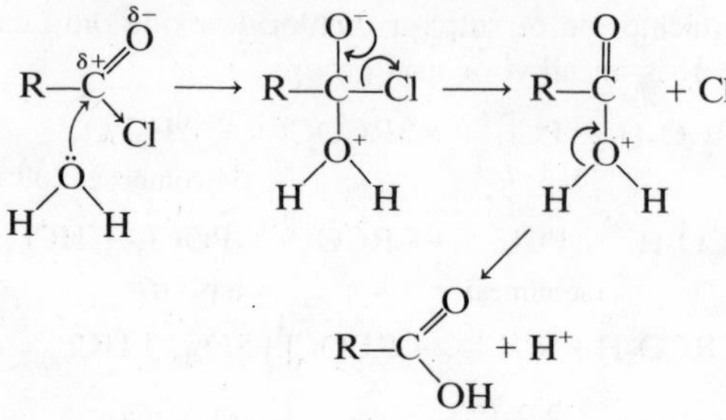

Aromatic acyl halides react in the same way but considerably more slowly.

(ii) **Ester formation.** Acyl halides react with alcohols or phenols to yield esters (see Units 12.6(d) and 13.6(d)):

$$RCOCl + R'OH \rightarrow RCO_2R' + HCl$$

The mechanism is the same as that described for the hydrolysis reaction, except that the nucleophile is the alcohol, $R—\ddot{O}H$, instead of water.

With aromatic acyl halides such as benzoyl chloride or benzenesulphonyl chloride, and in the esterification of phenols, an alkaline medium is used; for example:

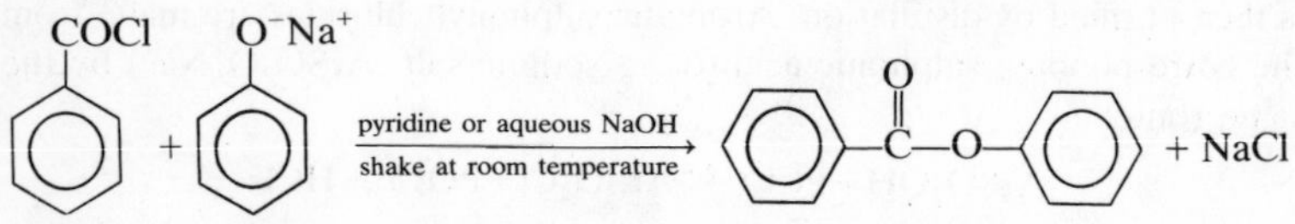

benzoyl   sodium   phenyl benzoate
chloride   phenoxide

This is an example of the *Schotten–Baumann reaction*; another is described in Experiment 13.1. The decreased reactivity of the aromatic acyl chloride is demonstrated by the use of dilute aqueous sodium hydroxide solution in these acylation reactions. The formation of esters from alcohols and phenols and that of amides from primary or secondary amines (see (iii) below) with benzoyl, 3,5-dinitrobenzoyl or 4-methylbenzenesulphonyl chlorides are used as methods of characterizing hydroxy- and amino-compounds. The melting-points of a number of 3,5-dinitrobenzoates of alcohols and phenols are listed in Appendix I.

(iii) **Amide formation.** The acyl halides form amides on reaction with ammonia or with primary or secondary amines:

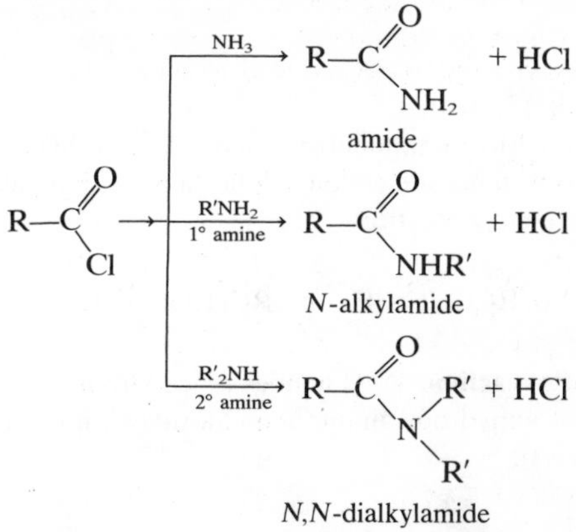

amide

N-alkylamide

N,N-dialkylamide

The corresponding reactions with benzenesulphonyl chloride yield benzenesulphonamide, $C_6H_5SO_2NH_2$, or its N-mono- or N,N-di-substituted benzenesulphonamides, $C_6H_5SO_2NHR$ and $C_6H_5SO_2NR_2$. Many valuable sulphonamide drugs are derivatives of 4-aminobenzenesulphonamide (sulphanilamide):

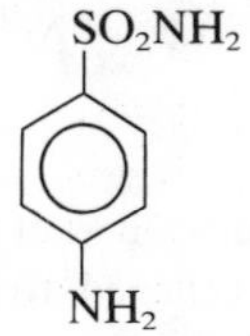

The artificial sweetening agent *saccharin*

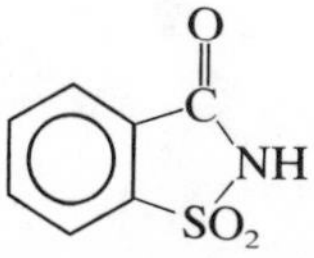

is also a benzenesulphonamide derivative.

(iv) **Anhydride formation.** Acyl halides react with sodium salts of carboxylic acids to yield acid anhydrides; for example, ethanoic anhydride may be prepared by the action of ethanoyl chloride on sodium ethanoate. The ethanoate ion acts as a nucleophile:

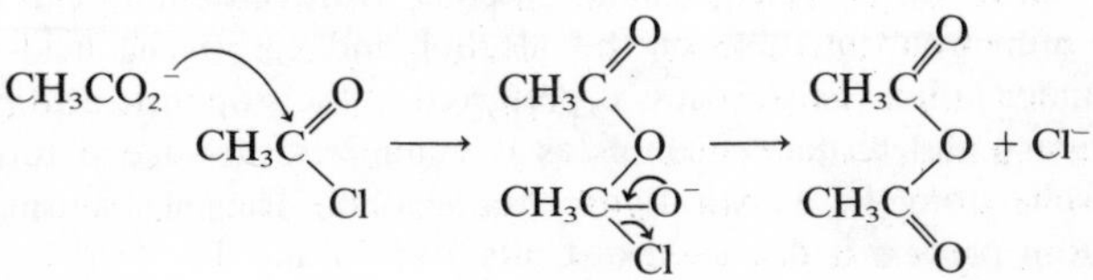

Aromatic acyl halides react similarly; for instance:

$$C_6H_5COCl + C_6H_5CO_2^-Na^+ \rightarrow (C_6H_5CO)_2O + NaCl$$
benzoic anhydride

(v) **Reduction.** Acyl halides are reduced to aldehydes by the *Rosenmund reaction* (see Unit 15.2(d)).

Lithium tetrahydridoaluminate(III), sodium tetrahydridoborate(III) or hydrogen in the presence of colloidal platinum or palladium reduce acyl halides to primary alcohols, thus:

$$RCOCl + 2H_2 \xrightarrow{Pd} RCH_2OH + HCl$$

(vi) **Friedel–Crafts reaction.** Acyl halides react with aromatic hydrocarbons in the presence of anhydrous aluminium chloride to form aromatic ketones (see Unit 9.6(b)(iv)).

17.5 Esters

(a) **General Formula and Nomenclature**
Esters have the general formula

R—C(=O)—OR'   or   Ar—C(=O)—OR'

and are named as alkyl or aryl derivatives of the parent carboxylic acid, the suffix of the acid name being changed from *-ic* to *-ate*. For example, $HCO_2C_2H_5$ is an ethyl derivative of methanoic acid, HCO_2H, and is known as ethyl methanoate. The simplest ester derived from an aromatic acid is $C_6H_5CO_2CH_3$, methyl benzoate.

(b) **Preparation**
(i) **From alcohols:**

$$RCO_2H + R'OH \rightleftharpoons RCO_2R' + H_2O$$
carboxylic acid   alcohol   ester   water

The reaction is reversible: the process from left to right is known as *esterification* while the reverse reaction is *ester hydrolysis*. A little concentrated sulphuric acid is added to the reaction mixture as a catalyst. Alternatively, in the *Fischer–Speier method*, gaseous hydrogen chloride is passed into the anhydrous mixture of the alcohol and carboxylic acid before heating under reflux. This process is preferred to the sulphuric acid method for secondary and tertiary alcohols as it minimizes the alkene formation which results from the dehydration of the alcohol. The mechanism of the esterification process is discussed in Units 16.5(b) and 17.5(d)(i).

(ii) **From acyl halides or acid anhydrides** (see Unit 12.6(d)). The Schotten–Baumann reaction (see Unit 17.4(d)(ii)) is particularly useful for preparing the esters of phenols, such as phenyl benzoate, $C_6H_5CO_2C_6H_5$, m.p. 70°.

Experiment 17.1 *Preparation of phenyl benzoate*
Add 1 cm^3 of benzoyl chloride to a solution of 0.5 g of phenol (**Care!**) in 10 cm^3 of 10 per cent sodium hydroxide in a boiling-tube. Cork the tube and shake it vigorously for five or ten minutes, loosening the cork from time to time to release any build-up of pressure. Filter off the precipitate of crude phenyl benzoate, wash well with water, recrystallize from hot ethanol and dry. Determine the melting-point of the product.

(iii) **From the reaction of a silver salt with a halogenoalkane.** See Unit 10.6(a)(iii):

$$R'CO_2^-Ag + RI \rightarrow R'CO_2R + AgI_{(s)}$$

(*c*) **Physical Properties**
The lower esters are colourless liquids with pleasant 'fruity' odours; for example, 3-methylbutyl ethanoate smells like pear-drops. The lower members of the series are moderately soluble in water but the solubility decreases rapidly with increasing molecular mass; esters are soluble in most organic solvents, however, and are excellent solvents in their own right. They are used as such in industry, and also for the preparation of synthetic perfumes and fruit essences.

Esters boil at considerably lower temperatures than do the isomeric carboxylic acids, owing to their inability to associate by intermolecular hydrogen bonding (see Unit 16.4).

(*d*) **Reactions**
(i) **Hydrolysis.** Esters yield an alcohol (or phenol) and a carboxylic acid on hydrolysis. This is the reverse of the esterification process used for their preparation. The reaction is catalysed by strong mineral acids (sulphuric acid, for instance) or bases (see Unit 12.3(a)).

Isotopes have been used to investigate the position of bond fission in ester hydrolysis. There are two possibilities:

Acyl–oxygen fission

Alkyl–oxygen fission

By hydrolysing the ester in water containing the oxygen-18 isotope it is possible to distinguish between the two mechanisms. In general, the heavier oxygen isotope appears in the acid constituent, indicating that acyl–oxygen fission is preferred:

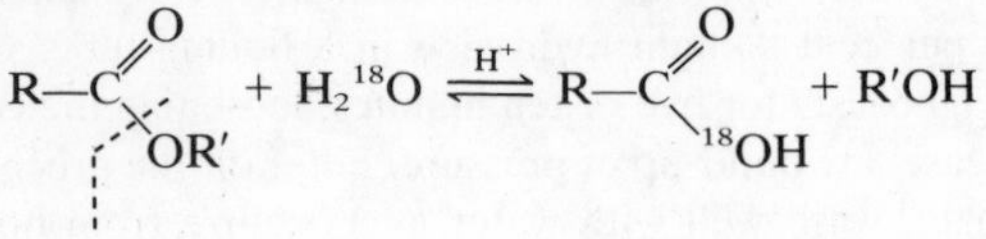

$$R-\overset{\displaystyle O}{\underset{OR'}{C}} + H_2{}^{18}O \rightleftharpoons R-\overset{\displaystyle O}{\underset{{}^{18}OH}{C}} + R'OH$$

The mechanism of the acid-catalysed hydrolysis (or esterification, as both the forward and reverse process in a reversible reaction take place by the same mechanism) is:

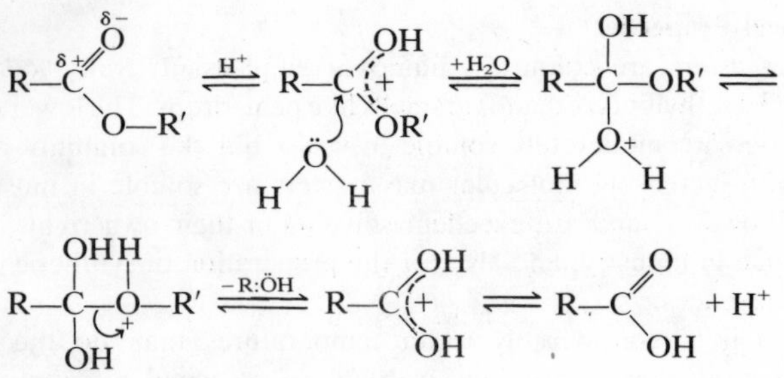

$$R-\overset{\delta-}{\underset{O-R'}{\overset{\delta+}{C}}} \rightleftharpoons^{H^+} R-\overset{OH}{\underset{OR'}{C}}+ \xrightarrow{+H_2O} R-\overset{OH}{\underset{\overset{+}{O}}{C}-OR'} \rightleftharpoons$$

$$R-\overset{OHH}{\underset{OH}{C}-\overset{}{O}-R'} \xrightarrow{-R:\ddot{O}H} R-\overset{OH}{\underset{OH}{C}+} \rightleftharpoons R-\overset{O}{\underset{OH}{C}} + H^+$$

This hydrolysis is described as an $A_{Ac}2$ process—it is acid-catalysed, fission occurs at the acyl carbon atom and the reaction is second-order (bimolecular), that is:

$$\text{Rate} = k[\text{ester}][H^+]$$

The mechanism for the corresponding base-catalysed (or $B_{Ac}2$) hydrolysis is:

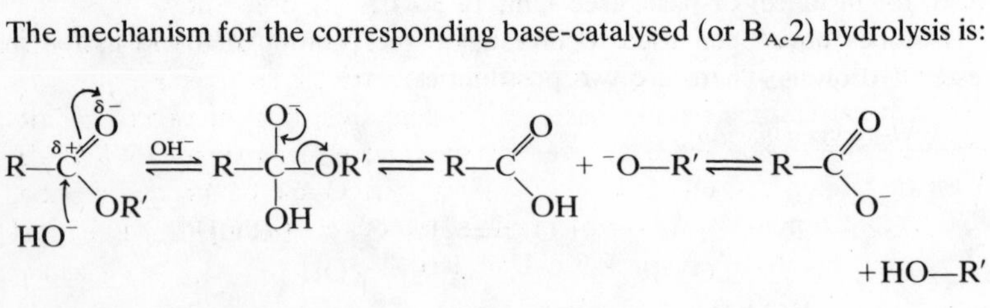

$$R-\overset{\delta-}{\underset{HO^-}{\overset{\delta+}{C}}}\overset{O}{\underset{OR'}{}} \xrightarrow{OH^-} R-\overset{O^-}{\underset{OH}{C}-OR'} \rightleftharpoons R-\overset{O}{\underset{OH}{C}} + {}^-O-R' \rightleftharpoons R-\overset{O}{\underset{O^-}{C}}$$

$$+HO-R'$$

(ii) **Amide formation.** Esters react with 0.880 aqueous ammonia or with primary or secondary amines in aqueous solution to yield amides:

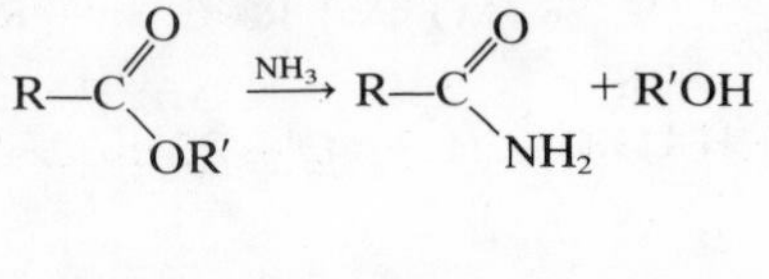

$$R-\overset{O}{\underset{OR'}{C}} \xrightarrow{NH_3} R-\overset{O}{\underset{NH_2}{C}} + R'OH$$

The reaction is catalysed by ammonium salts and proceeds by the expected addition–elimination:

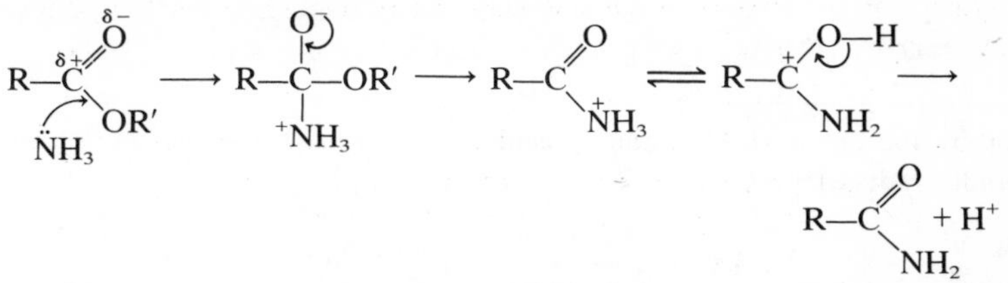

(iii) **Reduction.** Esters are reduced to alcohols—the acid constituent giving rise to a primary alcohol—by catalytic hydrogenation (for instance, at 250° under a pressure of 150 atmospheres using a copper chromate(III) catalyst), by lithium tetrahydridoaluminate(III) reduction or by the Bouveault–Blanc reaction (sodium plus ethanol or butanol—see Unit 12.3(c)).

$$RCO_2R' \xrightarrow{\text{reduction}} RCH_2OH + R'OH$$
$$1° \text{ alcohol}$$

17.6 Acid Anhydrides

(a) General Formula and Nomenclature
The acid anhydrides have the general formula:

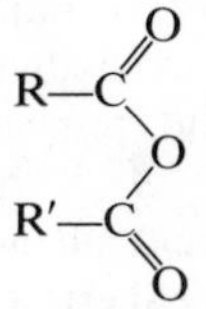

They are described as *simple* or *symmetrical* if R and R' are identical, and as *mixed* or *unsymmetrical* when the two groups are different.

Anhydrides are named as derivatives of the parent acid (or acids) by replacing the word *acid* with *anhydride*; thus $(CH_3CO)_2O$ is *ethanoic* (or *acetic*) *anhydride*. Mixed anhydrides are named by listing the two contributing acids in alphabetical order; for instance, *ethanoic propanoic anhydride*. The first member of the homologous series—methanoic anhydride, $(HCO)_2O$ is unknown, although mixed anhydrides containing the methanoyl group have been synthesized (see Unit 16.6).

(b) Preparation and Manufacture
Anhydrides are prepared by the action of an acyl halide on the sodium salt of a carboxylic acid (see Unit 17.4(d)(iv)).

Ethanoic anhydride is manufactured by passing ethenone (ketene) into glacial ethanoic acid:

$$CH_2{=}C{=}O + CH_3CO_2H \rightarrow (CH_3CO)_2O$$

Ethenone itself is obtained by passing propanone vapour over an alloy of nickel and chromium at about 750°:

$$CH_3COCH_3 \xrightarrow[Ni/Cr]{750-800°} CH_4 + CH_2{=}\overset{\cdot}{C}{=}O$$

or by the pyrolysis of ethanoic acid over a trimethyl phosphate catalyst under reduced pressure:

$$CH_3CO_2H \xrightarrow[(CH_3O)_3PO]{650-700°} CH_2{=}C{=}O + H_2O$$

(c) Physical Properties

The alkanoic acid anhydrides are colourless volatile liquids. They are insoluble in water, although the lower members of the series dissolve slowly in the cold, but more rapidly on warming, as they are hydrolysed to the alkanoic acids. Ethanoic anhydride, b.p. 136.5°, has a sharp, irritating odour and smells of ethanoic acid (vinegar). The aromatic carboxylic anhydrides are colourless, crystalline solids which are sparingly soluble (with hydrolysis) in water.

(d) Reactions

The chemical properties of the acid anhydrides are similar to those of the acyl halides. The reactions proceed via the same nucleophilic addition–elimination mechanism (see Unit 17.2) but the anhydrides are less reactive.

(i) **Hydrolysis.** The anhydrides are hydrolysed slowly by cold water, and rapidly by aqueous alkali, to yield, respectively, the carboxylic acid or the carboxylate anion.

(ii) **Ester formation.** Alcohols and phenols undergo acylation on treatment with an acid anhydride to yield esters (see Units 12.6(d) and 13.6(d)).

(iii) **Amide formation.** Acylation of ammonia with an acid anhydride yields an amide:

$$(RCO)_2O + 2NH_3 \longrightarrow RC\overset{\displaystyle O}{\underset{\displaystyle NH_2}{\big\langle}} + RCO_2^- NH_4^+$$

Primary and secondary amines react similarly to form N-alkyl- and N,N-dialkyl-amides, RCONHR' and RCONR'$_2$, respectively. For example,

$$C_6H_5NH_2 + (CH_3CO)_2O \rightarrow C_6H_5NHCOCH_3 + CH_3CO_2H$$

phenylamine   ethanoic anhydride   N-phenylethanamide

(iv) **Friedel–Crafts reaction.** See Unit 9.6(b)(iv).

(v) **Reduction.** Carboxylic anhydrides are reduced by catalytic hydrogenation or by the action of lithium tetrahydridoaluminate(III) to yield primary alcohols:

$$(RCO)_2O \xrightarrow{reduction} 2RCH_2OH + H_2O$$

(e) **Uses**

The principal industrial application of ethanoic anhydride is the preparation of ethanoate esters, such as poly(ethenyl ethanoate) (see Unit 7.6(j)) and cellulose ethanoate (see Unit 20.8(b)(ii)), in the plastics industry. Benzene-1,2-dicarboxylic anhydride is used in the manufacture of glyptal resins (see Unit 21.6(b)).

17.7 Amides

(a) **General Formula and Nomenclature**

The amides have the general formula:

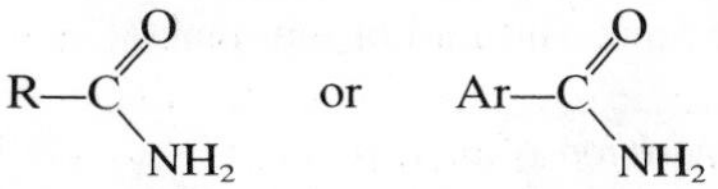

$$R-\overset{\displaystyle O}{\underset{\displaystyle NH_2}{C}} \qquad \text{or} \qquad Ar-\overset{\displaystyle O}{\underset{\displaystyle NH_2}{C}}$$

The hydrogen atoms of the amino-group can be substituted by alkyl (or aryl) groups to yield N-alkyl- and N,N-dialkyl-amides, RCONHR' and RCONR'$_2$, respectively.

The amides are named by adding the suffix -amide to the stem of the corresponding hydrocarbon or acid name, as in ethanamide (acetamide), CH_3CONH_2, and benzamide, $C_6H_5CONH_2$.

(b) **Preparation**

(i) **From ammonium salts.** The ammonium salts of carboxylic acids undergo dehydration on heating to yield amides; for instance:

$$CH_3CO_2^-NH_4^+ \xrightarrow[\text{heat}]{-H_2O} CH_3CONH_2$$

$$\text{ammonium ethanoate} \qquad\qquad \text{ethanamide}$$

The reaction is carried out in the presence of an excess of the free carboxylic acid so as to offset the dissociation that occurs when any ammonium salt is heated:

$$RCO_2^-NH_4^+ \overset{\text{heat}}{\rightleftharpoons} RCO_2H + NH_3$$

(ii) **From carboxylic acids.** Amides are formed in high yield by heating carboxylic acids with carbamide (urea):

$$RCO_2H + CO(NH_2)_2 \rightarrow RCONH_2 + CO_2 + NH_3$$

(iii) **From acyl halides, esters or anhydrides** (see Units 17.4(d)(iii), 17.5(d)(ii) and 17.6(d)(iii)). For example, a white precipitate of ethanediamide (oxamide) is obtained when diethyl ethanedioate (ethyl oxalate) is shaken with an excess of 0.880 aqueous ammonia.

$$\begin{matrix} CO_2C_2H_5 \\ | \\ CO_2C_2H_5 \end{matrix} + 2NH_3 \longrightarrow \begin{matrix} CONH_2 \\ | \\ CONH_2 \end{matrix} + 2C_2H_5OH$$

Similarly, white flakes of benzamide (m.p. 130°) separate when a concentrated aqueous solution of ammonia is treated with benzoyl chloride:

$$C_6H_5COCl + 2NH_3 \xrightarrow[\text{shake}]{\text{excess of aq. } NH_3} C_6H_5CONH_2 + NH_4Cl$$

Ethanediamide and benzamide are conveniently prepared by these methods as they are virtually insoluble in water; the freely soluble lower amides are usually obtained by the decomposition of the ammonium salt (method (i) above). N-Substituted amides may be prepared by this method, using a primary or secondary amine instead of ammonia.

Experiment 17.2 *Preparation of benzamide*
Add 1 cm³ of benzoyl chloride to 5 cm³ of 0.880 aqueous ammonia in a boiling-tube. Cork the tube securely and shake vigorously for five or ten minutes. **Care:** considerable amounts of heat are evolved during the reaction, so the cork must be loosened from time to time to release the pressure. Filter off the fine flakes of benzamide, wash them well with cold water and then recrystallize from boiling water. Determine the melting-point of the purified product.

(c) Physical Properties
Methanamide (m.p. 2.5°) is a liquid at room temperature, but the remaining amides are colourless crystalline solids whose solubility in water, with which they form hydrogen bonds, decreases with increasing molecular mass. Intermolecular hydrogen bonding also accounts for the high melting-points of amides as compared with those of other carboxylic acid derivatives (see Unit 17.3).

(d) Reactions
(i) **Hydrolysis.** Amides are slowly hydrolysed by refluxing with aqueous solutions of mineral acids or alkalis:

$$RCONH_2 + H_2O + H^+ \xrightarrow{\text{boil}} RCO_2H + NH_4^+$$

$$RCONH_2 + NaOH_{(aq)} \xrightarrow{\text{boil}} RCO_2^-Na^+ + NH_3$$

(ii) **Dehydration.** Amides are dehydrated by heating with phosphorus(v) oxide to yield nitriles:

$$R-C\underset{NH_2}{\overset{O}{<}} \xrightarrow[-H_2O]{P_2O_5} R-C\equiv N$$

Some dehydration and nitrile formation occurs when the amides of the higher alkanoic acids are heated to a high temperature:

$$2RCONH_2 \xrightarrow{\text{heat}} RCN + RCO_2H + NH_3$$

The yield of nitrile is almost quantitative when this dehydration is carried out in the presence of an excess of ammonia (*cf.* the preparation of amides; see Unit 17.7(*b*)(i)):

$$RCO_2H + NH_3 \rightarrow RCO_2^-NH_4^+ \xrightarrow[-H_2O]{\text{heat}} RCONH_2 \xrightarrow[-H_2O]{\text{heat}} RCN$$

(iii) **Reduction.** Amides are reduced catalytically or by dissolving metals (such as sodium in ethanol) or by lithium tetrahydridoaluminate(III) to primary amines (see Unit 18.2(*b*)):

$$RCONH_2 \xrightarrow{\text{reduction}} RCH_2NH_2$$

(iv) **Action of nitrous acid.** Amides, like other compounds containing a free primary amino-group (see Unit 18.5(g)), react with nitrous acid, liberating nitrogen:

$$RCONH_2 + \text{'}HNO_2\text{'} \rightarrow RCO_2H + H_2O + N_2$$

(v) **Hofmann degradation.** Treatment of an amide with bromine (or chlorine) in the presence of alkali yields a primary amine that contains one less carbon atom in its molecule than the starting material:

$$RCONH_2 + Br_2 + 4KOH \rightarrow RNH_2 + 2KBr + K_2CO_3 + 2H_2O$$
$$1° \text{ amine}$$

The reaction proceeds via substitution, rearrangement and elimination:

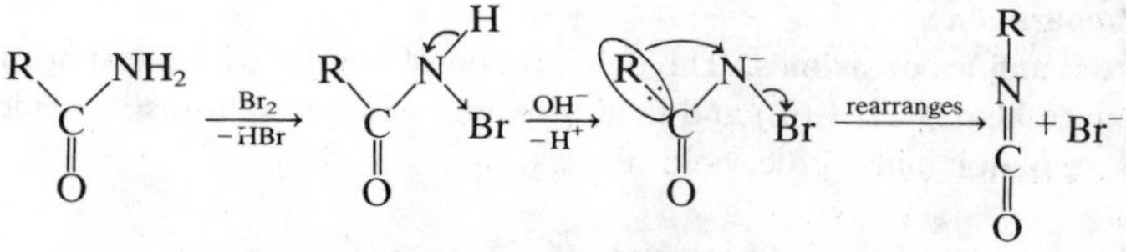

$$R-N{=}C{=}O \xrightarrow{2OH^-} RNH_2 + CO_3^{2-}$$

The various intermediates in this reaction have been isolated.

Experiment 17.3 *To demonstrate the reactions of amides*

1. *Solubility.* Add water to a few crystals of ethanamide in a test-tube. Note whether the amide is soluble and test the mixture with litmus or with Universal indicator paper.

2. *Hydrolysis.* Add about 5 cm³ of aqueous sodium hydroxide to some crystals of ethanamide in a test-tube and warm. Identify the gas evolved by

its smell and action on moist red litmus paper. This test may be used to distinguish ammonium salts, such as ammonium ethanoate, from amides; ammonium salts liberate ammonia when treated with aqueous sodium hydroxide *without* warming.

3. *Hofmann's degradation reaction.* Add 4 drops of bromine (**Care!**) and about 2 cm^3 of aqueous sodium hydroxide to about 0.1 g of ethanamide in a test-tube. Shake the mixture gently for a minute or so and then boil with about 5 cm^3 of sodium hydroxide solution. Test the gas evolved by its smell and its action on moist red litmus paper.

4. *Action of nitrous acid.* Add 1 cm^3 of dilute hydrochloric acid to 1 cm^3 of a concentrated aqueous solution of sodium nitrite in a test-tube cooled in a beaker containing ice and water. When any initial reaction has finished add a cold solution of ethanamide and note the immediate effervescence. What is the gas that is evolved?

17.8 Nitriles

(a) General Formula and Nomenclature
The nitriles have the general formula:

$$R—C\equiv N \quad \text{or} \quad Ar—C\equiv N$$

Their names are derived from those of the corresponding carboxylic acids: thus CH_3CN and C_6H_5CN, derived from ethanoic and benzoic acids respectively, are known as *ethanonitrile* and *benzonitrile*, though the trivial names for the former—acetonitrile (from acetic acid) and methyl cyanide—are still sometimes used, especially in industry.

The nitriles are isomeric with the isocyano-compounds; for instance, $CH_3C\equiv N$ (ethanonitrile) and $CH_3N\equiv C$ (isocyanomethane) are isomers.

(b) Preparation
(i) **From amides or oximes.** The dehydration of amides with phosphorus(v) oxide (see Unit 17.7(d)(ii)) and that of oximes with phosphorus(v) oxide or, better, ethanoic anhydride yield nitriles:

$$RCONH_2 \xrightarrow[-H_2O]{P_2O_5} RCN$$

$$RCH=NOH \xrightarrow[-H_2O]{(CH_3CO)_2O} RCN$$

(ii) **From iodoalkanes.** Nitriles can be prepared by the action of aqueous ethanolic potassium cyanide on iodoalkanes (see Unit 10.6(a)(iii)). Some isocyano-compound is also formed in this reaction, but this may be removed by shaking the product with dilute hydrochloric acid:

$$RNC + 3H_2O \xrightarrow{HCl} R\overset{+}{N}H_3Cl^- + HCO_2H$$

as the nitrile is not hydrolysed under these mild conditions. If silver cyanide is used in place of potassium cyanide, the isocyano-compound is the major product:

$$R\text{—}I + AgNC \rightarrow RNC + AgI$$

Isocyano-compounds may also be prepared by the *Hofmann isocyano-reaction*:

$$RNH_2 + CHCl_3 + 3KOH \xrightarrow[\text{ethanol}]{\text{warm}} RNC + 3KCl + 3H_2O$$

1° amine   isocyano-compound

(iii) **Aromatic nitriles** may be prepared from diazonium salts (see Unit 18.6(*c*)(ii)) or by fusing the sodium salt of an aromatic sulphonic acid with sodium cyanide:

$$C_6H_5SO_3{}^-Na^+ + NaCN \xrightarrow{\text{fuse}} C_6H_5CN + Na_2SO_3$$

(iv) **Propenonitrile** (acrylonitrile) may be prepared from ethyne, but it is now manufactured on the industrial scale from propene:

$$2CH_3CH{=}CH_2 + 2NH_3 + 3O_2 \xrightarrow[450°]{\text{Mo-based catalyst}} 2CH_2{=}CHCN + 6H_2O$$

The compound is used to prepare *polypropenonitrile* (polyacrylonitrile or Orlon) for man-made 'acrylic' fibres

$$\left[\begin{array}{c} CH_2\text{—}CH \\ | \\ CN \end{array} \right]_n$$

(*cf.* Unit 7.6(*j*)) and it forms a copolymer with buta-1,3-diene, *Buna-N synthetic rubber* (see Unit 21.8(*b*)).

(*c*) Properties

The nitriles are stable, neutral substances which generally have a pleasant smell (unlike the isocyano-compounds). Only the lower members of the aliphatic series dissolve in water but they are all readily soluble in organic solvents. The isocyano-compounds are virtually insoluble in water.

(*d*) Reactions

(i) **Hydrolysis.** Nitriles are hydrolysed by acids or alkalis via the intermediate formation of the amide to yield the corresponding carboxylic acid or its salt:

$$RCN + 2H_2O \xrightarrow[\text{boil}]{H^+} RCO_2H + NH_4{}^+$$

$$RCN + NaOH + H_2O \xrightarrow{\text{boil}} RCO_2{}^-Na^+ + NH_3$$

Isocyano-compounds are hydrolysed by dilute acid to give a primary amine and methanoic acid; for example:

$$CH_3NC + 2H_2O + HCl \rightarrow CH_3NH_3^+Cl^- + HCO_2H$$

but they are not hydrolysed by alkalis.

(ii) **Reduction.** Nitriles are reduced by sodium and ethanol (the *Mendius reduction*) or by lithium tetrahydridoaluminate(III) to primary amines; for instance:

$$CH_3CN \rightarrow CH_3CH_2NH_2$$

This reduction may also be carried out by catalytic hydrogenation. Isocyano-compounds yield secondary amines on reduction:

$$R—N{\equiv}C \xrightarrow{\text{reduction}} RNHCH_3$$

which confirms that the alkyl (or aryl) group in an isocyano-compound is attached to the nitrogen atom of the cyano-group.

Nitriles are reduced to aldehydes by the action of tin(II) chloride and hydrochloric acid (the *Stephen reaction*):

$$RC{\equiv}N \xrightarrow{\text{HCl}} [RC{\equiv}NH]^+Cl^- \xrightarrow[\text{SnCl}_2/\text{HCl}]{\text{e/H}^+} [RCH{=}NH_2]_2SnCl_6 \xrightarrow{\text{H}_2\text{O}} RCHO$$

This reaction may also be carried out by treating the nitrile with the calculated amount of lithium tetrahydridoaluminate(III):

$$4RCN \xrightarrow{\text{LiAlH}_4} [(RCH{=}N—)_4Al]^-Li^+ \xrightarrow{\text{H}_2\text{O}} 4RCHO$$

17.9 Soaps and Detergents

(a) Soap

Soap is manufactured by the alkaline hydrolysis of naturally occurring fats and oils. These substances are called *lipids* and are mostly esters of the trihydric alcohol propane-1,2,3-triol (glycerol), $CH_2OHCHOHCH_2OH$, with long-chain alkanoic acids. The acids in these esters usually contain an even number of carbon atoms; for example, palm oil is an ester of hexadecanoic (palmitic) acid, $CH_3(CH_2)_{14}CO_2H$, and many animal fats contain octadecanoic (stearic) acid, $CH_3(CH_2)_{16}CO_2H$. Octadec-9-enoic (oleic) acid is present in olive oil; as its name indicates it is an unsaturated acid:

$$CH_3(CH_2)_7CH{=}CH(CH_2)_7CO_2H$$

The hydrolysis

$$\text{fat or oil} + NaOH_{(aq)} \rightarrow \text{soap} + \text{propane-1,2,3-triol}$$

produces a homogeneous solution from which soap is precipitated by the addition of concentrated aqueous sodium chloride. This process is known as the *salting-out of soap*. The curds of soap are separated from the lower aqueous layer which consists of a solution of propane-1,2,3-triol and sodium chloride.

Hard soap consists mainly of the sodium salts $C_{15}H_{31}CO_2Na$ and $C_{17}H_{35}CO_2Na$. Soft soap and toilet soap are more soluble and consist mainly of the potassium salts, such as $C_{17}H_{35}CO_2K$, and some added triol. Soap powders for laundry purposes are made by adding sodium carbonate-10-water to powdered soap. (For a description of the action of soaps and detergents, see Unit 1.3(*b*).)

(*b*) Detergents

One disadvantage of soap is that in hard water it forms a scum or precipitate of the calcium or magnesium salt of the long-chain alkanoic acid. This problem is avoided in synthetic detergents by replacing the carboxylate group as the hydrophilic component of the molecule by a sulphonate, $-SO_2O^-Na^+$, or sulphate, $-OSO_2O^-Na^+$, group; the corresponding calcium or magnesium salts of these compounds are soluble in water, so no scum is produced. Detergents are of two types: *anionic* and *non-ionic* detergents.

(i) **Anionic detergents.** Anionic detergents are alkylbenzenesulphonates or alkyl sulphates in which the alkyl group contains from 10 to 14 carbon atoms. In the detergents that were first marketed, the alkyl group consisted of a branched chain synthesized from a polypropene; for instance:

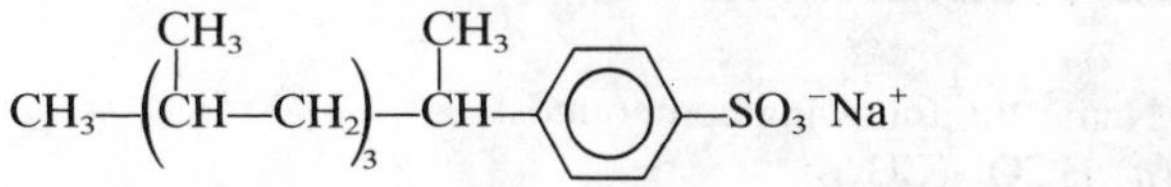

These detergents could not be degraded by bacteria, however, and therefore gave rise to obstinate pollution of rivers, lakes and other water supplies. *Biodegradable* detergents, such as Omo, Tide and Surf, contain unbranched or singly branched hydrocarbon chains and are synthesized from the long-chain alkanes obtained from the cracking of waxes (see Units 6.3 and 6.6) or from the polymerization of ethene in the presence of triethylaluminium (Ziegler process):

$$Al(C_2H_5)_3 + nC_2H_4 \rightarrow Al[(CH_2CH_2)_nC_2H_5]_3$$

$$\xrightarrow[\text{pressure}]{300°} Al(C_2H_5)_3 + 3RCH{=}CH_2$$

where R is an alkyl group containing between 8 and 12 carbon atoms.

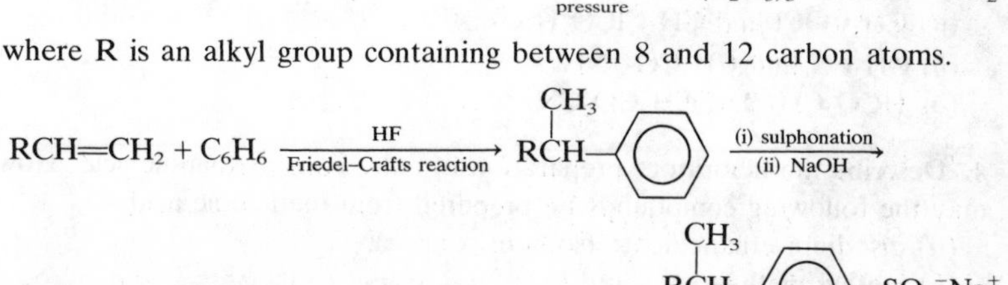

Alkyl sulphates are made from unbranched-chain C_{10}–C_{14} alcohols:

$$RCH_2OH \xrightarrow{H_2SO_4} RCH_2OSO_2OH \xrightarrow{NaOH} RCH_2OSO_2O^-Na^+$$

(ii) **Non-ionic detergents.** In non-ionic detergents, such as the ethoxylates, the hydrophilic part of the molecule consists of a number of ether groups which are able to form hydrogen bonds with water. Ethoxylates are manufactured by the action of epoxyethane on long-chain alcohols; for instance:

$$CH_3(CH_2)_8CH_2OH + nCH_2{-}CH_2 \longrightarrow CH_3(CH_2)_8CH_2(OCH_2CH_2)_n OH$$
$$\underset{O}{}$$

Detergent formulations for domestic use contain a number of additives. These include inorganic phosphates to remove calcium ions, bleaching agents such as sodium peroxoborate, and complex organic compounds (known as *fluorescers*) which absorb light in the ultra-violet region and re-emit it in the blue end of the visible spectrum, thus making yellowish clothes appear white.

Test Yourself on Unit 17

1. Name the following compounds:
   (a) $HCON(CH_3)_2$;
   (b) $HCO_2CH(CH_3)_2$;
   (c) $C_6H_5CH_2COCl$;
   (d) $CH_3COOCOC_2H_5$;
   (e) $(CH_3)_3CCN$.

2. Outline the laboratory preparation of ethyl ethanoate. How and under what conditions does ethyl ethanoate react with (a) water, (b) ammonia, (c) hydrogen and (d) ethylmagnesium bromide?

3. Suggest one test in each case to distinguish between the following pairs of compounds:
   (a) CH_3COCl and CH_2ClCO_2H;
   (b) CH_3CN and $CH_3CO_2^-NH_4^+$;
   (c) HCO_2CH_3 and $CH_3CO_2CH_3$.

4. Describe the laboratory preparation of anhydrous methanoic acid. How may the following compounds be prepared from methanoic acid:
   (a) disodium ethanedioate (sodium oxalate),
   (b) methyl methanoate,
   (c) methanamide?

Assertion–reason questions

In Questions 5 to 13, select A if both assertion and reason are true statements and the reason is a correct explanation of the assertion;

B if both assertion and reason are true statements but the reason is not a true explanation of the assertion;

C if the assertion is true, but the reason is a false statement;

D if the assertion is false, but the reason is a true statement;

E if both the assertion and the reason are false statements.

5. Methanoic acid will reduce ammoniacal silver nitrate while ethanoic acid will not, *because* methanoic acid is a considerably stronger acid than ethanoic acid.

6. Anhydrous methanoic acid cannot be obtained by distillation of its aqueous solution, *because* the boiling-point of methanoic acid is the same as that of water.

7. Anhydrous ethanol cannot be obtained by fractional distillation of the products of the hydrolysis of ethyl ethanoate with aqueous sodium hydroxide, *because* the boiling-point of pure ethanol is approximately the same as that of water.

8. A solution of ethanoic acid in benzene gives virtually twice the expected freezing-point depression, *because* the nearly complete ionization of the acid almost doubles the number of particles present.

9. A little concentrated acid is added to the reaction mixture in the hydrolysis of ethyl ethanoate, *because* the reaction is reversible.

10. Ethanamide is hydrolysed by dilute hydrochloric acid more rapidly than ethanoyl chloride, *because* the —NH$_2$ group in ethanamide shows some basic properties.

11. Chloroethanoic acid is a stronger acid than ethanoic acid, *because* the inductive effect of the chlorine atom facilitates the loss of the proton from the carboxyl group.

12. Ester hydrolysis in H$_2$^{18}O generally yields an alcohol containing the ^{18}O isotope, *because* most esters hydrolyse with fission of the acyl–oxygen bond.

13. The boiling-point of an ethyl ester is lower than that of the corresponding carboxylic acid *because* ester molecules cannot associate via intermolecular hydrogen bonding.

14. A compound P, C$_5$H$_{10}$O$_2$, yields two compounds, Q and R, on hydrolysis. Q effervesces with sodium carbonate solution while R does not. When the product of the reaction of R with sodium bromide and sulphuric acid was treated with silver cyanide, two compounds of formula C$_3$H$_5$N, S

and *T*, were obtained. On hydrolysis *S* forms *Q*.
  (*a*) State whether the compound *P* is:
      A: butyl methanoate;
      B: propyl ethanoate;
      C: 1-methylethyl ethanoate;
      D: methyl butanoate;
      E: ethyl propanoate.
  (*b*) State whether, on hydrolysis, *T* forms:
      A: methanoic acid and ethylamine;
      B: methanoic acid and dimethylamine;
      C: ethanoic acid, carbon dioxide and ammonia;
      D: propanoic acid and ammonia;
      E: ethanoic acid and methylamine.

15. Starting with ethanoic acid as the only organic compound, outline the preparation of (*a*) ethanamide, (*b*) ethanoic anhydride, (*c*) ethylamine (aminoethane), (*d*) ethane and (*e*) methane.

16. Discuss the mechanisms of the following reactions:
  (*a*) the hydrolysis of methyl ethanoate,
  (*b*) the formation of methyl ethanoate by the esterification of methanol, and
  (*c*) the formation of methylamine from ethanamide.

17. Compare and contrast the structure, reactivity and general reactions of esters, amides, acyl halides and carboxylic anhydrides.

18. Write an essay on soaps and detergents.

Amines

18.1 General Formula and Nomenclature

Amines may be regarded as derivatives of ammonia in which one or more of the hydrogen atoms in the ammonia molecule have been replaced by alkyl or aryl groups. They are classified as *primary*, *secondary* or *tertiary* amines, depending on whether one, two or three hydrogen atoms have been replaced. The general formulae of the three classes of amines are thus:

Class	Functional group	Aliphatic amine	Aromatic amine
1°	$-NH_2$	RNH_2	$ArNH_2$
2°	$\diagdown NH \diagup$	R_2NH or $R-NH-R'$	Ar_2NH or $Ar-NH-R$
3°	$\diagdown N \diagup$	R_3N or $R-N(R')(R'')$	Ar_3N or $ArNR_2$ or Ar_2NR

The names of the simple aliphatic or aromatic amines are formed by adding the suffix *-amine* to the name of the corresponding alkyl or aryl group or groups, thus:

CH_3NH_2 $(C_2H_5)_2NH$ $(CH_3)_3N$ $C_6H_5NH_2$ $CH_3NHC_2H_5$

methylamine   diethylamine   trimethylamine   phenylamine   ethylmethylamine

More complex substances are named by adding the suffix *amino-* to the name of the parent compound, thus:

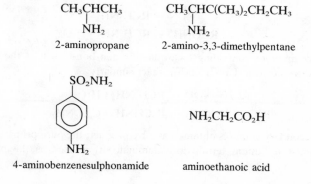

$$CH_3\underset{\underset{NH_2}{|}}{C}HCH_3$$

2-aminopropane

$$CH_3\underset{\underset{NH_2}{|}}{C}HC(CH_3)_2CH_2CH_3$$

2-amino-3,3-dimethylpentane

4-aminobenzenesulphonamide

$NH_2CH_2CO_2H$

aminoethanoic acid

18.2 Preparation of Amines

(a) From Nitro-compounds
Nitro-compounds yield primary amines on reduction:

$$R-N{\overset{O}{\underset{O}{\diagup}}} \xrightarrow{\text{reduction}} R-NH_2$$

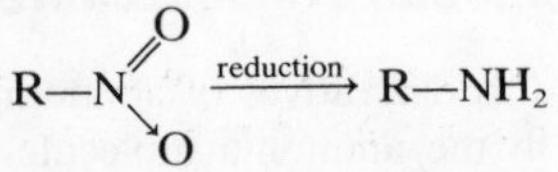

Nitroalkanes are reduced by hydrogen in the presence of Raney nickel or with lithium tetrahydridoaluminate(III) or a dissolving metal such as tin in hydrochloric acid.

Primary aromatic amines are prepared in the laboratory by reducing the corresponding nitro-compound with granulated tin and hydrochloric acid. The amine is a base and is therefore obtained in acid solution as a salt, from which it is liberated by the action of sodium hydroxide. The reaction sequence for the reduction of nitrobenzene to phenylamine is:

$$Sn \xrightarrow{H^+} Sn^{2+} + 2e$$

$$Sn^{2+} \longrightarrow Sn^{4+} + 2e$$

$$2C_6H_5NO_2 \xrightarrow{Sn/HCl} [C_6H_5NH_3]_2SnCl_6$$

The phenylamine–hexachlorostannate(IV) complex is decomposed by the addition of alkali:

$$(C_6H_5NH_3)_2SnCl_6 + 8NaOH \rightarrow 2C_6H_5NH_2 + Na_2SnO_3 + 6NaCl + 5H_2O$$

and the liberated phenylamine is separated from the reaction mixture by either steam-distillation (see Unit 2.1(b)) or ether extraction (see Unit 2.4). Iron filings and aqueous hydrochloric acid are used as the reducing agent in industry.

(b) From Nitriles or Amides
Nitriles and amides yield primary amines on reduction by dissolving metals (such as sodium in ethanol) or catalytic hydrogenation:

$$RCN \rightarrow RCH_2NH_2$$

$$RCONH_2 \rightarrow RCH_2NH_2 + H_2O$$

Other compounds containing a carbon–nitrogen bond, such as the oximes and hydrazones (see Unit 15.6(b)), react similarly:

$$RCH{=}NOH \rightarrow RCH_2NH_2 + H_2O$$

$$R_2C{=}NNHC_6H_5 \rightarrow R_2CHNH_2 + C_6H_5NH_2$$

Some secondary amine is obtained as a by-product; the pure primary amine is obtained if lithium tetrahydridoaluminate(III) is used as the reducing agent.

The reduction of isocyano-compounds yields secondary amines containing a methyl group:

$$RNC \xrightarrow{\text{reduction}} RNHCH_3$$

(c) From Halogenoalkanes

The reaction of primary halogenoalkanes with ammonia (*Hofmann's ammonolysis reaction*) yields a mixture of the primary, secondary and tertiary amines (in the form of their salts) as well as the quaternary salt or tetra-alkylammonium halide (see Unit 10.6(*a*)(iv)).

2-Bromopropane is the only secondary halogenoalkane to form an amine by this method; the other secondary and the tertiary halogenoalkanes yield alkenes on heating with ammonia by elimination of hydrogen halide; for example:

$$(CH_3)_3CBr + NH_3 \rightarrow (CH_3)_2C{=}CH_2 + NH_4Br$$
$$\text{2-methylpropene}$$

Aromatic amines cannot in general be prepared by this method as the halogen atom in halogenoarenes is too firmly bound to the aromatic nucleus to react with ammonia under normal conditions. Secondary and tertiary alkylphenylamines may, however, be prepared by the reaction between phenylamine and a halogenoalkane; for instance:

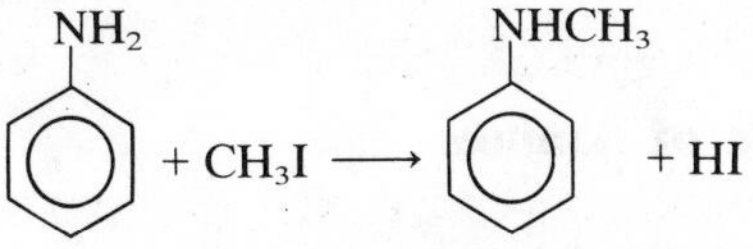

N-methylphenylamine

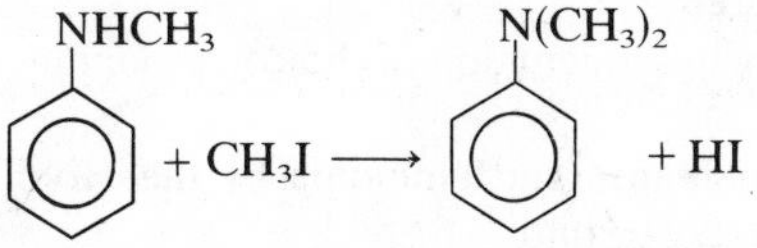

N,N-dimethylphenylamine

Phenylamine may be synthesized by the ammonolysis of chlorobenzene in the presence of copper(I) oxide:

$$2C_6H_5Cl + 2NH_{3(aq)} + Cu_2O \rightarrow 2C_6H_5NH_2 + 2CuCl + H_2O$$

(d) From Alcohols

A mixture of primary, secondary and tertiary amines is obtained when an alcohol is heated with ammonia under pressure in the presence of a copper chromate(III), cobalt or alumina catalyst:

$$ROH + NH_3 \rightarrow RNH_2 + H_2O$$
$$ROH + RNH_2 \rightarrow R_2NH + H_2O$$
$$ROH + R_2NH \rightarrow R_3N + H_2O$$

This reaction and the Hofmann amine synthesis ((c) above) are called *ammonolysis* reactions as they both involve fission of covalent bonds (carbon–oxygen and carbon–nitrogen respectively) by the action of ammonia; for example:

$$C_2H_5Br + NH_3 \rightarrow C_2H_5NH_2 + HBr$$
$$C_2H_5OH + NH_3 \rightarrow C_2H_5NH_2 + H_2O$$

These may be compared with *hydrolysis* reactions, in which a covalent bond is broken by the action of water, as in

$$C_2H_5Br + H_2O \rightarrow C_2H_5OH + HBr$$

Aromatic amines cannot be prepared by the action of ammonia on phenols. However, the secondary and tertiary amines *N*-methyl- and *N,N*-dimethyl-phenylamine are obtained commercially by heating phenylamine with methanol and sulphuric acid at 230°:

$$C_6H_5NH_2 + CH_3OH \xrightarrow[230°]{H_2SO_4} C_6H_5NHCH_3 + H_2O$$
$$C_6H_5NH_2 + CH_3OH \longrightarrow C_6H_5N(CH_3)_2 + H_2O$$

(e) Hofmann Degradation of Amides
See Unit 17.7(d)(v)).

18.3 Manufacture of Amines

(a) Aliphatic Amines
These are manufactured:

(i) by the catalytic hydrogenation of the corresponding nitro-compounds (see Unit 18.2(a));

(ii) from halogenoalkanes and ammonia by the Hofmann ammonolysis reaction (see Unit 18.2(c)); and

(iii) by the action of ammonia on alcohols under pressure in the presence of a catalyst; for instance:

$$CH_3OH + NH_3 \xrightarrow{Al_2O_3/high\ pressure} CH_3NH_2 + H_2O$$

(b) Aromatic Amines
Phenylamine is manufactured by the reduction of nitrobenzene with iron and hydrochloric acid or by hydrogenation using a nickel catalyst (see Unit 18.2(a)).

18.4 Physical Properties of Amines

The lower alkylamines are gases with an ammoniacal, 'fishy' odour. They dissolve in organic solvents and the lower members are very soluble in water owing to their ability to form hydrogen bonds. This solubility in water decreases with increasing molecular mass.

The aromatic amines, such as phenylamine and N-methylphenylamine, are colourless liquids when freshly distilled, but gradually darken on exposure to air as they are sensitive to oxidation. Phenylamine is slightly soluble in water (about 3 per cent) and is steam-volatile. It dissolves readily in aqueous acids and organic solvents. Phenylamine has a characteristic unpleasant odour and its vapour is poisonous.

18.5 Chemical Properties of Amines

(a) Basic Properties

Amines are basic compounds because the unshared pair of electrons on the nitrogen atom are able to form a co-ordinate bond with a proton:

$$RN\begin{matrix} H \\ \\ H \end{matrix} + H_2O \rightleftharpoons \left[\begin{matrix} H \\ | \\ R-N-H \\ | \\ H \end{matrix} \right]^+ + OH^-$$

base
(proton acceptor)   conjugate acid

The position of equilibrium in this reaction (and hence the basic strength of the amine) is determined by the availability of this unshared pair of electrons for co-ordination and by the stability of the conjugate acid ion. It is represented by K_b, the basic dissociation constant, or pK_b, where $pK_b = -\log K_b$ (see Unit 4.8). The values of K_b and pK_b for a number of amines are listed in Table 18.1.

The availability of the unshared pair of electrons on the nitrogen atom is increased by the inductive effect (+I) of an alkyl group; thus methylamine

$$CH_3 \rightarrow \ddot{N}H_2 \qquad K_b = 4.4 \times 10^{-4}$$

is a stronger base than ammonia ($K_b = 1.8 \times 10^{-5}$). The introduction of a

Table 18.1 Dissociation constants of amines

Name	K_b	pK_b
Ammonia	1.8×10^{-5}	4.74
Methylamine	4.4×10^{-4}	3.36
Ethylamine	5.4×10^{-4}	3.28
Dimethylamine	5.9×10^{-4}	3.23
1-Aminopropane	6.9×10^{-4}	3.16
Trimethylamine	6.3×10^{-5}	4.20
Phenylamine	4.2×10^{-10}	9.38
Phenylmethylamine	2.2×10^{-5}	4.66
N-Methylphenylamine	7.09×10^{-10}	9.15

second alkyl group into the molecule further increases the basic strength:

$$\begin{array}{c} CH_3 \\ \diagdown \\ NH \qquad K_b = 5.9 \times 10^{-4} \\ \diagup \\ CH_3 \end{array}$$

It might be expected that the tertiary amine would be an even stronger base owing to the inductive effect of the third methyl group. This is not the case, however; K_b for trimethylamine is 6.3×10^{-5}. This decrease in basic strength is explained by the lower hydration stabilization of the trialkyl-ammonium ion, which has only one hydrogen atom available for hydrogen bonding in aqueous solution, compared with that of the corresponding conjugate acid cation of the secondary amine which has two. This decrease in solvation more than counteracts the increase in electron availability on the nitrogen atom resulting from the inductive effect of the third alkyl group. Hydration stabilizes the conjugate acid cation of the base by spreading the charge over a first and—to a far lesser extent—a second solvation 'shell'. Support for this is provided by the fact that in solution in chlorobenzene, where no hydrogen bonding is possible, the basic strength does increase in the order $NH_3 < RNH_2 < R_2NH < R_3N$.

Phenylamine and the other aromatic amines are considerably less basic than ammonia owing to the interaction of the unbonded pair of electrons on the nitrogen atom with the π orbital of the ring (see Fig. 18.1). This partial delocalization reduces their availability for conjugation with a proton. (Phenylmethyl)amine, $C_6H_5CH_2NH_2$, $K_b = 2.2 \times 10^{-5}$, has a basic strength similar to that of the alkylamines. The compound contains a benzene ring but delocalization of the unbonded electron pair on the nitrogen atom is not possible as the p orbital of the nitrogen atom is separated from the π orbital of the aromatic nucleus by a —CH_2 group.

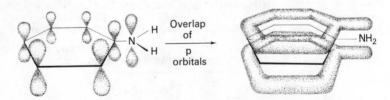

Fig. 18.1   Structure of phenylamine

Substitution by alkyl groups of the hydrogen atoms in the amino-group of phenylamine produces the expected increase in basic strength (cf. $C_6H_5NH_2$, $K_b = 4.2 \times 10^{-10}$, and $C_6H_5NHCH_3$, $K_b = 7.09 \times 10^{-10}$). The presence in the ring of electron-withdrawing groups, such as halogen atoms or nitro-groups, decreases the basic strength.

The loss of the basicity of the nitrogen atom in amides, imides and sulphonamides is a result of the electron-withdrawing effect of the carbonyl or sulphonyl groups:

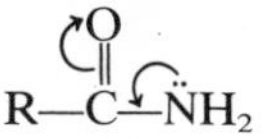

R—C(=O)—NH₂   *amides* are neutral or slightly acidic.

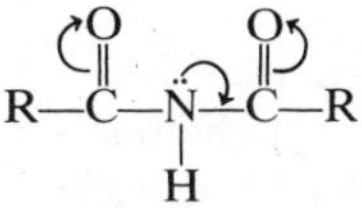

R—C(=O)—N(H)—C(=O)—R   the *imide* hydrogen atom is acidic and can be replaced by alkali metals to form salts.

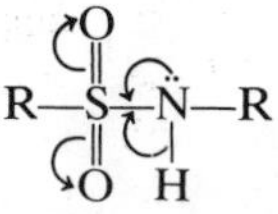

R—S(=O)(=O)—N(H)—R   *sulphonamides* can form water-soluble alkali-metal salts.

(b) Salt Formation

Amines dissolve in aqueous solutions of mineral acids to form salts containing an alkyl- or aryl-substituted ammonium ion; for instance:

$$(C_2H_5)_2NH + HCl \rightarrow \quad (C_2H_5)_2\overset{+}{N}H_2Cl^-$$

diethylamine   diethylammonium chloride
                      (diethylamine hydrochloride)

$$C_6H_5NH_2 + HCl \rightarrow \quad C_6H_5\overset{+}{N}H_3Cl^-$$

phenylamine   phenylamine hydrochloride

These compounds may be isolated as crystalline solids. The salts of aromatic amines are strongly hydrolysed in aqueous solution (especially those of secondary aromatic amines such as diphenylamine, $(C_6H_5)_2NH$) and effervesce with sodium carbonate solution. Triphenylamine, however, is too weak a base to form salts with acids.

Phenylamine hydrogen sulphate is used to manufacture 4-amino-benzenesulphonic acid (sulphanilic acid) by the 'baking process':

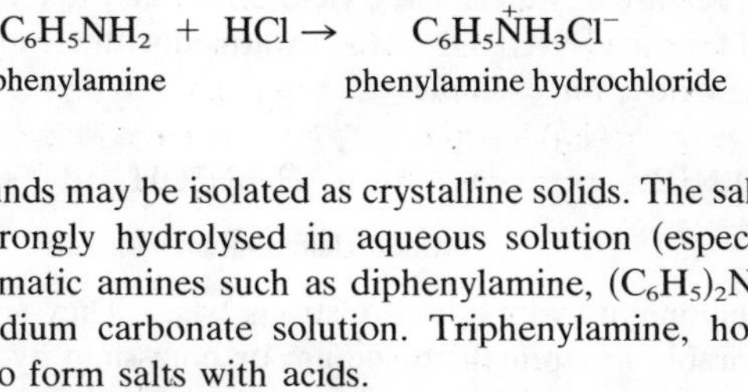

$$NH_3{}^+HSO_4{}^- \xrightarrow[200°/several\ hours]{conc.\ H_2SO_4} \quad + H_2O$$

The product is an important starting compound for the manufacture of methyl orange and other azo-dyes (see Unit 18.6(c)(iii)) and of 4-aminobenzenesulphonamide (sulphanilamide) and sulphonamide drugs (see Unit 17.4(d)(iii)).

(c) Combustion

Aliphatic amines burn in air with a yellow flame, whereas ammonia burns in oxygen but not in air.

Phenylamine burns in air with a very sooty flame.

(d) Acylation

Primary and secondary amines are readily acylated by acid anhydrides or acyl halides to yield the corresponding *N*-alkyl- or *N*-aryl-amides (see Units 17.4(*d*)(iii) and 17.6(*d*)(iii)). The reaction with benzoyl chloride (or 3,5-dinitrobenzoyl chloride) in the presence of aqueous sodium hydroxide— the Schotten–Baumann reaction—is used to prepare solid derivatives for the identification of amines (see Unit 17.4(*d*)(ii) and Experiment 17.1).

(e) Formation of Quaternary Ammonium Salts

Quaternary ammonium salts are obtained by the action of a halogenoalkane on a tertiary amine; for example:

$$(C_2H_5)_3N + C_2H_5Br \xrightarrow{\text{heat}} (C_2H_5)_4N^+Br^-$$

tetraethylammonium bromide

or by Hofmann's ammonolysis reaction in the presence of an excess of the halogenoalkane (see Units 10.6(*a*)(iv) and 18.2(*c*)). This process is known as *exhaustive alkylation*.

Quaternary ammonium salts are colourless, odourless crystalline solids which dissolve readily in water. They yield *quaternary ammonium hydroxides* of general formula $[NR_4]^+OH^-$ when warmed with an aqueous suspension of silver(I) oxide; for example:

$$(C_2H_5)_4N^+Br^- \xrightarrow{Ag_2O/H_2O} (C_2H_5)_4N^+OH^- + AgBr$$

tetraethylammonium hydroxide

Quaternary ammonium hydroxides are strong bases. They are fully ionized and are comparable in strength to sodium or potassium hydroxides. They decompose on heating to yield a tertiary amine, an alkene and water; for example:

$$(C_2H_5)_4N^+OH^- \xrightarrow{120-150°} (C_2H_5)_3N + C_2H_4 + H_2O$$

(f) Hofmann's Isocyano-reaction

Primary aliphatic and aromatic amines yield an isocyano-compound on warming with trichloromethane and an alcoholic solution of potassium hydroxide:

$$RNH_2 + CHCl_3 + 3KOH \xrightarrow[\text{ethanol}]{\text{warm}} RNC + 3KCl + 3H_2O$$

The product has an unpleasant odour, and its readily detectable formation in this reaction is used as a test for primary amines.

(g) Action of Nitrous Acid

The products obtained from the reaction between nitrous acid and an amine depend on the class and type of amine and the experimental conditions:

(i) **Primary amines.** *Primary aliphatic amines* yield nitrogen on treatment with nitrous acid owing to the decomposition of the unstable alkyldiazonium cation which is formed as an intermediate:

$$RNH_2 \xrightarrow[\text{(NaNO}_2/\text{HCl)}]{\text{'HNO}_2\text{'}} R\overset{+}{N}\equiv N \rightarrow R^+ + N_{2(g)}$$

$$1° \text{ amine} \qquad\qquad \begin{array}{c}\text{alkyldiazonium}\\\text{ion}\end{array} \qquad \begin{array}{c}\text{carbonium}\\\text{ion}\end{array}$$

The subsequent reaction of the carbonium ion results in the formation of a wide variety of products, depending on the nature of the alkyl group. Methylamine yields methoxymethane by reaction of the methyl carbonium ion with water

$$CH_3^+ + :OH_2 \longrightarrow CH_3\overset{+}{O}\begin{smallmatrix}H\\ \diagup\\ \diagdown\\H\end{smallmatrix} \longrightarrow CH_3OH + H^+$$

$$\downarrow CH_3^+$$

$$(CH_3)_2\overset{+}{O}\begin{smallmatrix}H\\ \diagup\\ \diagdown\\H\end{smallmatrix} \longrightarrow (CH_3)_2O + H^+$$

Nitromethane and chloromethane are formed by the reaction of the carbonium ion with the nitrite and chloride ions in solution respectively. Ethylamine and the higher primary alkylamines yield a mixture of alcohols, ethers and alkenes; ethylamine, for example, forms ethanol as the major product (60 per cent), whereas propylamine yields a mixture of propanol (7 per cent), propan-2-ol (32 per cent) and propene (28 per cent).

Primary aromatic amines yield a considerably more stable diazonium ion on treatment with nitrous acid at a low temperature:

$$C_6H_5NH_2 + NaNO_2 + 2HCl \xrightarrow{5-10°} C_6H_5N_2^+Cl^- + NaCl + 2H_2O$$

$$\begin{array}{c}\text{benzenediazonium}\\\text{chloride}\end{array}$$

The structure and synthetic uses of the aromatic diazonium salts are described in Unit 18.6.

At higher temperatures primary aromatic amines produce phenols, with loss of nitrogen:

$$ArNH_2 \xrightarrow[>25°]{\text{'HNO}_2\text{'}} ArOH + N_2 + H_2O$$

(ii) **Secondary amines.** Secondary aliphatic and aromatic amines react with nitrous acid to form *N-nitrosamines*, which are obtained as yellow oils; nitrogen is not evolved.

$$R_2NH + HONO \rightarrow R_2NNO + H_2O$$

For instance:

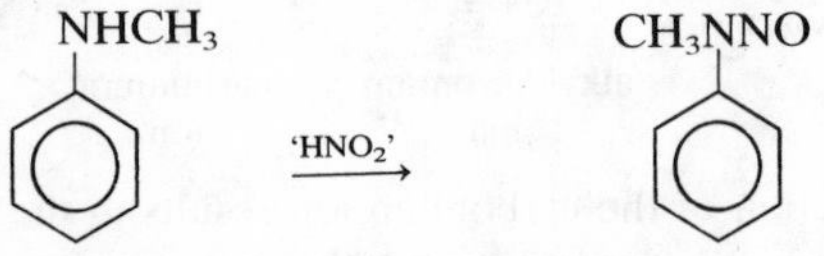

N-methylphenylamine   N-nitroso-N-methylphenylamine

(iii) **Tertiary amines.** Aliphatic tertiary amines react with nitrous acid to form salts, which remain in solution:

$$R_3N + HNO_2 \rightarrow R_3NH^+NO^-$$

Tertiary aromatic amines undergo *nitrosation* on treatment with nitrous acid:

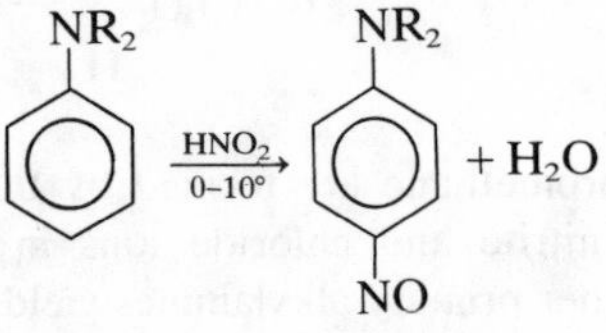

The active electrophile is the nitrosonium ion, NO^+.

(*h*) **Electrophilic Substitution of Aromatic Amines**
The amino-group activates the aromatic ring with respect to electrophilic substitution and in benzene derivatives it is *ortho*- and *para*-directing (see Unit 9.9). Bromination and chlorination of phenylamine, for example, take place in aqueous solution at room temperature to yield a white precipitate of the trihalogeno-derivative:

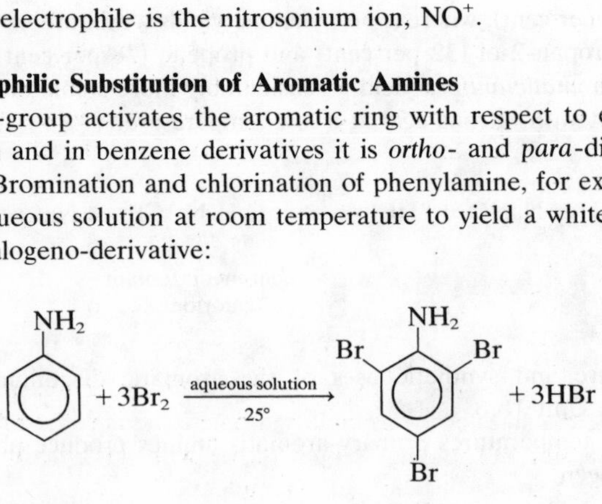

The monohalogeno-compounds and other 2- and 4-substituted phenylamine derivatives are usually prepared via *N*-phenylethanamide; for example:

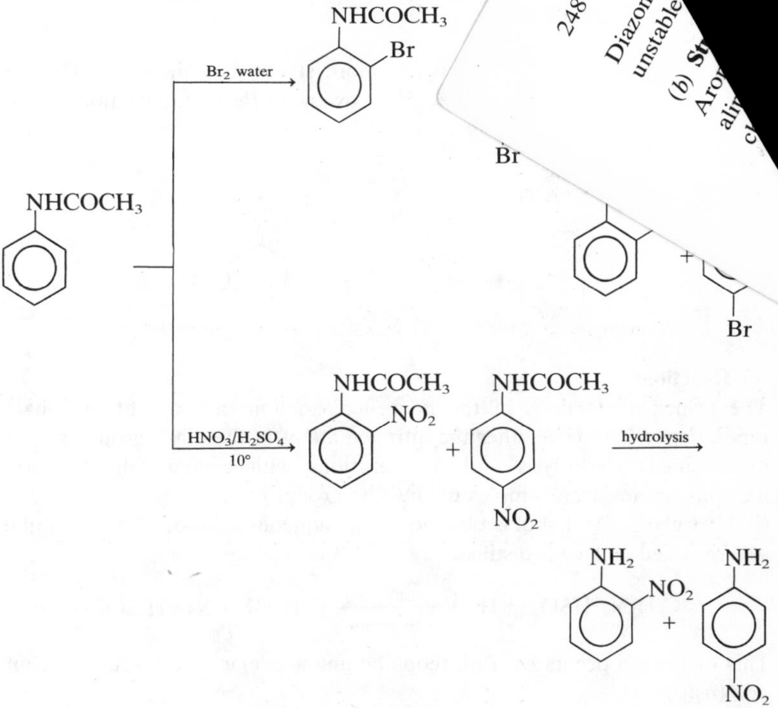

NHCOCH$_3$ → (Br$_2$ water) → ortho-bromo NHCOCH$_3$

NHCOCH$_3$ → (HNO$_3$/H$_2$SO$_4$, 10°) → ortho-NO$_2$ NHCOCH$_3$ + para-NO$_2$ NHCOCH$_3$ → (hydrolysis) → ortho-NO$_2$ NH$_2$ + para-NO$_2$ NH$_2$

248

Successful

Diazonium
unstable

(b) S...
Aro...
ali...
c...

This indirect route avoids the oxidation which occurs when phenylamine is treated with nitric acid. Electrophilic substitution of aromatic amines is more difficult in strongly acid media owing to the powerful electron-withdrawing effect of the protonated amino-group. This protonated group is *meta*-directing; thus a mixture of 2-, 3-, and 4-aminobenzenesulphonic acids is obtained when phenylamine is sulphonated with fuming sulphuric acid at room temperature.

18.6 Diazonium Salts

(a) Preparation
Aromatic diazonium compounds are prepared by the action of nitrous acid on a cold acidic solution of a primary aromatic amine (the nitrous acid is generated *in situ* by treating sodium nitrite with an aqueous solution of hydrochloric or sulphuric acid); for example:

$$C_6H_5NH_2 \xrightarrow[5-10°]{NaNO_2/H_2SO_4} C_6H_5N_2{}^+HSO_4{}^-$$

salts are used in aqueous solution as they are explosively
in the solid anhydrous state.

ucture

atic diazonium compounds are more stable than the corresponding
hatic derivatives (see Unit 18.5(g)) owing to the delocalization of the
arge on the ion by resonance:

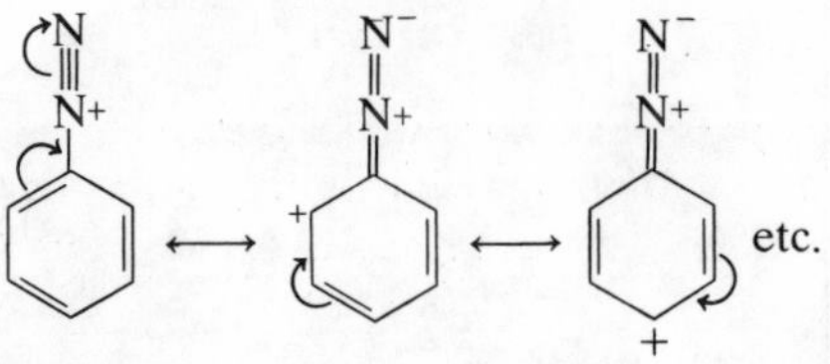

etc.

(c) **Reactions**

The principal reactions of the benzenediazonium salts are of two main
types, depending on whether the nitrogen atoms of the diazo-group are lost
or retained. Hydrolysis and the reactions with copper salts to form
halogenoarenes are examples of the first group.

(i) **Hydrolysis.** A phenol is obtained if the aqueous solution of a diazonium
salt is boiled or steam-distilled:

$$C_6H_5N_2^+HSO_4^- + H_2O \xrightarrow[\text{or steam-distil}]{\text{boil}} C_6H_5OH + N_2 + H_2SO_4$$

This hydrolysis occurs by a nucleophilic unimolecular mechanism (cf. Unit
10.6(a)(i)).

(ii) **Action of copper or copper salts.** Chlorobenzene and bromobenzene
may be prepared by warming an aqueous solution of a benzenediazonium
salt with copper(ɪ) chloride or copper(ɪ) bromide in the presence of the
corresponding halogen acid (*Sandmeyer reaction*):

$$C_6H_5N_2^+Cl^- \xrightarrow{\text{CuCl/HCl}} C_6H_5Cl + N_2$$

$$C_6H_5N_2^+Cl^- \xrightarrow{\text{CuBr/HBr}} C_6H_5Br + N_2 + Cl^-$$

These compounds may also be prepared by the *Gattermann reaction*, in
which the benzenediazonium chloride or bromide is warmed with copper
powder:

$$C_6H_5N_2^+Br^- \xrightarrow[\text{warm}]{\text{Cu powder}} C_6H_5Br + N_2$$

Iodobenzene is obtained by boiling a solution of a benzenediazonium salt
with aqueous potassium iodide:

$$C_6H_5N_2^+HSO_4^- + KI_{(aq)} \xrightarrow{\text{boil}} C_6H_5I + N_2 + KHSO_4$$

This reaction is probably the best method of preparing iodoarenes.

The nitrogen atoms of the diazo-group are replaced by a cyano-group when the aqueous solution of the diazonium salt is treated with a solution of copper(I) cyanide in aqueous potassium cyanide or a mixture of powdered copper and potassium cyanide solution:

$$C_6H_5N_2^+Cl^- + KCN \xrightarrow[\text{CuCN}]{\text{Cu or}} C_6H_5CN + KCl + N_2$$

(iii) **Coupling with phenols or aromatic amines.** Diazonium salts react with phenols in alkaline solution, or with tertiary aromatic amines in neutral solution, to form brightly coloured *azo-dyes*; for example:

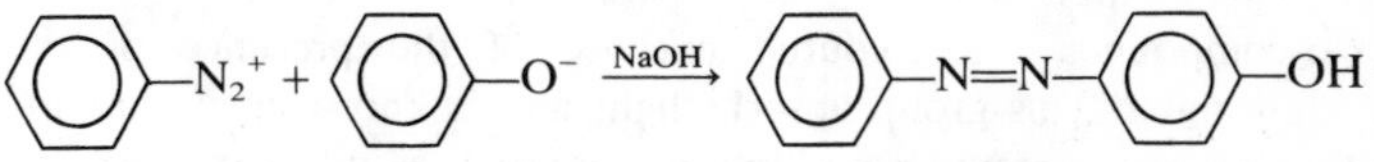

from phenol

4-hydroxyazobenzene
(yellow)

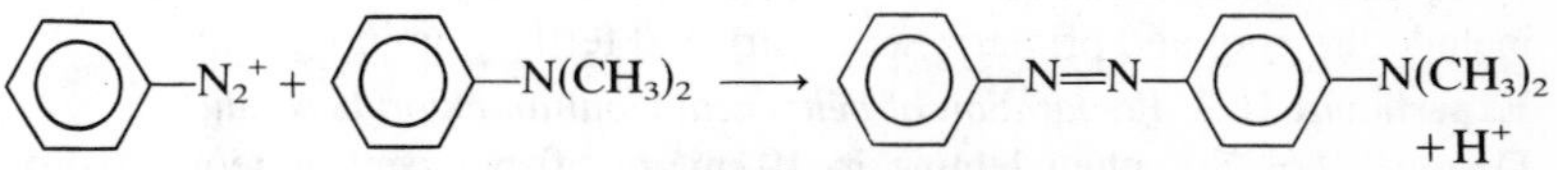

4-dimethylaminoazobenzene
(yellow)

Naphthalen-2-ol yields a bright scarlet azo-dye:

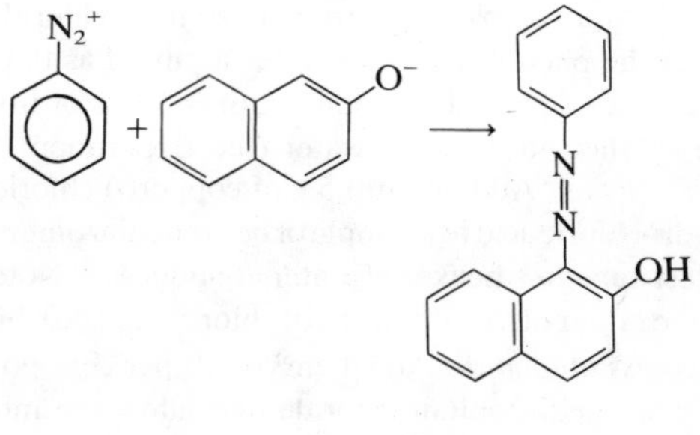

This reaction may be used for the detection of primary aromatic amines: a red precipitate forms when a cooled solution of such an amine in hydrochloric acid is treated with sodium nitrite and then poured into a cold alkaline solution of naphthalen-2-ol. For example, 4-aminobenzenesulphonic acid (see Unit 18.5(*b*)) yields the dye Orange II:

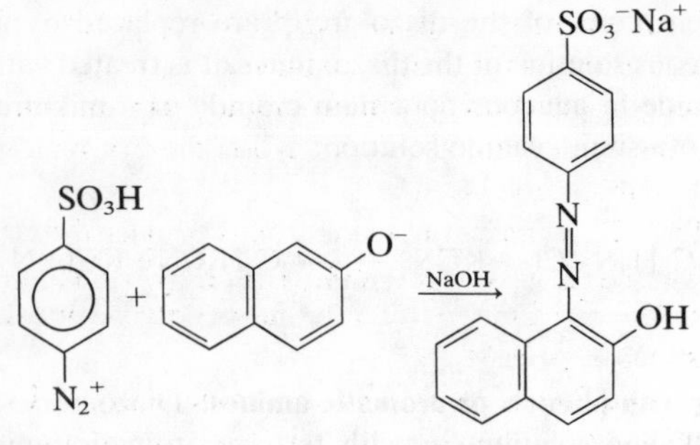

Orange II

Sulphonic acid groups are often introduced into the azo-dyes to increase their solubility in water.

The azo-compounds are coloured because of the presence of the —N=N— grouping. This group absorbs light and is known as a *chromophore*. Other groups containing multiple bonds, such as nitro-, nitroso- or carbonyl groups, can also act as chromophores. The actual colour of a compound containing a chromophore depends on the nature of other substituents, called *auxochromes*, in the molecule; common auxochromes include the enol and primary, secondary and tertiary amino-groups.

Experiment 18.1 *Preparation of benzenediazonium chloride solution*
Dissolve 2 cm^3 of phenylamine in 10 cm^3 of 50 per cent aqueous hydrochloric acid in a test-tube and cool the mixture in a beaker of ice and water. Cool 5 cm^3 of a 20 per cent aqueous solution of sodium nitrite to about 5° and add it to the solution of phenylamine hydrochloride, ensuring that the temperature of the mixture does not exceed 10°.

Experiment 18.2 *To demonstrate the reactions of benzenediazonium chloride*
Divide the benzenediazonium chloride solution prepared in the previous experiment into six equal portions for the following reactions.

1. *Hydrolysis.* Boil a sample of benzenediazonium chloride solution and note the odour of the phenol which separates as an oil as the mixture cools. Confirm the presence of phenol by adding 2 or 3 drops of iron(III) chloride to 1 cm^3 of the solution in 5 cm^3 of water (see Experiment 13.2).

2. *Sandmeyer reaction.* Add about 0.5 g of copper(I) chloride dissolved in concentrated hydrochloric acid to a sample of benzenediazonium chloride solution. Place the test-tube in a beaker of water at about 60°. Note the evolution of nitrogen and the odour of the oily drops of chlorobenzene which are formed.

3. *Action of potassium iodide.* Add 1 cm^3 of 10 per cent potassium iodide solution to the benzenediazonium chloride and allow the mixture to stand for about five minutes before boiling gently. Note the formation of dense drops of iodobenzene.

4. *Formation of azo-compounds.* (i) Add the cold benzenediazonium chloride solution drop by drop to a cold solution of about 0.3 g of phenol in dilute sodium hydroxide. Note the formation of a yellow precipitate of 4-hydroxyazobenzene.

Repeat this experiment with naphthalen-2-ol instead of phenol and observe the formation of the scarlet azo-dye.

(ii) Add phenylamine drop by drop to about 1 cm³ of benzenediazonium chloride solution cooled to about 5°. Note the formation of a yellow precipitate of 4-aminoazobenzene.

Experiment 18.3 *To demonstrate the reactions of phenylamine*

Note: Phenylamine is a toxic liquid. Use only small amounts of the compound and do not allow it to come into contact with the skin. Avoid inhaling its vapour unnecessarily.

1. *Solubility.* Add 7 or 8 drops of phenylamine to about 1 cm³ of water in a test-tube and shake. Determine the pH of the aqueous suspension with Universal indicator paper. Add dilute hydrochloric acid and note whether the phenylamine dissolves. Observe what happens when the mixture is made alkaline by adding an excess of sodium hydroxide.

2. *Diazotization and azo-dye formation.* See Experiments 13.2.4 and 18.2.4.

3. *Action of nitrous acid.* Add 1 or 2 cm³ of a 20 per cent solution of sodium nitrite to 5 drops of phenylamine dissolved in 2 cm³ of dilute hydrochloric acid. Warm the mixture gently and note the odour of phenol.

4. *Acylation: formation of N-phenylethanamide.* Add 5 drops of ethanoic anhydride to 5 drops of phenylamine in a test-tube and warm the mixture gently. Note the formation of a white solid as the mixture cools. The crude product may be recrystallized from a small amount of boiling water. Allow the crystals of the pure product to dry in air and determine their melting-point (*N*-phenylethanamide, m.p. 114°).

5. *Action of bromine water.* Add bromine water to 5 drops of phenylamine in 2 cm³ of water and observe (and account for) any changes that occur.

6. *Colorations with oxidizing agents.* (i) *Bleaching powder.* Add a few drops of bleaching powder solution to one drop of phenylamine in 10 cm³ of water. Note the formation of a purple coloration which rapidly changes to brown.

(ii) *Iron*(III) *chloride.* Add 2 drops of iron(III) chloride solution to a solution of 2 drops of phenylamine in 2 cm³ of dilute hydrochloric acid. A pale green coloration is obtained which darkens on warming.

(iii) *Action of hydrogen peroxide and iron*(II) *sulphate.* Dissolve 5 drops of phenylamine in about 2 cm³ of concentrated hydrochloric acid and add 1 cm³ of 10-volume hydrogen peroxide followed by 2 drops of freshly prepared iron(II) sulphate solution. A bright-green coloration is obtained and the deep-green dye *emeraldine* is slowly precipitated.

18.7 Uses of Amines

Dimethylamine is used for the manufacture of solvents such as dimethyl-methanamide:

$$HCO_2CH_3 + (CH_3)_2NH \rightarrow HCON(CH_3)_2 + CH_3OH$$

and for the preparation of drugs and detergents.

Phenylamine is a starting material for the manufacture of dyestuffs and for the synthesis of drugs. Some phenylamine is used to prepare antioxidants and accelerators for the vulcanization of rubber.

Test Yourself on Unit 18

1. Name the isomers of formula C_3H_9N and classify them as primary, secondary or tertiary amines.

2. Arrange the following in order of increasing basic strength: A, dimethylamine; B, ethanamide; C, ammonia; D, phenylamine; E, N-phenyl(benzenesulphonamide); F, methylamine; G, tetramethylammonium hydroxide.

3. Describe how you would carry out the following changes:
   (a) $C_6H_5NO_2 \rightarrow C_6H_5NC$;
   (b) $CH_3NH_2 \rightarrow (CH_3)_2O$;
   (c) $C_2H_5NH_2 \rightarrow C_2H_4$;
   (d) $C_2H_5Br \rightarrow (C_2H_5)_4N^+OH^-$;
   (e) $C_2H_5Br \rightarrow C_2H_5CH_2NH_2$

4. Discuss the factors which determine the relative basic strength of aliphatic and aromatic amines.

5. Compare and contrast the preparation and reactions of ethylamine with those of phenylamine. How do you account for the differences in the chemistry of these two compounds?

6. Discuss the preparation, stability and synthetic uses of the aromatic diazonium compounds.

7. Describe how you would prepare a pure sample of phenylamine in the laboratory. How may phenylamine be converted into (a) bromobenzene and (b) N-phenylethanamide?

8. A white, crystalline solid, A, and an oily liquid, B, were obtained by the hydrolysis of C, $C_{15}H_{15}NO$. A dissolves in aqueous sodium carbonate with effervescence and the solid which is obtained by evaporating this solution to dryness yields D, C_7H_8, when heated with soda-lime. On treatment with powerful oxidizing agents A or D yields E, $C_7H_6O_2$. A bright scarlet precipitate is obtained when sodium nitrite is added to a solution of B in cold hydrochloric acid and the mixture is poured into cold alkaline naphthalen-2-ol. Identify the compounds A to E and elucidate the reactions.

Stereoisomerism

19.1 Introduction

You will recall that compounds which have the same molecular formula but different chemical and/or physical properties are said to be *isomeric*, and that there are various kinds of isomers. *Structural isomers*, having different molecular structures, were discussed in detail in Unit 1.6; in this Unit we shall consider *stereoisomers*, that is, compounds having the same molecular structure but different spatial arrangements of the atoms within it, or *configurations*.

19.2 Geometrical Isomerism

(a) *cis*- and *trans*-Butenedioic Acids

Geometrical isomerism occurs in compounds in which free rotation about a particular covalent bond is prevented by the presence of a double bond or of ring structures, or because of steric factors. The best-known example is *butenedioic acid*, which exists in two isomeric forms in which the carbonyl groups lie respectively on the same side and on opposite sides of the double bond in the planar molecule:

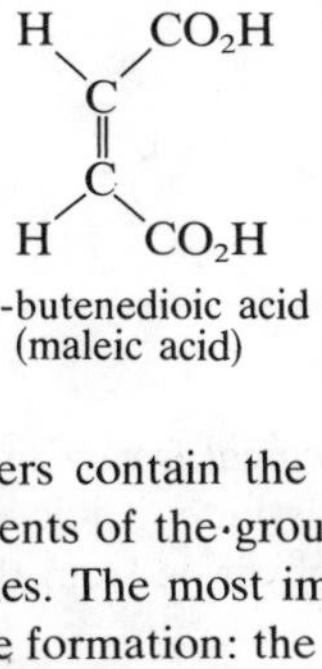

cis-butenedioic acid
(maleic acid)

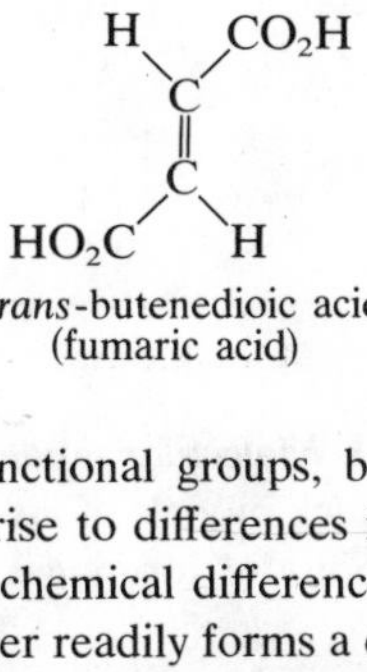

trans-butenedioic acid
(fumaric acid)

The two isomers contain the same functional groups, but the different spatial arrangements of the·groups give rise to differences in chemical and physical properties. The most important chemical difference is the relative ease of anhydride formation: the *cis*-isomer readily forms a cyclic anhydride on heating to 170°.

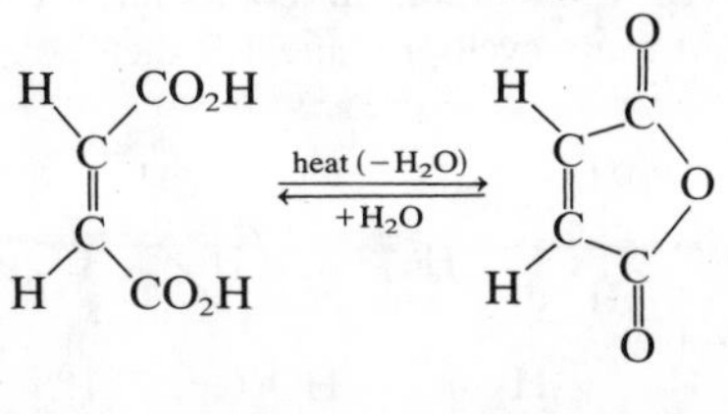

The reaction is reversed on adding water. *trans*-Butenedioic acid remains unchanged under these conditions, although on strong heating it sublimes and some rearrangement occurs to yield a certain amount of the *cis*-anhydride.

Reactions such as the formation of the cyclic anhydride, and its subsequent hydrolysis with cold water to yield the *cis*-acid, provide the principal chemical method of distinguishing between geometrical isomers of this type. Physical methods include X-ray crystallography and spectroscopic techniques. The principal differences in the physical properties of *cis*- and *trans*-butenedioic acids are summarized in Table 19.1. The *cis*-isomer is a considerably stronger acid than the *trans*-isomer for the first ionization owing to stabilization of the resulting anion by intramolecular hydrogen bonding (see Unit 16.5). This order is reversed for the second ionization, for which *trans*-butenedioic acid is approximately 15 times stronger than the *cis*-isomer. The lower acid strength of *cis*-butenedioic acid for this second ionization is partly a result of the stability of the monoanion, but it also reflects the difficulty of removing the second proton from a carboxyl group which is close to the site of the anionic charge.

Table 19.1 Geometrical isomerism: differences in physical properties of *cis*- and *trans*-butenedioic acids

Property	*cis*-Butenedioic acid	*trans*-Butenedioic acid
m.p. (°C)	130–31	286 (dec.)
density (g cm^{-3})	1.590	1.635
solubility in water (g 100 cm^{-3})	79	0.7
pK_a'	1.92	3.02
pK_a''	6.23	4.38
K_a'/K_a''	20 420	23

Experiment 19.1 *Molecular models* (*geometrical isomerism*)
Make ball-and-stick models of *cis*- and *trans*-butenedioic acids and demonstrate the possibility of forming a cyclic anhydride from the *cis*-isomer.

(b) Cyclic Compounds

Geometrical isomerism is common in compounds containing saturated rings, such as *cis*- and *trans*-cyclopropane-1,2-dicarboxylic acid:

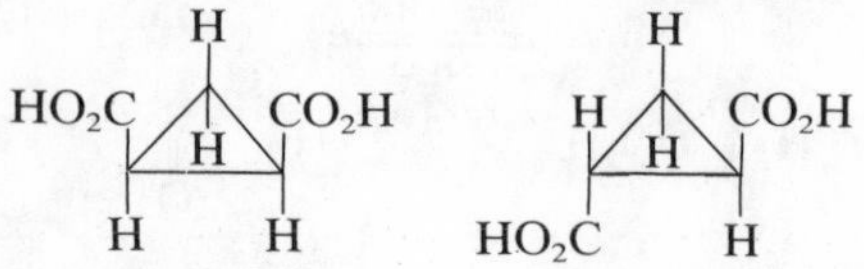

cis-form
m.p. 139°

trans-form
m.p. 175°

19.3 Optical Isomerism

Sunlight, or light from an ordinary electric lamp, is made up of electromagnetic waves, the vibrations of which take place in any plane at right
angles to the direction of propagation (Fig. 19.1). If, however, the light
passes through a piece of Polaroid or a Nicol prism (a *polarizer*) the waves
of the light that emerges are found to be vibrating in *one plane only*, and the
light is said to be *plane-polarized*. If this polarized light is now passed
through a second piece of Polaroid or Nicol prism (or *analyser*), light will
only be transmitted if the plane of polarization is the same as that which the
analyser will transmit. This may be demonstrated using small squares of
Polaroid sheet or the lenses of Polaroid sun-glasses (Fig. 19.2). As one

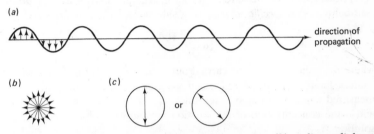

(a)

direction of
propagation

(b)   (c)

or

Fig. 19.1   Diagrams of (a) a transverse wave motion, (b) ordinary light—
the vibrations take place in any plane at right angles to the direction of
propagation, and (c) plane-polarized light—the vibrations take place in one
plane only

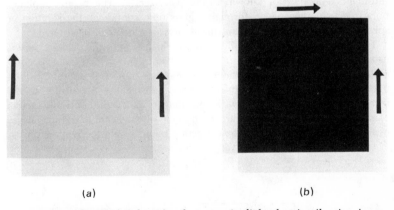

(a)   (b)

Fig. 19.2   A piece of Polaroid only transmits light that is vibrating in one
specific plane—the polarizing axis; thus when two pieces of Polaroid are
superimposed so that their polarizing axes coincide (a) most of the incident
light is transmitted, but when the axes are at right angles (b) little or no light
can pass through

sheet is rotated relative to the other through an angle of 90° the field of view rapidly changes from light to dark as the amount of light transmitted decreases almost to zero.

Solutions of certain substances are able to rotate the plane of plane-polarized light; such substances are said to be *optically active.* *Optical isomers* are optically active substances which have the same molecular structure but differ in their effect on plane-polarized light. One isomer, the (+) or *dextrorotatory* form, rotates the plane of polarization to the right, while the other rotates it to the left and is known as the (−) or *laevorotatory* form. The two isomers have the same chemical and physical properties; they differ only in their effect on plane-polarized light and in reactions involving other optically active substances.

Optical activity is measured with an instrument known as a *polarimeter* (see below). The *specific rotation* of a substance, $[\alpha]_D^t$ is defined by:

$$[\alpha]_D^t = \frac{100\alpha}{l \times c}$$

where the measurement was carried out at temperature t using light from a sodium lamp (the 'D-line' of mean wavelength 589.3 nm), and α is the measured angle of rotation. l the thickness of the solution (in decimetres) and c the concentration of the solution in grams of solute per 100 cm^3 of solution.

The polarimeter. The construction of a simple polarimeter—sometimes called a *saccharimeter*, as the instrument is used, especially in the brewing and wine-making industries, for the estimation of sugars—is shown diagrammatically in Fig. 19.3. Light from a monochromatic (single-wavelength) source, S, such as a sodium lamp, is polarized by passing it (via a lens) through a Nicol prism known as the *polarizer*, P. The beam of plane-polarized light then passes through a glass tube containing the solution or solvent to a second Nicol prism (the *analyser*) which can be rotated.

The tube is first filled with the solvent (which is optically inactive, and is usually water) and the analyser is rotated until the field of view is completely dark. The reading on the analyser scale is noted. If the tube is then filled with a solution of an optically active substance and returned to the instrument, the field of view is no longer dark: the optically active compound has rotated the polarization plane of the beam and the analyser needs to be turned to regain the extinction point. Again the reading on the

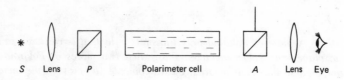

S   Lens   P   Polarimeter cell   A   Lens   Eye

Fig. 19.3   Diagram of a polarimeter

analyser scale is noted. The angle through which the analyser has to be turned—the difference between the two readings—is the angle of rotation, α.

19.4 Molecular Asymmetry

The existence of optical isomers of a substance is a result of the *asymmetry* of its molecules. The dextrorotatory and laevorotatory isomers have the same structure but are mirror images of each other; because of their asymmetry, the two mirror images are not identical—they cannot be superimposed one on another. The two forms are known as *enantiomorphs* or *enantiomers*. The simplest examples are compounds containing one *asymmetric carbon atom*, that is, a carbon atom attached to four different groups, which we may write as *Cabcd*. The bonds are arranged tetrahedrally about the central carbon atom and the configurations of the mirror images are shown in Fig. 19.4: the dotted line represents a bond directed into the plane of the page and the solid triangle a bond pointing out of the plane of the paper.

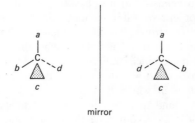

mirror

Fig. 19.4 Non-superimposable mirror images

The specific rotations of the two enantiomorphs have the same value, but are of opposite signs. An equimolecular mixture of the two isomers thus has no effect on plane-polarized light and is said to be *optically inactive*. Such a mixture is known as a *racemate* or *racemic mixture* (the DL-form). The letters D and L refer to the configurations of the groups within the molecule; this convention is discussed in Unit 19.5.

2-Aminopropanoic acid (alanine), $CH_3CH(NH_2)CO_2H$, and 2-hydroxypropanoic acid (lactic acid), $CH_3CH(OH)CO_2H$, are both examples of naturally occurring optically active substances. L(+)-2-Aminopropanoic acid is an important component of proteins (see Unit 20.9). L(+)-2-Hydroxypropanoic acid is found in muscle, while its D(−)-isomer is a product of the fermentation of sucrose by *Bacillus acidi laevolactiti*, and the racemate occurs in sour milk.

Experiment 19.2 *Molecular models (optical isomerism)*
Make a ball-and-stick model of a molecule in which an sp³ hybridized carbon atom is attached tetrahedrally to four different groups (four differently coloured balls will be suitable) and compare this with a model of its mirror image. Attempt to superimpose the two forms; you should satisfy yourself that however you twist and turn your models, the one cannot be superimposed on the other.

Repeat this with models in which two of the substituent groups are identical and two different.

19.5   Configuration

(a) Arbitrary Configuration

Enantiomorphism—non-superimposable mirror-image asymmetry—is quite common. Our hands have the same structure but different configurations: a left-hand glove will not fit the right hand and vice versa, because the left hand is a non-superimposable mirror image of the right. We can say unequivocally which is the right hand and which is the left. But how can we distinguish between the two isomers of, say, 2-hydroxypropanoic acid? Which of the two possible configurations is the dextrorotatory and which the laevorotatory isomer?

The early stereochemists had no physical methods for determining the *actual* positions of groups within a molecule. One substance, (+)-2,3-dihydroxypropanal (dextrorotatory glyceraldehyde), was therefore chosen as an *arbitrary standard* and assigned the configuration shown on the left in Fig. 19.5. Any substance which could be related by an unambiguous series of reactions to this compound was said to have the D-configuration, irrespective of the direction in which it rotated the plane of polarized light. Similarly, any compound unambiguously related to its mirror image (on the right in Fig. 19.5) was said to have the L-configuration.

For convenience, these configurations are represented as planar diagrams (such as Fig. 19.5(c) and (d)), in which—by convention—the asymmetric carbon atom is at the point where the lines cross, while vertical lines represent groups below the plane of the paper and horizontal lines groups above the plane; where no substituent group is named in a planar diagram, the presence of a hydrogen atom is understood. The planar diagram of a

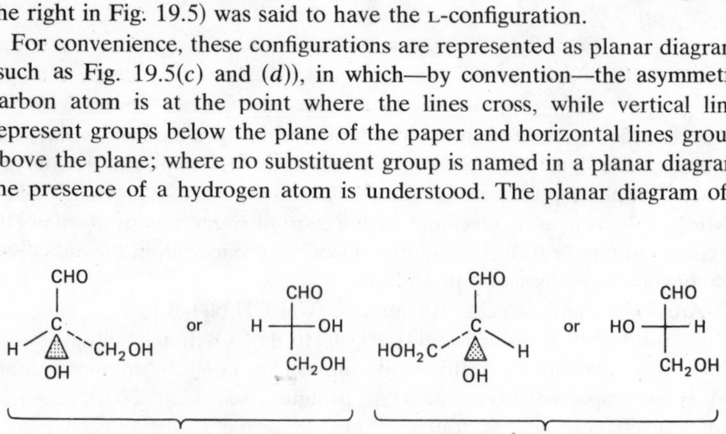

D (+)-2,3-dihydroxypropanal   L (−)-2,3-dihydroxypropanal

Fig. 19.5   Configurations of 2,3-dihydroxypropanal

compound containing an asymmetric carbon atom cannot be superimposed on its mirror image *within the plane of the paper.*

Compounds containing more than one asymmetric carbon atom, such as the sugars (see Unit 20.2(*b*)), are classified into D- and L-series depending on whether the configuration of the carbon atom at the end of the chain is related to that of D(+)- or L(−)-2,3-dihydroxypropanal:

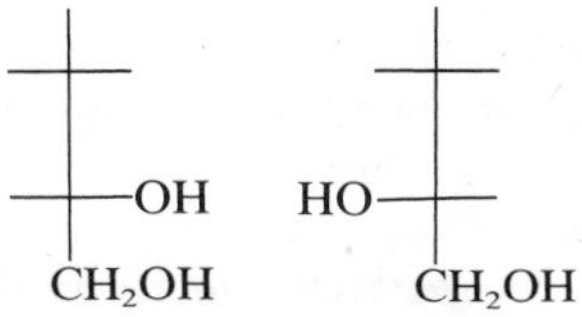

D-series   L-series

Thus, for example, naturally occurring glucose (Fig. 19.6) is called D(+)-glucose, as it has a D-configuration and is dextrorotatory.

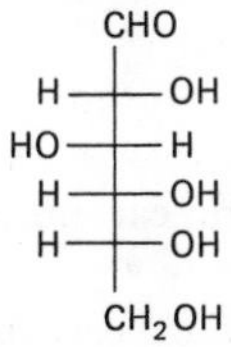

Fig. 19.6   Configuration of D(+)*-glucose*

(b) Absolute Configuration

All the configurations assigned on this system were purely arbitrary as they depended on a guess for the configuration of the standard, D(+)-2,3-dihydroxypropanal. What then if this guess was wrong? Would all the assigned configurations have to be altered?

In 1951, by X-ray crystallographic studies of crystals of sodium rubidium 2,3-dihydroxybutanedioate, Bijvoet was able to check the actual arrangement of the groups in dextrorotatory 2,3-dihydroxybutanedioic acid (D(+)-tartaric acid). This substance occurs in grape-juice and had been assigned the configuration shown in Fig. 19.7 by Emil Fischer about sixty years earlier. Bijvoet's results confirmed that the guess was correct and that the arbitrary configurations based on D(+)-2,3-dihydroxypropanal are actual or *absolute configurations.* The D(+)- and L(−)-2,3-dihydroxybutanedioic acids are used as *absolute standards.*

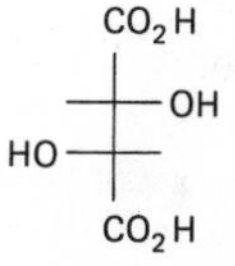

Fig. 19.7   D(+)-2,3-Dihydroxybutanedioic acid (D(+)-tartaric acid)

19.6 Properties of Enantiomers

(a) Physical Properties

The physical properties (melting-point, boiling-point, solubility, acid strength, density and so forth) of any pair of isomers are all identical, *except* for their effect on plane-polarized light.

(b) Chemical Properties

The chemical properties of optical isomers are identical, except in some reactions that involve the participation of other optically active substances. Many enzyme-catalysed reactions occur readily with one optically active isomer while its mirror image reacts either very slowly or not at all. For example, lactate dehydrogenase, an enzyme found in muscle, catalyses the dehydrogenation of L(+)-2-hydroxypropanoic acid to 2-oxopropanoic acid:

$$CH_3\overset{*}{C}H(OH)CO_2H \underset{(\pm 2H)}{\overset{\text{lactate dehydrogenase}}{\rightleftharpoons}} CH_3COCO_2H$$

L(+)-2-hydroxypropanoic   2-oxopropanoic acid
acid

where $\overset{*}{C}$ represents an asymmetric carbon atom. The same enzyme catalyses the reverse reaction, but only the L(+)-acid is obtained from the optically inactive 2-oxopropanoate. Reactions of this type indicate that a similar *stereospecificity* exists in the structure of enzyme molecules, that is, that both the nature and the stereochemical configuration of the reactant are important for enzyme action. The stereospecificity of enzymes probably explains why optical isomers frequently have different physiological properties; L(+)-ascorbic acid (vitamin C), for instance, is more effective in preventing scurvy than is its D-isomer, and many sugars, amino-acids, antibiotics, drugs and hormones are only physiologically active in one form.

19.7 Resolution of Optical Isomers

Some optically active substances may be isolated in the form of a pure enantiomer from natural sources or from the products of an enzyme reaction. But when a compound containing an asymmetric carbon atom is synthesized in the laboratory from optically inactive starting materials, the product is almost invariably a racemic mixture. 2-Hydroxypropanoic acid, for example, is obtained from ethanal as a racemate by the following reaction sequence (since there is an equal chance of attack on either side of the planar carbonyl group):

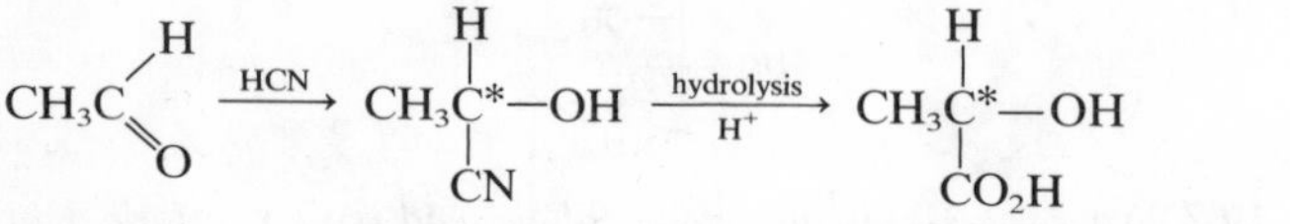

$$CH_3C\overset{H}{\underset{O}{\diagdown}} \xrightarrow{HCN} CH_3\overset{H}{\underset{CN}{\overset{|}{\underset{|}{C}}}}{}^*\!-OH \xrightarrow[H^+]{\text{hydrolysis}} CH_3\overset{H}{\underset{CO_2H}{\overset{|}{\underset{|}{C}}}}{}^*\!-OH$$

ethanal   DL-2-hydroxypropanonitrile   DL-2-hydroxypropanoic acid

There are three principal methods of separating or *resolving* such a racemic mixture into optical isomers.

(a) Mechanical Separation

This technique, often called *crystal picking*, was first used by Pasteur in 1848 to separate the two forms of sodium ammonium 2,3-dihydroxybutanedioate and is of mainly historical interest. The method depends on the fact that the crystals of the two enantiomers of this salt are themselves enantiomorphous—an unusual phenomenon—and can be separated with tweezers under a lens or a low-powered microscope.

(b) Biochemical Separation

Occasionally it is possible to find a micro-organism which metabolizes one form in a racemic mixture and leaves the other isomer unchanged. For example, *Penicillium glaucum* destroys L(+)-2-hydroxypropanoic acid and thus enables the D(−)-isomer to be isolated from the racemic mixture.

(c) Chemical Separation

This technique, which was also developed by Pasteur, is generally the most convenient. It usually depends on salt formation: a racemic acid, for example, is treated with an enantiomer of an optically active base, generally a compound that occurs naturally in optically pure form, such as brucine, quinine, strychnine or morphine:

$$\underbrace{\text{D-acid} + \text{L-acid}}_{\text{racemic mixture}} + 2\text{D-base} \rightarrow (\text{D-acid–D-base}) + (\text{L-acid–D-base})$$

The product consists of a mixture of isomeric optically active (but not enantiomorphous) salts which, if their solubilities are sufficiently different, may be separated by fractional crystallization. The separate acid isomers are then regenerated by hydrolysis of the salt.

19.8 Stereospecific Reactions

Certain elimination, addition and substitution reactions are known to be stereospecific, such as the *anti*-addition of bromine to an alkene (see Unit 7.6(b)). An S_N2 hydrolysis (see Unit 10.6(a)(i)) is accompanied by an inversion of configuration; thus the hydrolysis of an optically active halide with a D-configuration yields an L-alcohol if the reaction proceeds by an S_N2 mechanism:

An S_N1 mechanism results in racemization. Any reaction in which the configuration of a compound is inverted in this way is known as a *Walden inversion*.

Test Yourself on Unit 19

1. Discuss the isomerism of compounds of the following molecular formulae: (*a*) $C_2H_2Cl_2$, (*b*) $C_4H_{10}O$ and (*c*) $C_3H_4Cl_2$.

2. Explain what is meant by the following terms: (*a*) configuration, (*b*) stereoisomer, (*c*) plane-polarized light, (*d*) enantiomorphism.

3. Describe how you would prepare a sample of 2-hydroxypropanoic acid in the laboratory, starting from ethanol. Outline the procedure you would follow to resolve the product into its optical isomers.

4. Describe the polarimeter and explain how you would use it to demonstrate the optical activity of D(−)-fructose.

5. What is an asymmetric carbon atom? Write an essay on the optical isomerism of compounds containing an asymmetric carbon atom.

6. Outline the methods available for the resolution of racemic mixtures.

7. Explain, with reference to suitable examples, what is meant by the term *isomerism*.

Carbohydrates and Proteins

20.1 Introduction

Carbohydrates and proteins are two of the principal classes of naturally occurring organic compounds. They are both important constituents of foodstuffs and form vital structural and functional components of all plant and animal tissues. Muscle, blood, skin, hair and enzymes—the catalysts which control the thousands of chemical reactions which make up the life process itself—all consist largely or wholly of protein. Sugars, starch and glycogen—all carbohydrates—constitute the energy sources and food reserves of innumerable millions of living organisms, while cellulose is the structural component of all plant cell walls.

The chemical structure and properties of the carbohydrates and proteins are discussed separately in this Unit.

20.2 Carbohydrates

(a) Definition

The carbohydrates contain carbon, hydrogen and oxygen only, and the hydrogen and oxygen are usually present in the same ratio as in water. Their general empirical formula is therefore $C_xH_{2y}O_y$. These compounds are in no sense 'hydrates of carbon', however, and many substances are known which fit this general formula but which are not carbohydrates, while a number of carbohydrates, such as the sugars rhamnose, $C_6H_{12}O_5$, and deoxyribose, $C_5H_{10}O_4$, do not fit the general formula. Methanal, ethanoic acid, 2-hydroxypropanoic acid and glucose, for example, all have the empirical formula CH_2O, but only glucose is a carbohydrate:

$$CH_2O \text{ (methanal)}$$

$$C_2H_4O_2 \text{ or } CH_3CO_2H \text{ (ethanoic acid)}$$

$$C_3H_6O_3 \text{ or } CH_3CHOHCO_2H \text{ (2-hydroxypropanoic acid)}$$

$$C_6H_{12}O_6 \text{ (glucose)}$$

Carbohydrates are better defined as *optically active polyhydroxy-aldehydes or -ketones and their derivatives.*

(b) Classification and Nomenclature

The carbohydrates are divided into two main classes: the *sugars* and the *polysaccharides* (see Fig. 20.1).

(i) **The sugars.** Sugars are crystalline solids of comparatively low relative molecular mass (from about 10^2 to 10^3) which dissolve readily in water and have a sweet taste. They are subdivided into the *monosaccharides*, *disaccharides* and *trisaccharides*, according to their behaviour on hydrolysis.

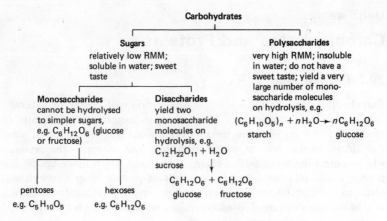

Fig. 20.1   Classification of carbohydrates

Glucose and fructose, for example, have the formula $C_6H_{12}O_6$ and are monosaccharides and cannot be hydrolysed into simpler sugar molecules. Disaccharides yield two monosaccharide molecules on hydrolysis, and trisaccharides three.

The monosaccharides, like other sugars, all have names ending with the suffix *-ose*; they are classified according to the number of carbon atoms in the molecule and the nature of the carbonyl group, that is, whether it acts as an aldehydic or a ketone group. Glucose is thus an *aldohexose* as it contains an aldehyde group and has six carbon atoms:

$$
\begin{array}{lll}
\text{CHO} & \text{CH}_2\text{OH} & \text{CHO} \\
(\text{CHOH})_4 & \text{CO} & (\text{CHOH})_3 \\
\text{CH}_2\text{OH} & (\text{CHOH})_3 & \text{CH}_2\text{OH} \\
 & \text{CH}_2\text{OH} & \\
\text{glucose} & \text{fructose} & \text{ribose}
\end{array}
$$

Fructose, $C_6H_{12}O_6$, which is isomeric with glucose, is a *ketohexose*, while ribose, $C_5H_{10}O_5$, is an *aldopentose*.

Sucrose and maltose are both disaccharides of formula $C_{12}H_{22}O_{11}$. On hydrolysis, they each yield two monosaccharide units—a glucose and fructose molecule and two glucose molecules respectively.

(ii) **The polysaccharides.** Polysaccharides have a considerably greater relative molecular mass than have the sugars (about 10^4 to 10^7 or higher) and are generally insoluble in water and do not have a sweet taste. Each polysaccharide molecule yields many hundreds or thousands of monosaccharide molecules on hydrolysis. Starch, for example, has the formula

$(C_6H_{10}O_5)_n$ and is hydrolysed to glucose by the action of enzymes or by boiling with aqueous acid:

$$(C_6H_{10}O_5)_n + nH_2O \xrightarrow{\text{hydrolysis}} nC_6H_{12}O_6$$

starch   glucose

20.3 Preparation of Sugars

The most important sugars are glucose, fructose, maltose and sucrose. *Glucose* and *fructose* are obtained by hydrolysing starch with boiling aqueous sulphuric acid under pressure: they are separated by fractional crystallization. DL-Fructose is a constituent of formose (see Unit 15.6(*a*)(vi)).
Starch is hydrolysed to *maltose* by the action of the enzymes of malt:

$$(C_6H_{10}O_5)_n + \frac{n}{2}H_2O \xrightarrow{\text{enzyme action}} \frac{n}{2}C_{12}H_{22}O_{11}$$

starch   maltose

Sucrose is obtained from either sugar-cane or sugar-beet. The juices pressed from the crushed cane or beet are made alkaline with calcium hydroxide and the precipitated impurities are filtered off. Steam is passed through the liquid to coagulate the proteins and the clear filtrate is concentrated by evaporation under reduced pressure. Sucrose crystallizes out as the syrup cools and further sugar is recovered from the thick residual liquid (*molasses*) by dilution and recrystallization.

The sugar so obtained is brown in colour and is purified by dissolving it in water and treating the solution with calcium hydroxide and carbon dioxide. The filtrate is boiled with charcoal to decolorize it (*cf.* Unit 2.2) and the filtered solution is concentrated by vacuum distillation and allowed to crystallize. The remaining molasses is used in cattle-foods or is fermented to yield ethanol (see Unit 12.4(*b*)(i)).

20.4 Structure of Glucose and Fructose

Glucose is a pentahydroxyaldehyde, $CHO(CHOH)_4CH_2OH$, and fructose is a pentahydroxyketone, $CH_2OHCO(CHOH)_3CH_2OH$. These unbranched open-chain structures account for most of the physical and chemical properties of glucose and fructose. For example, they explain the ready formation of oximes and cyanohydrins with hydroxylamine and hydrogen cyanide respectively which are characteristic reactions of the carbonyl group (see Units 15.6(*b*) and 15.6(*a*)(ii)). The aldehyde group of glucose is easily oxidized by bromine water to yield a carboxylic acid, but the ketone group of fructose is unaffected by this reagent (see Unit 20.6(*b*)).

The glucose molecule has been shown by X-ray crystallography and chemical methods to exist as a six-membered ring. In aqueous solution, however, this cyclic structure is in equilibrium with the open-chain form; thus glucose solution readily reduces Fehling's solution and undergoes other reactions characteristic of the free aldehyde group. The ring is formed by a hemiacetal bond between the aldehyde group and the hydroxyl on carbon atom 5 (see Unit 15.6(a)(iv)):

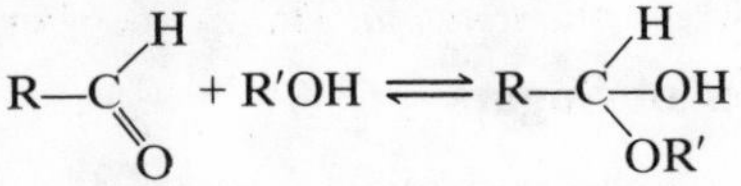

aldehyde   hemiacetal

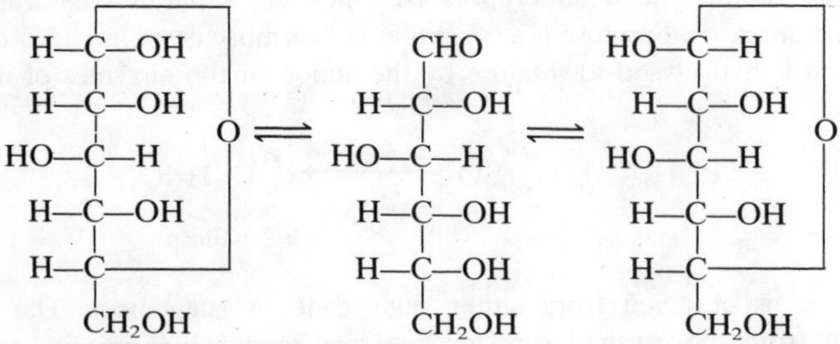

α-D(+)-glucose β-D(+)-glucose

Two different cyclic structures are possible, depending on whether the hydroxyl group attached to carbon atom 1 is above or below the ring (Fig. 20.2). These two forms have different specific rotations (see Unit 19.3): that for the α-form, α-D(+)-glucose, is +112° and that for the β-isomer

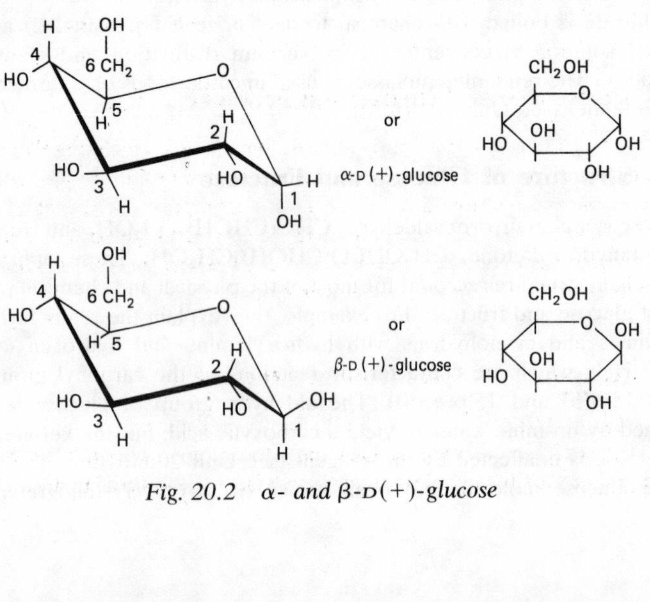

Fig. 20.2 α- and β-D(+)-glucose

+ 18.5°. The two forms are in equilibrium in aqueous solution and if either is dissolved in water the specific rotation slowly changes to + 52.6°:

α-D(+)-glucose:$[\alpha]_D^{20} = +112°$

β-D(+)-glucose:$[\alpha]_D^{20} = +18.5°$

Equilibrium mixture:
$[\alpha]_D^{20} = +52.6°$

This process is known as *mutarotation*. The six-membered ring is described as the *pyranose* structure, *cf.*

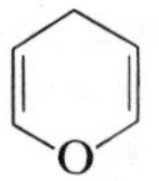

pyran

and is represented in simple block diagrams of sugars and polysaccharides as:

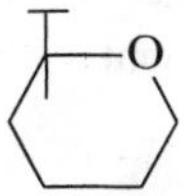

Fructose also exists in a cyclic form which contains a five-membered ring:

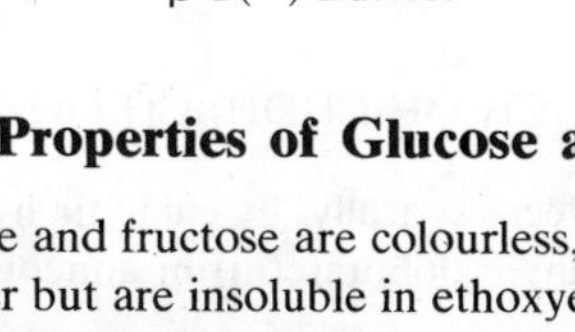

β-D(−)-fructose α-D(−)-fructose

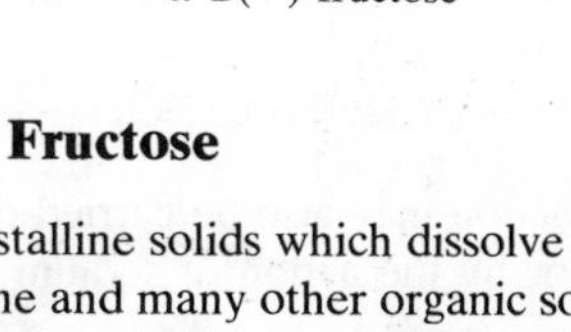

20.5 Properties of Glucose and Fructose

Glucose and fructose are colourless, crystalline solids which dissolve readily in water but are insoluble in ethoxyethane and many other organic solvents; they are sparingly soluble in ethanol. They decompose on heating (glucose, m.p. 146° (dec.), and fructose, m.p. 102° (dec.)). Both glucose and fructose have a sweet taste, though they are not as sweet as sucrose. D-Glucose is dextrorotatory and D-fructose is laevorotatory.

20.6 Reactions of Glucose and Fructose

(a) Action of Heat

Glucose, fructose and other sugars melt to colourless liquids on heating. The liquid gradually becomes increasingly viscous as it turns first yellow and then brown. The product smells of caramel or toffee. Water is progressively lost on further heating and the residue chars.

(b) Oxidation

Glucose and fructose are both strong reducing agents and will reduce ammoniacal silver nitrate (Tollen's reagent) and Fehling's solution to metallic silver and copper(I) oxide respectively. Glucose is oxidized to *gluconic acid*, $CO_2H(CHOH)_4CH_2OH$, by bromine water, but fructose does not react.

Stronger oxidizing agents, such as dilute nitric acid, oxidize the primary alcohol group as well as the aldehyde group in glucose to yield *glucaric acid* (2,3,4,5-tetrahydroxyhexanedioic acid):

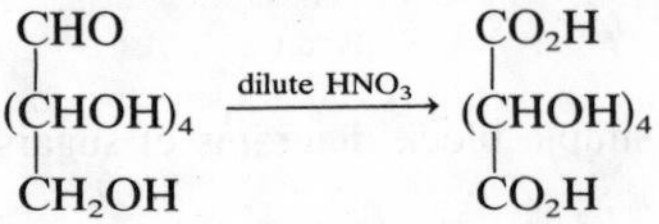

$$\begin{array}{c} CHO \\ | \\ (CHOH)_4 \\ | \\ CH_2OH \end{array} \xrightarrow{\text{dilute } HNO_3} \begin{array}{c} CO_2H \\ | \\ (CHOH)_4 \\ | \\ CO_2H \end{array}$$

Fructose breaks down on treatment with nitric acid to form a mixture of acids:

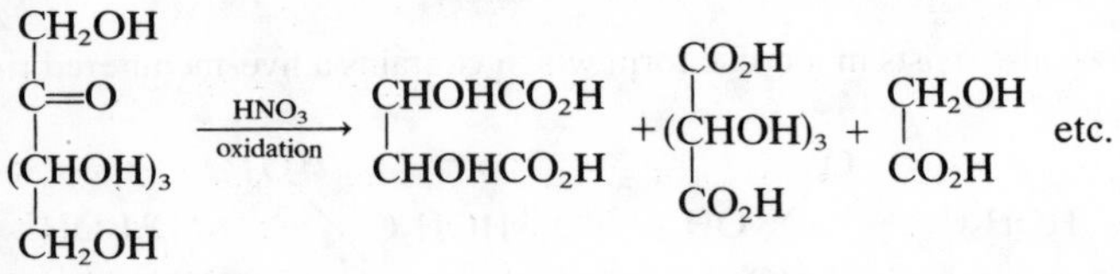

$$\begin{array}{c} CH_2OH \\ | \\ C{=}O \\ | \\ (CHOH)_3 \\ | \\ CH_2OH \end{array} \xrightarrow[\text{oxidation}]{HNO_3} \begin{array}{c} CHOHCO_2H \\ | \\ CHOHCO_2H \end{array} + \begin{array}{c} CO_2H \\ | \\ (CHOH)_3 \\ | \\ CO_2H \end{array} + \begin{array}{c} CH_2OH \\ | \\ CO_2H \end{array} \text{ etc.}$$

(c) Reduction

Glucose is reduced to the hexahydric alcohol *sorbitol* by the action of sodium amalgam in aqueous solution:

$$CHO(CHOH)_4CH_2OH \xrightarrow{\text{reduction}} CH_2OH(CHOH)_4CH_2OH$$

This reaction may also be carried out electrolytically, by catalytic hydrogenation or by the action of sodium tetrahydridoborate(III) in aqueous solution.

(d) Action of Sodium Hydroxide

All sugars turn yellow and then brown when their aqueous solution is warmed with sodium hydroxide. The mixture has a characteristic odour.

(e) Action of Sulphuric Acid

Sugars undergo dehydration and charring on warming with concentrated sulphuric acid; for instance:

$$C_6H_{12}O_6 \xrightarrow{\text{conc. } H_2SO_4} 6C + 6H_2O$$

(f) Fermentation

Glucose and fructose are fermented to ethanol by the action of yeast under anaerobic conditions (see Unit 12.4(b)(i)):

$$C_6H_{12}O_6 \xrightarrow{\text{yeast}} 2C_2H_5OH + 2CO_2$$

20.7 Disaccharides

The three most important naturally occurring disaccharides are sucrose, maltose and lactose. These three sugars have the same molecular formula, $C_{12}H_{22}O_{11}$, and have similar physical properties; they are all sweet, water-soluble, colourless solids. They each yield two hexose sugar molecules on hydrolysis.

(a) Sucrose

(i) **Hydrolysis.** Each sucrose molecule yields a molecule of glucose and a molecule of fructose on hydrolysis with dilute mineral acid:

$$C_{12}H_{22}O_{11} + H_2O \xrightarrow[\text{H}^+\text{ catalyst}]{\text{hydrolysis}} C_6H_{12}O_6 + C_6H_{12}O_6$$

D(+)sucrose   D(+)glucose   D(−)fructose

The reaction takes place with an inversion of the direction of rotation of plane-polarized light (see Unit 19.3). Sucrose and glucose are both dextrorotatory but fructose is laevorotatory and has a higher numerical specific rotation than glucose, so that the net change is from (+) to (−). The hydrolysis is therefore known as the *inversion of sucrose* and the course of the reaction may be followed using a polarimeter. The resulting mixture of glucose and fructose is called *invert sugar*. The hydrolysis is also catalysed by the enzyme *invertase*, found in yeast.

(ii) **Properties and structure.** Sucrose has no reducing properties; it does not affect Fehling's solution or ammoniacal silver nitrate. The two monosaccharide residues in the sucrose molecule must therefore be joined together via the reducing groups, that is, the aldehyde group of glucose is linked to the keto-group of fructose. The structure is:

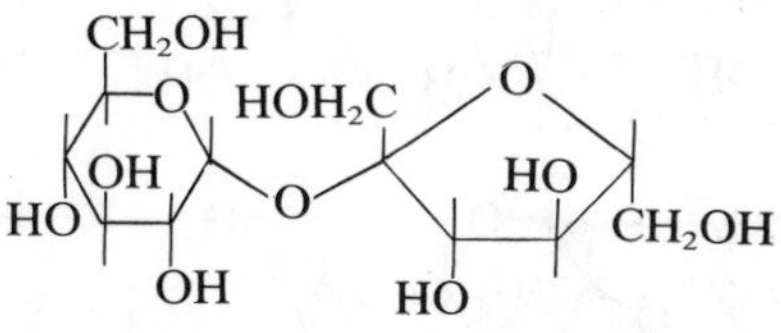

Sucrose is dehydrated by concentrated sulphuric acid to yield *sugar charcoal*, which is virtually pure carbon.

(b) **Maltose and Lactose**

(i) **Preparation.** Maltose is produced from starch by the action of an enzyme obtained from malt (see Unit 20.3). Lactose ('milk sugar') is found in the milk of all animals. It is obtained commercially by evaporating to crystallization the whey produced as a by-product in cheese manufacture.

(ii) **Properties and structure.** Both lactose and maltose are reducing sugars: they give a silver mirror with ammoniacal silver nitrate and reduce Fehling's solution to copper(I) oxide, indicating that at least one aldehyde group must be free in the disaccharide molecule. Maltose yields two molecules of D(+)-glucose on hydrolysis. Its structure is:

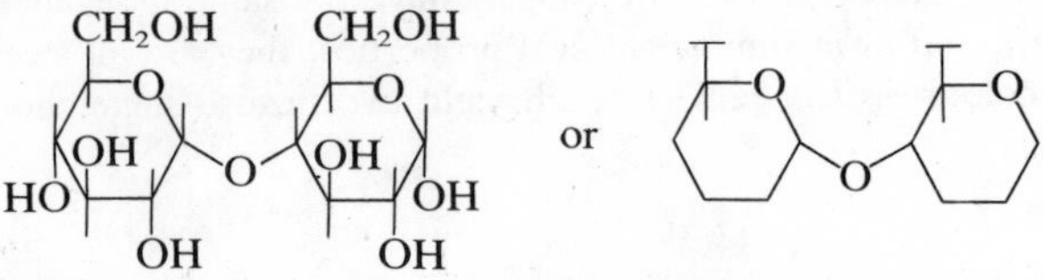

Lactose is hydrolysed to glucose and galactose (an aldohexose).

20.8 Polysaccharides

The general formula of the polyhexoses is $(C_6H_{10}O_5)_n$ where n can be as high as 10^5. They are found in plants as starch and cellulose, and in animals as glycogen.

(a) **Starch**

Starch is found in all green plants where it is the principal carbohydrate food reserve material. It is especially plentiful in potatoes and in rice and other cereal crops. Starch consists of two components: α-amylose and β-amylose. *α-Amylose* is the water-soluble fraction and constitutes about 15 per cent of starch. It has a relative molecular mass of between 10^4 and 10^5 and consists of long chains of glucose units joined together in the 1–4α position:

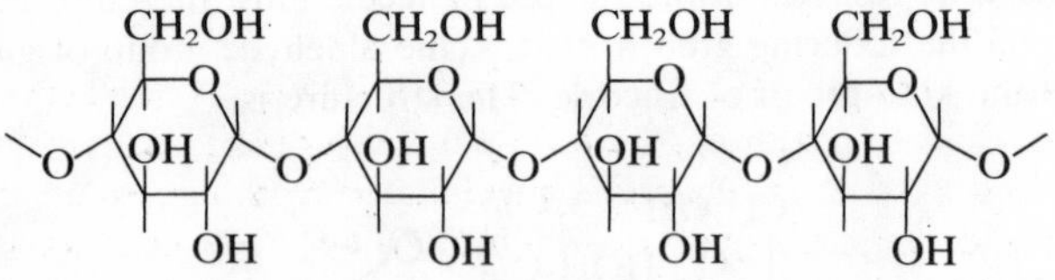

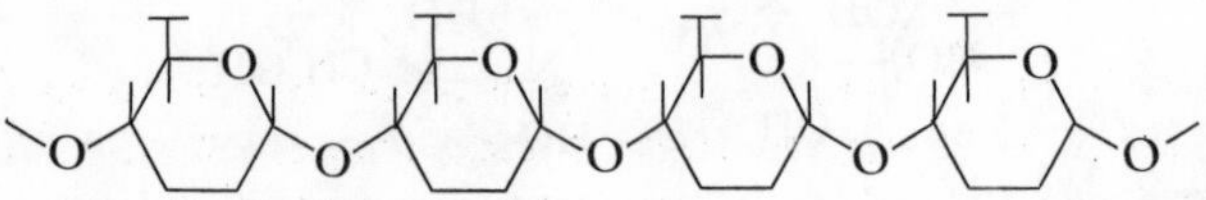

It gives a blue coloration with iodine solution.

β-Amylose (or *amylopectin*) is insoluble in water and has a considerably

larger relative molecular mass (from 10^5 to 10^6). It consists of branched chains of glucose units and gives a violet colour with iodine.

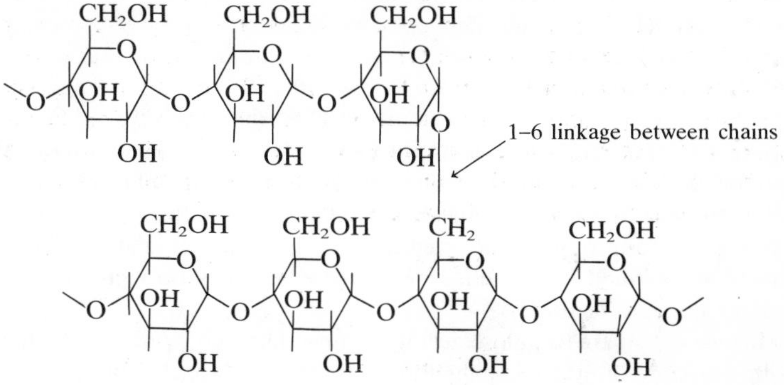

Starch is hydrolysed to maltose by the action of the enzyme amylase (present in human saliva or malt) and to glucose by boiling aqueous acids:

$$(C_6H_{10}O_5)_n + nH_2O \xrightarrow[\text{heat in sealed tube}]{\text{aq. } H_2SO_4} nC_6H_{12}O_6$$

(b) Cellulose

Cellulose is the principal structural component of the cell walls of plants and is the major constituent of cotton, hemp and paper. It is an important raw material for the manufacture of synthetic fibres, paper and plastics: cotton-wool and filter-paper are virtually pure cellulose. Cellulose consists of a complex network of chains of glucose units linked together in the 1–4β position:

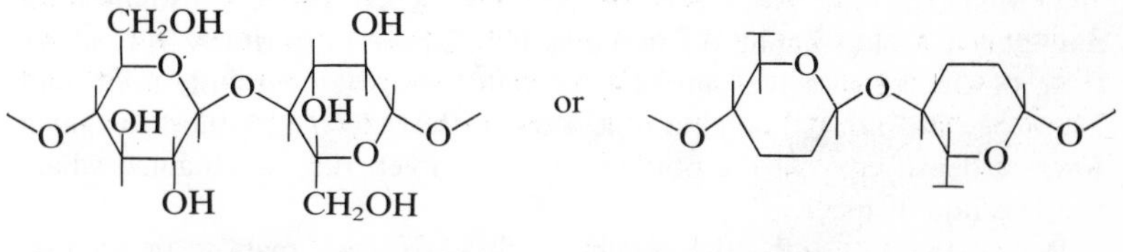

Cellulose is a white solid which is insoluble in water, but which dissolves readily in solutions containing the tetra-amminecopper(II) ion, $[Cu(NH_3)_4]^{2+}$ (*Schweitzer's reagent*). Cellulose is precipitated from this solution by the action of acids; by forcing the solution through fine holes in a metal plate (a *spinneret*) into an acid bath threads of artificial silk ('cupra silk') are obtained.

(i) *Manufacture.* Cellulose is manufactured by treating wood shavings with an aqueous solution of calcium hydrogensulphite at 130–150°. Wood is a mixture of cellulose and lignin; the latter is dissolved and the insoluble cellulose is removed by filtration.

(ii) *Uses.* Cellulose is used to manufacture man-made fibres known as *rayon. Viscose rayon* is made by treating cellulose with a mixture of sodium hydroxide and carbon disulphide:

$$Cel\text{-}OH + CS_2 + NaOH \longrightarrow \begin{array}{c} Cel\text{---}O \\[-2pt] \diagdown \\[-4pt] C\text{=}S \\[-4pt] \diagup \\[-2pt] Na^+ \ ^-S \end{array} \quad + H_2O$$

sodium cellulose xanthate

where Cel–OH represents cellulose with its many hydroxy-groups. The sodium cellulose xanthates are soluble in aqueous alkali and form a viscous solution which is forced through a spinneret into a bath of sulphuric acid causing cellulose to be precipitated in the form of fine threads. *Cellophane* sheets are formed by injecting the viscose solution through long, very narrow slits into acid.

Cellulose ethanoate (cellulose acetate) is manufactured by treating cellulose with a mixture of ethanoic anhydride and ethanoic acid. It is used to make films, varnishes, lacquers, shatter-proof glass and 'Celanese' rayon.

Nitrocellulose. The cellulose nitrates are prepared by treating cellulose with a mixture of concentrated nitric and sulphuric acids. Cellulose trinitrate is used as an explosive (gun-cotton).

(c) Glycogen

Glycogen is the carbohydrate storage material of animals. It is stored in the muscles and in the liver and acts as a short-term energy reserve. It has a branched structure similar to that of β-amylose, but with chains consisting of about a dozen 1–4α-linked glucose units between the branches.

Glycogen gives a reddish-brown coloration with iodine.

Experiment 20.1 *To demonstrate the reactions of carbohydrates*

1. *Molisch's test.* Add 2 or 3 drops of a 20 per cent solution of naphthalen-1-ol (1-naphthol) in industrial methylated spirit (IMS) to about 0.1 g of glucose dissolved in 2 cm³ of water and then **carefully** pour 1 or 2 cm³ of concentrated sulphuric acid down the side of the tube so that it forms a dense layer at the bottom. A deep-violet 'ring' is obtained where the two liquids meet.

Repeat this test with other sugars, such as fructose, maltose or sucrose, and with about 2 cm³ of 'starch solution'. Molisch's test is given by all carbohydrates.

2. *Action of heat.* Warm about 0.5 g of glucose or sucrose in a dry test-tube **gently and slowly** over a Bunsen burner flame. Carefully observe all the changes which take place and note the gradual change in odour.

3. *Action of sulphuric acid.* Add about 1 cm³ of concentrated sulphuric acid to 0.2 to 0.3 g of glucose or sucrose and warm the mixture gently. Remove the tube from the flame and observe the immediate charring. Heat the mixture more strongly and test for the evolution of carbon monoxide, carbon dioxide and sulphur dioxide.

Repeat this experiment with starch.

4. *Reduction of ammoniacal silver nitrate.* Add 2 or 3 cm^3 of ammoniacal silver nitrate solution (see Appendix II) to a solution of about 0.1 g of glucose in 2 cm^3 of water in a clean test-tube. Place the tube in a beaker of boiling water and note the formation of a silver mirror.

Fructose, lactose and maltose behave similarly, but sucrose is not a reducing sugar and therefore does not produce a silver mirror.

5. *Action of Fehling's solution.* Boil a solution of about 0.1 g of glucose in 2 cm^3 of water with about 1 cm^3 each of Fehling's solutions I and II. Reducing sugars (glucose, fructose, lactose and maltose) reduce the copper(II) ion to an orange-red precipitate of copper(I) oxide. Starch and sucrose have no effect.

6. *Hydrolysis of sucrose.* Add 1 cm^3 of dilute sulphuric acid to 0.3 g of sucrose dissolved in 4 cm^3 of water. Heat the mixture on a boiling water bath for 5 minutes. Neutralize the cooled solution by adding aqueous ammonia and carry out tests to show the presence of glucose and fructose.

Experiment 20.2 *To demonstrate the reactions of starch*

1. *Action of iodine.* Add 1 or 2 drops of dilute iodine solution to 2 or 3 cm^3 of a solution of soluble starch. Note the deep-blue colour. Observe what happens when this mixture is boiled and then allowed to cool.

2. *Appearance.* Place a little dry starch on a microscope slide, add a drop of water and cover it with a slip. Examine the starch grains under the microscope and draw one in your notebook.

3. *Hydrolysis.* Prepare three test-tubes, *A*, *B* and *C*, each containing about 2 cm^3 of a dilute solution of soluble starch.

Add 1 cm^3 of dilute sulphuric acid to *A* and place in a boiling water-bath for 15 minutes. Neutralize the solution and divide it into two parts. Test one portion with 1 or 2 drops of iodine solution and the other with Fehling's solution to show the presence of glucose.

Add a little saliva to each of the two remaining portions, *B* and *C*. Boil *B* for 2 or 3 minutes and then place both the tubes in a water-bath at 40° for 20 minutes. At the end of this time test the contents of the two tubes with iodine and with Fehling's solution.

20.9 Proteins

(a) Amino-acids and the Structure of Proteins

Proteins contain carbon, hydrogen, nitrogen, oxygen and some sulphur. They are polymers of high relative molecular mass (approximately 10^3 to 10^6) and consist of chains of amino-acid residues:

$$a_1—a_2—a_3—a_4—a_2—a_4—a_5—a_1—a_6—$$

where a_1, a_2 and so on are different amino-acids. Proteins containing less than 30 or 40 amino-acid residues are known as *polypeptides*.

About twenty amino-acids are commonly found in nature, and all proteins are made up of different combinations of these, arranged in specific sequences. The naturally occurring amino-acids are virtually all 2-aminocarboxylic acids (α-amino-acids), that is, the amino- and carboxyl groups are attached to the same carbon atom, and their general formula is:

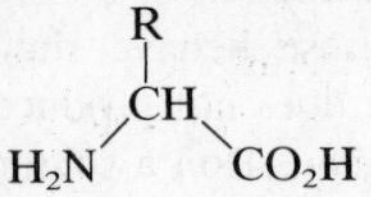

$$
\begin{array}{c}
R \\
| \\
CH \\
H_2N \qquad CO_2H
\end{array}
$$

The various amino-acids differ in the nature of the substituent group R. Some common amino-acids are:

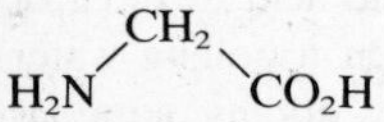

aminoethanoic acid
(glycine)

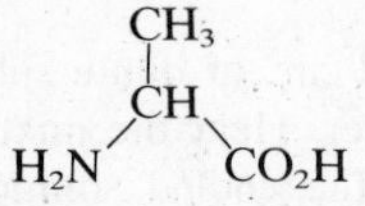

2-aminopropanoic acid
(α-alanine)

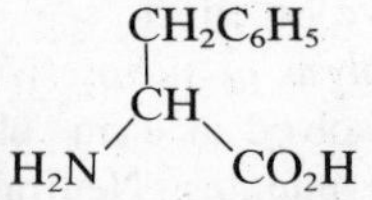

2-amino-3-phenylpropanoic acid
(phenylalanine)

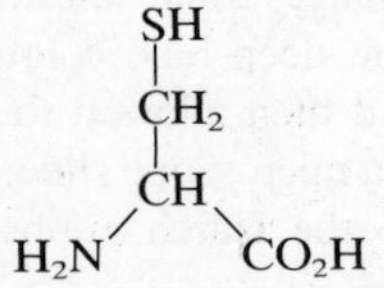

2-amino-3-mercaptopropanoic acid
(cysteine)

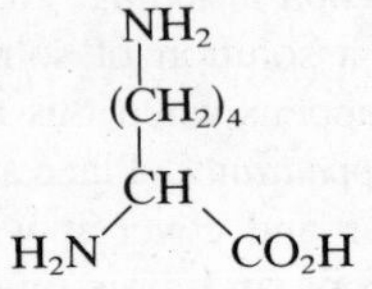

2,5-diaminohexanoic acid
(lysine)

Proteins are hydrolysed by boiling aqueous acid, or at about 40° by the action of enzymes, to yield a mixture of amino-acids. The general structure and hydrolysis of a polypeptide chain are illustrated in Fig. 20.3. The amino-acids are joined together in the polypeptide chain via the amino-

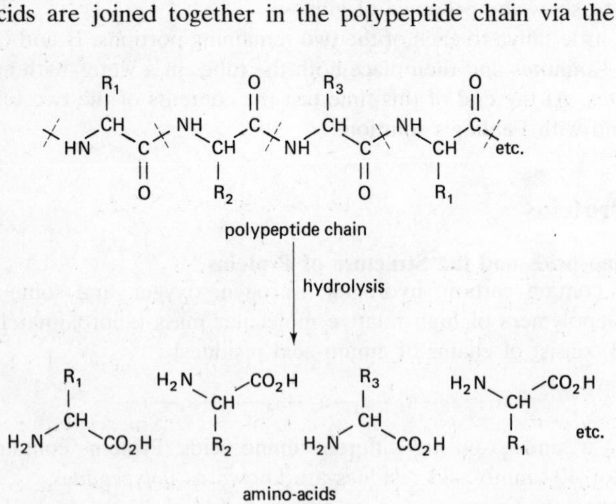

polypeptide chain

hydrolysis

amino-acids

Fig. 20.3 Structure and hydrolysis of a polypeptide chain

group of one amino-acid and the carboxyl group of the next. The resulting —CO—NH— grouping is known as the *peptide link* and is common to all proteins and polypeptides.

(b) Shape of Polypeptide Molecules

The shape of the polypeptide molecule is largely determined by the configuration of the bonds about the atoms forming the backbone of the chain—the planar carbonyl carbon atom, the tetrahedral sp^3 hybridized saturated carbon atom and the pyramidal nitrogen atom. Hydrogen bonding between the —NH group of one amino-acid residue and the carbonyl group of another holds the protein chain in a coil or spiral, known as the α-helix. The spacing between the turns is about 0.54 nm. Many proteins, such as enzymes and egg-white, lose their physiological activity on heating, and are said to be *denatured*; this effect is largely due to the unfolding of the coiled chain by breaking the intramolecular hydrogen bonds. Thus the *shape* of a polypeptide molecule, as well as the amino-acid sequence in its chains, is important for protein function.

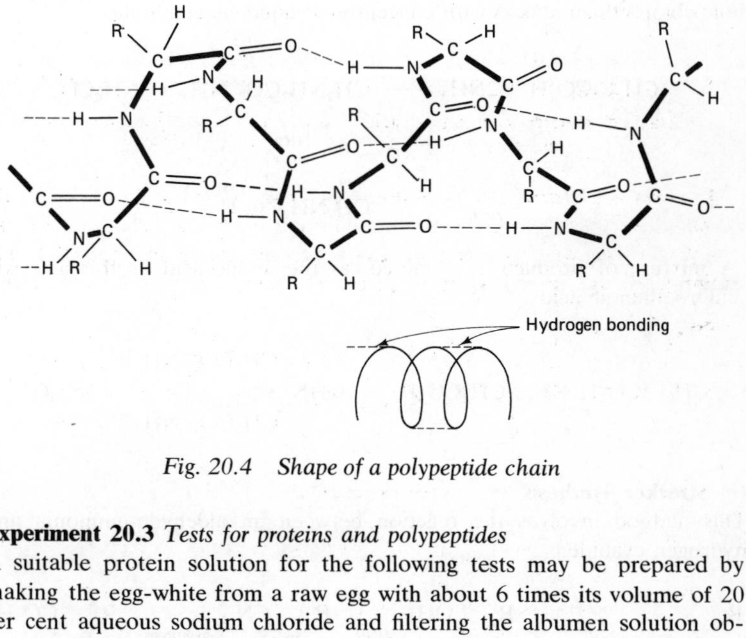

Fig. 20.4   *Shape of a polypeptide chain*

Experiment 20.3 *Tests for proteins and polypeptides*

A suitable protein solution for the following tests may be prepared by shaking the egg-white from a raw egg with about 6 times its volume of 20 per cent aqueous sodium chloride and filtering the albumen solution obtained through a muslin cloth.

1. *Denaturation.* Boil a 2 cm³ sample of the albumen solution and note the formation of a white precipitate.

2. *Xanthoproteic test.* Add 1 cm³ of concentrated nitric acid to about 1 cm³ of the protein solution. A yellow coloration is obtained which turns orange on the addition of an excess of ammonia solution.

3. *Biuret reaction.* Add 1 or 2 drops of copper(II) sulphate solution to 1 cm^3 of the protein solution and 2 to 3 cm^3 of dilute sodium hydroxide. A violet or pink coloration is obtained, indicating the presence of the peptide link.

4. *Action of ninhydrin.* Add 3 or 4 drops of aqueous ninhydrin solution to 2 cm^3 of the protein solution and warm. Amino-acids and polypeptides give a blue coloration with ninhydrin.

5. *Millon's test.* Add 1 or 2 drops of mercury(II) nitrate solution and 1 drop of dilute sulphuric acid to about 1 cm^3 of the protein solution and boil. Allow the mixture to cool and then add 1 drop of sodium nitrite to the mixture. A red coloration is obtained indicating the presence of tyrosine in the protein.

20.10 Preparation of Amino-acids

(a) From 2-Chloroalkanoic Acids

Aminoethanoic acid (glycine), for example, may be prepared by treating monochloroethanoic acid with concentrated aqueous ammonia:

$$CH_2ClCO_2H + 2NH_3 \longrightarrow CH_2NH_2CO_2^-NH_4^+ + NH_4Cl$$

$$\downarrow HCl$$

$$CH_2NH_2CO_2H$$

A mixture of products is obtained, as the amino-acid itself reacts with chloroethanoic acid:

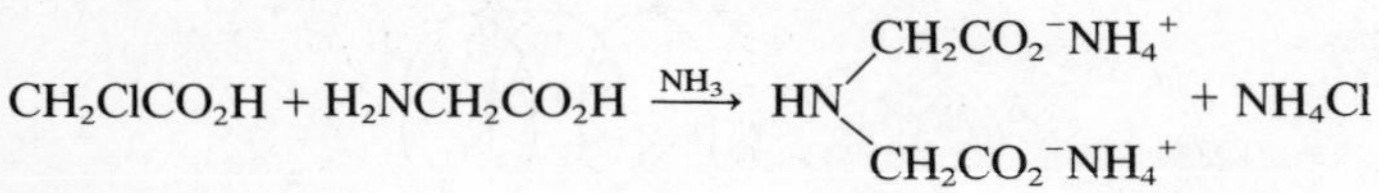

$$CH_2ClCO_2H + H_2NCH_2CO_2H \xrightarrow{NH_3} HN\begin{matrix} CH_2CO_2^-NH_4^+ \\ \\ CH_2CO_2^-NH_4^+ \end{matrix} + NH_4Cl$$

(b) Strecker Synthesis

This method involves the reaction between an aldehyde-ammonia and hydrogen cyanide:

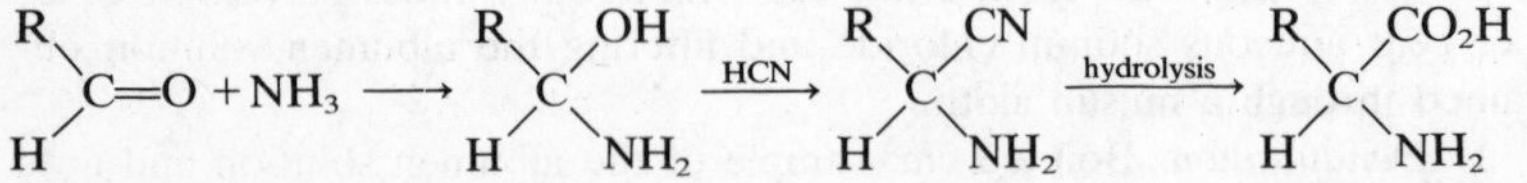

$$\underset{H}{\overset{R}{>}}C{=}O + NH_3 \longrightarrow \underset{H}{\overset{R}{>}}C\underset{NH_2}{\overset{OH}{<}} \xrightarrow{HCN} \underset{H}{\overset{R}{>}}C\underset{NH_2}{\overset{CN}{<}} \xrightarrow{hydrolysis} \underset{H}{\overset{R}{>}}C\underset{NH_2}{\overset{CO_2H}{<}}$$

In practice, a mixture of potassium cyanide and ammonia (or potassium cyanide and ammonium chloride) is used. For example, 2-aminopropanoic acid (α-alanine) may be synthesized from ethanal by the following reaction sequence:

$$CH_3CHO \xrightarrow[\text{(or NH}_4\text{Cl)}]{\text{NH}_3} \left[CH_3-\overset{\overset{\text{OH}}{|}}{\underset{\underset{\text{NH}_2}{|}}{C^*}}-H \right] \xrightarrow{-H_2O} [CH_3-CH=NH]$$

$$\xrightarrow{CN^-} \left[CH_3-\overset{\overset{\text{CN}}{|}}{\underset{\underset{\text{NH}_2}{|}}{C}}-H \right]^- \xrightarrow{H^+} \left[CH_3-\overset{\overset{\text{CN}}{|}}{\underset{\underset{\text{NH}_2}{|}}{C^*}}-H \right] \xrightarrow{\text{hydrolysis}} CH_3-\overset{\overset{\text{CO}_2\text{H}}{|}}{\underset{\underset{\text{NH}_2}{|}}{C^*}}-H$$

An asymmetric carbon atom (denoted by an asterisk) is formed in this reaction and, as there is equal chance of addition to either side of the planar carbonyl group, the product is the optically inactive racemate (or DL-form).

20.11 Properties of Amino-acids

The common amino-acids are white, crystalline solids with very high melting-points and boiling-points. Aminoethanoic acid and 2-aminopropanoic acid dissolve in water to form a neutral solution but are insoluble in ethanol or ethoxyethane. Amino-acids (except aminoethanoic acid) contain an asymmetric carbon atom and may be resolved into optically active forms. The naturally occurring amino-acids all have the L-configuration (*cf.* the naturally occurring sugars, which all have the D-configuration—see Unit 19.5).

20.12 Reactions of Amino-acids

The amino-acids are bifunctional compounds and undergo reactions which are characteristic of the amino-group and of the carboxylic acid group. Some reactions are due to the presence of both groups.

(a) Reactions of the Amino-group
(i) **Action of nitrous acid.** Nitrogen is evolved when an amino-acid is treated with a mixture of sodium nitrite and hydrochloric acid:

$$RCH(NH_2)CO_2H + \text{`HNO}_2\text{'} \rightarrow RCHOHCO_2H + H_2O + N_2$$

This reaction is characteristic of primary amino-groups (see Unit 18.5(g)).
(ii) **Salt formation.** Amino-acids form salts with mineral acids and with alkalis, thus:

$$\underset{\overset{|}{CO_2H}}{RCHNH_2} + HCl \longrightarrow \underset{\overset{|}{CO_2H}}{RCHNH_3^+Cl^-}$$

$$\underset{\overset{|}{CO_2H}}{RCHNH_2} + NaOH \longrightarrow \underset{\overset{|}{CO_2^-Na^+}}{RCHNH_2}$$

(b) Reactions of the Carboxyl Group

(i) **Salt formation.** See Unit 20.12(a)(ii) above.

(ii) **Esterification.** The carboxyl group forms an ester on treatment with an alcohol in the presence of a catalyst:

$$\underset{\overset{|}{R}}{H_2NCHCO_2H} + R'OH \xrightarrow{H+} \underset{\overset{|}{R}}{H_2NCHCO_2R'} + H_2O$$

(iii) **Decarboxylation.** Amino-acids undergo decarboxylation on heating with soda-lime to yield primary amines (*cf.* carboxylic acids, Unit 5.3); for example, methylamine is obtained by the action of soda-lime on aminoethanoic acid:

$$\underset{\text{soda-lime}}{H_2NCH_2CO_2H + 2'NaOH'} \xrightarrow{\text{heat}} \underset{\text{methylamine}}{CH_3NH_2} + Na_2CO_3 + H_2O$$

(c) Reactions Depending on the Presence of Both Groups

(i) **Zwitterion formation.** Amino-acids contain both an acidic and a basic group, and exist as 'internal salts' or *zwitterions*, which accounts for their high melting-points and insolubility in organic solvents:

$$R—CH\underset{\diagdown CO_2H}{\overset{\diagup NH_2}{}} \longrightarrow R—CH\underset{\diagdown CO_2^-}{\overset{\diagup NH_3^+}{}}$$

a zwitterion

The melting-point of aminoethanoic acid (262° with decomposition), for example, is considerably higher than would be expected for a compound of such a low relative molecular mass. Amino-acids are thus neutral or amphoteric substances and cannot be titrated directly against alkalis or acids.

(ii) **Formation of copper complexes.** Aminoethanoic acid gives a deep-blue colour with aqueous copper(II) sulphate owing to the formation of a copper(II) complex:

$$2H_2NCH_2CO_2H + Cu^{2+} \longrightarrow \overset{\displaystyle O}{\underset{CH_2—NH_2}{\overset{\parallel}{C}—O}} \underset{}{\overset{H_2N—CH_2}{\underset{O—C}{Cu}}} + 2H^+$$

Experiment 20.4 *To demonstrate the reactions of amino-acids*

1. *Action of heat.* Warm a few crystals of aminoethanoic acid (glycine) in a dry test-tube and note the high melting (and decomposition) point.

2. *Action of sodium carbonate solution.* Add 2 cm³ of sodium carbonate

solution to a solution of aminoethanoic acid in water. Note the evolution of carbon dioxide.

3. *Action of nitrous acid.* Add 1 cm³ of dilute ethanoic acid to 2 cm³ of aqueous sodium nitrite solution. Cool the mixture and then add a few crystals of aminoethanoic acid. Note the evolution of nitrogen.

4. *Formation of copper(II) complex.* Add some crystals of aminoethanoic acid to 3 or 4 cm³ of copper(II) sulphate solution containing 2 drops of dilute sodium hydroxide. Note the blue coloration; deep-blue needle-shaped crystals usually separate on allowing the warmed solution to stand.

Test Yourself on Unit 20

1. Describe how you would distinguish between the following pairs of compounds:
   (a) glucose and fructose,
   (b) glucose and sucrose,
   (c) starch and cellulose,
   (d) a carbohydrate and a protein,
   (e) maltose and sucrose.

2. What are the reactions (if any) between sucrose and (a) silver nitrate, (b) sulphuric acid and (c) nitric acid?

3. Explain what is meant by the terms *polysaccharide, mutarotation, amino-acid residue, zwitterion* and *peptide link.*

4. Explain the following:
   (a) A yellow coloration is obtained when concentrated nitric acid comes into contact with the skin.
   (b) The melting-points of propanoic acid and aminoethanoic acid are $-22°$ and $262°$ (decomp.) respectively, yet the two compounds have approximately the same relative molecular mass.
   (c) The rate of an enzyme-catalysed reaction increases with increasing temperature, but above a certain temperature it falls to zero.
   (d) Sucrose does not react with Fehling's solution.
   (e) The specific rotation of a freshly prepared solution of α-D($+$)-glucose slowly decreases.

5. Write an account of the structure, properties and uses of two naturally occurring polysaccharides.

6. Discuss the general structure of polypeptides and describe how you would separate and identify the hydrolysis products of a polypeptide containing 6 amino-acid residues.

7. Compare and contrast polypeptides and polysaccharides.

Synthetic Polymers

21.1 Introduction

A *polymer* is a substance of high relative molecular mass which is formed by the combination of a large number of smaller molecules, or *monomers*. Polymers whose molecules are composed of chemically identical units

$$-A-A-A-A-A-A-A-A-$$

are known as *homopolymers*; the simple polyalkenes are examples. *Copolymer* molecules are composed of more than one type of monomer:

$$-A-B-A-B-A-B-A-B-$$

Bakelite (see Unit 13.7(*b*)(v)) and Buna-N synthetic rubber (see Unit 21.8(*b*)) are both examples of copolymers.

A number of synthetic polymers were described in earlier Units. This Unit summarizes some of the general properties of *macromolecules* (very large molecules) and introduces a number of other useful plastics and polymeric materials.

21.2 Polymerization

Polymerization is a result of the reaction of compounds with more than one functional group or, in the case of the polyalkenes (see Unit 7.6(*j*)), of reaction by addition to a carbon–carbon double bond. Suppose that we represent two bifunctional compounds as —Ⓐ— and —B̄—, and that —Ⓐ— can only react with —B̄— or —B̄— with —Ⓐ—. The formation of a polymer chain can then be represented diagrammatically as:

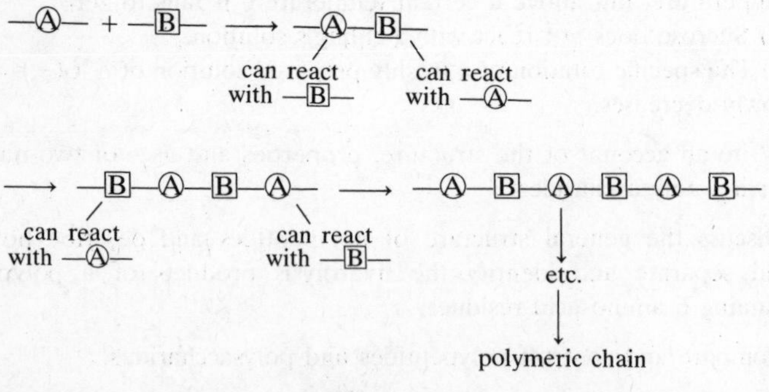

Similar polymerization of a bifunctional compound —B̄— with a trifunctional substance ⟨X⟩ yields branched chains that can then combine to form cross-linked structures:

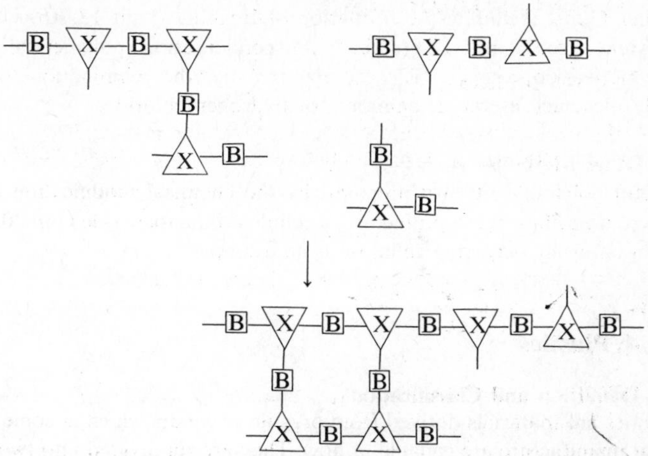

Polypeptides (see Unit 20.9(a)), polysaccharides (see Unit 20.8) and nylon-6 (see Unit 21.5) are examples of polymers of the $[A—B]_n$ type, in which two different functional groups are present in a single monomer molecule.

21.3 Types of Polymerization

There are two principal types of polymerization, depending on whether the polymer is built up by *addition* or *condensation* reactions.

(a) Addition Polymerization

An addition homopolymer has the same empirical formula but a considerably higher relative molecular mass than the monomer. The simplest examples of addition polymers are the polyalkenes (see Unit 7.6(j)):

$$n\,CH_2{=}\underset{Y}{CH} \longrightarrow \left[CH_2{-}\underset{Y}{CH}\right]_n$$

Copolymers may be formed by an addition reaction involving two different alkenes:

$$n\,CH_2{=}\underset{X}{CH} + n\,CH_2{=}\underset{Y}{CH} \longrightarrow \left[CH_2{-}\underset{X}{CH}{-}CH_2{-}\underset{Y}{CH}\right]_n$$

Their properties are different from those of either of the two homopolymers $[CH_2CHX]_n$ and $[CH_2CHY]_n$.

(b) Condensation Polymerization

A number of examples of condensation polymerization were described in earlier Units, including the formation of Bakelite (Unit 13.7(b)(v)) and of Terylene (see Unit 12.8(a)(iii)). In condensation polymerization, the polymerization process is accompanied by the elimination of small molecules such as water, ammonia or hydrogen chloride.

(c) Other Methods

Useful polymers are also prepared by the chemical modification of other macromolecules; the manufacture of cellulose ethanoate (see Unit 20.8(b)(ii)) from naturally occurring cellulose is an example.

21.4 Plastics

(a) Definition and Classification

Plastics are materials derived from organic polymers which at some stage of their manufacture are capable of flow. They are subdivided into two groups: the *thermosoftening* and the *thermosetting* plastics depending on their behaviour on heating.

(b) Fillers and Additives

Plastics frequently contain other materials to modify their properties. These include *plasticizers* to increase flexibility, *pigments* to provide colour and *fillers* to increase strength or to reduce costs—or frequently both—by replacing part of the bulk of the polymer with a cheaper material such as sawdust or wood shavings.

21.5 Thermosoftening Plastics

Thermosoftening polymers (or *thermoplastics*) have a linear structure—that is, the molecules consist of long chains of monomer units which have no chemical bonds between them and which can thus easily slide past one another when the polymer is heated. The softened polymer can then be moulded into a new shape which is retained when the material resolidifies on cooling, and this heating, reshaping and cooling process can be repeated indefinitely. The polyalkenes are the simplest examples of linear polymers. They are shaped by extrusion, blow-moulding, rolling or injecting the molten material. Other thermoplastic polymers include the polyester *Terylene* (see Unit 12.8(a)(iii)), and the polyamide *nylon*, which was the first synthetic fibre to be prepared by polymerization.

Nylon is formed by the condensation of hexanedioic acid (or of the corresponding acyl chloride) with 1,6-diaminohexane:

$$n\,HO_2C(CH_2)_4CO_2H + n\,H_2N(CH_2)_6NH_2 \rightarrow \text{-}[OC(CH_2)_4CONH(CH_2)_6NH]\text{-}_n$$

nylon-6,6

The product contains the peptide link —CO—NH—, a group that is also found in polypeptides and proteins (see Unit 20.9(*a*)), including wool, which is a naturally occurring protein fibre. This particular nylon is known as nylon-6,6, as it is formed by the reaction of two substances each of which contains six carbon atoms. If monomers with different numbers of carbon atoms are used, nylons with slightly different properties are obtained: nylon-6,10, for example, is made by the reaction of decanedioic acid, $HO_2C(CH_2)_8CO_2H$, and 1,6-diaminohexane, while nylon-6 is produced by the polymerization of caprolactam:

caprolactam

$$\xrightarrow[\text{trace of moisture}]{250°}$$

$+CO(CH_2)_5NH+_n$

nylon-6

Caprolactam is manufactured from cyclohexanone:

cyclohexanone

$$\xrightarrow[100°]{H_2NOH/H_2SO_4}$$

cyclohexanone oxime

$$\xrightarrow[\text{heat}]{20\% \text{ oleum}}$$

caprolactam

Nylon-6 is softer and melts at a lower temperature than either nylon-6,6 or nylon-6,10. Nylon and Terylene fibres are made by forcing the molten polymer through fine jets.

Experiment 21.1 *Preparation of nylon-6,6*

Pour 10 to 15 cm^3 of a 5 per cent solution of hexanedioyl dichloride (adipyl chloride) in tetrachloromethane into a dry 100 cm^3 beaker. Pour an equal volume of a 5 per cent aqueous solution of 1,6-diaminohexane **carefully** on top of the tetrachloromethane layer so that the solutions do not mix. A thin film of nylon is formed at the interface between the two layers.

$$n\,ClCO(CH_2)_4COCl + n\,H_2N(CH_2)_6NH_2 \xrightarrow[\text{interface}]{\text{reaction at}}$$

$$+CO(CH_2)_4CONH(CH_2)_6NH+_n$$

Remove this nylon with forceps and wind it round a glass rod (Fig. 21.1). By rotating the rod slowly the nylon can be removed as it is formed as a continuous thread until one or other of the reactants is exhausted. The material should be washed well with water and then with a little propanone (**Care! propanone is flammable**) before handling it as hexanedioyl dichloride should not be allowed to come into contact with the skin.

Nylon-6,10 may be prepared in the same way by substituting decanedioyl dichloride (sebacoyl chloride) for hexanedioyl dichloride.

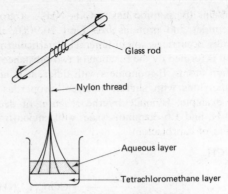

Fig. 21.1 Preparation of nylon

Experiment 21.2 *Preparation of nylon fibres*
Melt some nylon pellets or some colourless nylon (from an old comb, for
example) in a test-tube over a small flame. Dip a thin wire into the melt and
withdraw a fibre of nylon. Allow the fibre to cool and then test its strength
and elasticity. Examine a fibre through a piece of Polaroid; then stretch it
tightly, and examine it again. The altered appearance of the fibre is due to
the changes in its crystalline structure induced by strain.

21.6 Thermosetting Plastics

Thermosetting polymers have complex cross-linked three-dimensional
structures. They do not soften on heating and are therefore moulded during
the polymerization stage of their manufacture; unlike the thermoplastics,
they cannot then be reshaped. Bakelite (see Unit 13.7(*b*)(v)), carbamide–
methanal and melamine–methanal plastics, epoxy-resins, glyptal resins and
the polyurethans are all thermosetting polymers.

(*a*) Epoxy-resins
Epoxy-resins are prepared by the action of chloroepoxyalkanes on
diphenols; for example:

$$n\text{CH}_2\text{—CHCH}_2\text{Cl} + n\text{HO—}\bigcirc\text{—}\underset{\underset{\text{CH}_3}{|}}{\overset{\overset{\text{CH}_3}{|}}{\text{C}}}\text{—}\bigcirc\text{—OH}$$

1-chloro-2,3-epoxypropane   2,2-bis-(4-hydroxyphenyl)propane

$$\left[\text{CH}_2\text{—CH—CH}_2\text{—O—}\bigcirc\text{—}\underset{\underset{\text{CH}_3}{|}}{\overset{\overset{\text{CH}_3}{|}}{\text{C}}}\text{—}\bigcirc\text{—O—}\right]_n$$

The polymer chains are cross-linked through the epoxy-group. Epoxy-resins are used as electrical insulators, adhesives (such as Araldite) and surface coatings, often with the addition of hardeners to give an infusible, insoluble cross-linked solid.

(b) Glyptal Resins

These are polyesters formed from the reaction between propane-1,2,3-triol (glycerol) and benzene-1,2-dicarboxylic anhydride (phthalic anhydride):

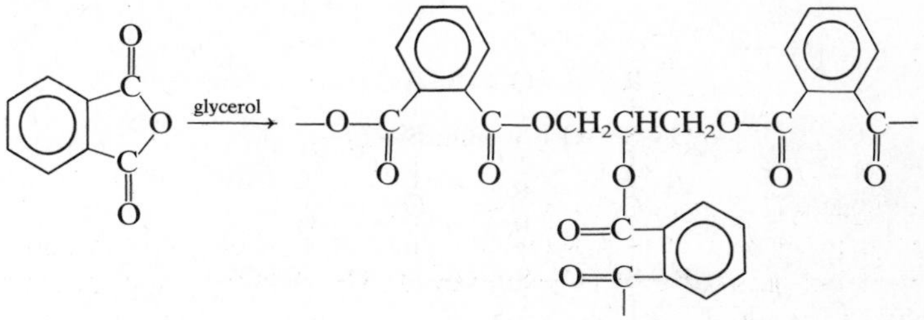

21.7 Silicones

Silicon is in the same group of the Periodic Table as carbon and has a similar electronic configuration ($1s^2 2s^2 p^6 3s^2 p^2$). It has a covalency of four and forms compounds with hydrogen, halogens and alkyl groups of similar formula to the corresponding carbon derivatives; for example,

silanes SiH_4, Si_2H_6; *cf.* hydrocarbons CH_4, C_2H_6

alkyl-substituted chlorosilanes R_2SiCl_2, $RSiCl_3$; *cf.* chloroalkanes R_2CCl_2, $RCCl_3$

(a) Preparation of Substituted Chlorosilanes

Chlorosilane derivatives may be prepared by the reaction between silicon and chloroalkanes at high temperatures in the presence of a copper or silver catalyst; for instance:

$$Si + 2CH_3Cl \xrightarrow[300°]{Cu} (CH_3)_2SiCl_2$$

or by the action of tetrachlorosilane on a Grignard reagent:

$$RMgX + SiCl_4 \longrightarrow RSiCl_3 \xrightarrow{RMgX} R_2SiCl_2 \longrightarrow \text{etc.}$$

(b) Polymerization

The dialkyldichlorosilanes are readily hydrolysed to yield dialkylsilanediols, $R_2Si(OH)_2$, which condense spontaneously and polymerize to form linear polymeric chains known as *silicones*:

$$n R_2SiCl_2 \xrightarrow{H_2O} n R_2Si(OH)_2 \longrightarrow -O-\underset{\underset{R}{|}}{\overset{\overset{R}{|}}{Si}}-O-\underset{\underset{R}{|}}{\overset{\overset{R}{|}}{Si}}-O-etc.$$

silicone

Copolymerization of these diols with trichlorosilane derivatives $RSiCl_3$, gives a cross-linked three-dimensional structure in which the oxygen atoms and substituent groups are arranged tetrahedrally about the silicon atoms:

$$
\begin{array}{ccccccc}
 & & R & & O & & R \\
 & & | & & | & & | \\
-O- & Si & -O- & Si & -O- & Si & -O- \\
 & | & & | & & | & \\
 & O & & R & & O & \\
 & | & & | & & | & \\
R- & Si & -O- & Si & -O- & Si & -O- \quad Si-O- \\
 & | & & | & & | & \\
 & O & & R & & R & R \\
\end{array}
$$

Cross-linking is also obtained by adding di(benzoyl) peroxide as a catalyst.

The structure of alternating silicon and oxygen atoms, resembling that in silica, is extremely stable to heat, while the hydrocarbon substituents (where R is an alkyl or aryl group) make the polymer flexible and water-repellent and also increase its solubility in organic solvents.

(c) Uses

Silicones are used in constant-viscosity lubricating oils and in the manufacture of paints, polishes and waterproof surfaces. Silicone rubber is chemical-resistant and is more stable than natural rubber at high and low temperatures.

21.8 Rubbers

(a) Natural Rubber

Natural rubber is obtained from *latex*, the milky fluid produced by the bark of the tree *Hevea brasiliensis*. Latex is an emulsion of rubber in water and is coagulated by the addition of methanoic acid or ethanoic acid. Most of the world's natural rubber comes from Malaysia and other parts of South East Asia.

Rubber has the structure:

$$-CH_2-\underset{\underset{CH_3}{|}}{C}=CH-CH_2-CH_2-\underset{\underset{CH_3}{|}}{C}=CH-CH_2- \text{ etc.}$$

Its molecular formula is $(C_5H_8)_n$ and it may be regarded as a polymer of 2-methylbuta-1,3-diene, $CH_2\!=\!C(CH_3)CH\!=\!CH_2$, which is formed in poor yield when rubber is distilled. A polymer similar to natural rubber may be obtained by heating 2-methylbuta-1,3-diene under pressure in the presence of a Ziegler catalyst (triethylaluminium and titanium(IV) chloride; see Unit 7.6(j)).

Pure rubber does not wear well and becomes soft and sticky in warm weather. These properties are improved and its strength and elasticity are greatly increased by heating it with a little sulphur to 100–150°. This process is known as *vulcanization* and involves the formation of cross-links between neighbouring polymer chains. The time required for the vulcanization process is reduced by the addition of nitrogen and sulphur compounds, known as *accelerators*. Carbon, zinc oxide and other substances are added as fillers and to increase the strength and wearing qualities of the rubber, together with aromatic amines as antioxidants.

(b) Synthetic Rubbers

Supplies of natural rubber are limited and are highly susceptible to political pressures, and a number of synthetic rubbers have therefore been developed. The simplest of these are based on buta-1,3-diene and its derivatives. For example, *neoprene rubber* is formed by the polymerization of 2-chlorobuta-1,3-diene:

$$n\text{CH}_2=\text{CH}-\underset{\underset{\text{Cl}}{|}}{\text{C}}=\text{CH}_2 \xrightarrow[\text{catalyst}]{(\text{NH}_4)_2\text{S}_2\text{O}_8} \left[\text{CH}_2-\text{CH}=\underset{\underset{\text{Cl}}{|}}{\text{C}}-\text{CH}_2\right]_n$$

neoprene rubber

Many useful synthetic rubbers are manufactured by the copolymerization of buta-1,3-diene with another unsaturated compound, such as phenylethene or propenonitrile; for example:

$$2n\text{CH}_2=\text{CH}-\text{CH}=\text{CH}_2 + n\text{CH}_2=\text{CHCN} \longrightarrow$$

$$\left[\text{CH}_2-\text{CH}=\text{CH}-\text{CH}_2-\text{CH}_2-\text{CH}=\text{CH}-\text{CH}_2-\text{CH}_2-\underset{\underset{\text{CN}}{|}}{\text{CH}}\right]_n$$

Buna-N rubber

Synthetic rubber is superior to natural rubber for some applications; neoprene, for example, is very strong and is resistant to oil and organic solvents. These man-made materials are, however, frequently more expensive than the natural product.

Test Yourself on Unit 21

1. Explain the meaning of the following terms: (a) plastic, (b) thermosetting polymer, (c) filler, (d) plasticizer, (e) vulcanization. (f) cross-linking, (g) monomer, (h) copolymerization, (i) macromolecule.

2. What is a polymer? Discuss, with suitable examples, the formation and structure of addition and condensation polymers.

3. Write an account of the structure, properties and uses of the following naturally occurring macromolecules: (a) polysaccharides, (b) proteins and (c) rubber.

4. 'Polymers are classified as thermoplastic (thermosoftening) or thermosetting.' Discuss this statement by reference to the structure, preparation and properties of THREE different examples of each type.

5. Write an essay on the uses of synthetic and naturally occurring macromolecules. What are the principal properties of each polymer which particularly suit it for the purposes you describe?

6. Outline the preparation, properties and structures of (a) nylon, (b) poly(chloroethene), (c) silicones.

7. Discuss the mechanisms of alkene polymerization.

Further Reading

Allinger, N. L. *et al.*: *Organic Chemistry*. Worth Publishers (New York, 1976).

Cross, A. D. and Jones, R. A.: *An Introduction to Practical Infra-red Spectroscopy*. Butterworth (London, 1969).

Everett, K. and Jenkins, E. W.: *A Safety Handbook for Science Teachers*. John Murray (London, 1977).

Finar, I. L.: *Organic Chemistry. Volume 1: The Fundamental Principles*. Longman (Harlow, 1973).

Gilbert, B. C.: *Investigation of Molecular Structure*. Mills and Boon (London, 1976).

Mann, F. G. and Saunders, B. C.: *Practical Organic Chemistry*. Longman (Harlow, 1974).

Stark, J. G. and Wallace, H. G.: *Chemistry Data Book*. John Murray (London, 1970).

Sykes, P.: *A Guidebook to Mechanism in Organic Chemistry*. Longman (Harlow, 1975).

Melting-points of Derivatives of Organic Compounds

(a) **3,5-Dinitrobenzoates of alcohols and phenols** (see Schotten–Baumann reaction, Experiment 13.1)

Compound	m.p. of derivative (°C)	Compound	m.p. of derivative (°C)
Methanol	109	Phenylmethanol	112
Ethanol	93	Cyclohexanol	113
Propan-1-ol	74	Phenol	146
Propan-2-ol	122	2-Methylphenol	134
Butan-1-ol	63	3-Methylphenol	165
Butan-2-ol	75	4-Methylphenol	188
Ethane-1,2-diol	169		

(b) **2,4-Dinitrophenylhydrazones of aldehydes and ketones** (see Experiment 15.1.9)

Compound	m.p. of derivative (°C)	Compound	m.p. of derivative (°C)
Methanal	166	Propanone	128
Ethanal	168	Butan-2-one	115
Propanal	155	Pentan-2-one	143
Butanal	122	Pentan-3-one	156
Benzaldehyde	237	Cyclohexanone	162
3-Phenylpropenal (cinnamaldehyde)	255 (decomposes)	Phenylethanone	242

Special Reagents

Alcoholic (ethanolic) potassium hydroxide. Reflux 10 g of potassium hydroxide (**Care!**) in 100 cm^3 of industrial rectified spirit for 20 minutes. Allow the mixture to cool and decant into a reagent bottle fitted with a rubber bung.

Ammoniacal silver nitrate solution. See **Tollen's reagent.**

Bleaching powder solution. Shake about 10 g of bleaching powder with about 100 cm^3 of water; allow the mixture to stand and then filter.

Brady's reagent (or **DNPH**). Dissolve 1 g of 2,4-dinitrophenylhydrazine in 30 cm^3 of methanol and 10 cm^3 of water. Add 2 cm^3 of concentrated sulphuric acid and mix well. Allow the mixture to stand and filter if necessary.

Bromine water. Shake 4 or 5 cm^3 of bromine (**Care!**) with 100 cm^3 of water and decant the supernatant aqueous solution as required.

Fehling's solution I. Dissolve 7 g of copper(II) sulphate in 100 cm^3 of water.
Fehling's solution II. Dissolve 10 g of sodium hydroxide pellets (**Care!**) and 5 g of potassium sodium 2,3-dihydroxybutanedioate (tartrate), $C_6H_4O_6KNa \cdot 4H_2O$ (Rochelle salt), in 100 cm^3 of water. **Fehling's solution** is prepared as required by mixing equal volumes of solutions I and II.

Hydrogen peroxide. '10 volumes' solution may be used.

Iodine solution. Use 1 per cent solution in aqueous 10 per cent potassium iodide.

Iron(III) chloride solution. Dissolve 7 g of $FeCl_3 \cdot 6H_2O$ in 100 cm^3 of water and add 1 cm^3 of concentrated hydrochloric acid. Neutral iron(III) chloride solution is prepared by adding dilute aqueous ammonia to some iron(III) chloride solution until a precipitate appears and then adding the original aqueous iron(III) chloride drop by drop until the precipitate just dissolves.

Mercury(II) chloride solution. Use 5 per cent aqueous solution.

Potassium manganate(VII) solution. 1 per cent aqueous solution. *Acidic* potassium manganate(VII) solution is prepared by adding about 10 cm^3 of dilute sulphuric acid to 100 cm^3 of 1 per cent aqueous potassium manganate(VII). *Alkaline* potassium manganate(VII) is prepared by adding 5 g of potassium carbonate to about 100 cm^3 of 1 per cent aqueous potassium manganate(VII).

Schiff's reagent. Dissolve 0.1 g of fuchsin (rosaniline) in 100 cm^3 of warm water. Allow the solution to cool and then pass sulphur dioxide through it until the colour disappears.

Sodium pentacyanonitrosylferrate(II) solution (sodium nitroprusside). Shake one small crystal of the compound with about $10 \, cm^3$ of distilled water in a test-tube and decant the pale-pink supernatant solution; use at once.

Tollen's reagent (ammoniacal silver nitrate). This reagent should be prepared in *small* quantities immediately before use by adding aqueous ammonia drop by drop to about $5 \, cm^3$ of aqueous 1 per cent silver nitrate solution until the precipitate which forms almost dissolves. Always wash unused reagent down the sink at once; it can become explosively unstable on standing.

Answers to Test Questions

Unit One

1. (a) False. Organic compounds are usually covalent and the velocity of their reactions is generally controlled by the rate at which covalent bonds are broken.

(b) False. It is determined by the ready solubility of the hydrocarbon chain in oil or grease and of the polar carboxylate ion in water.

(c) True.

(d) False. There is only one compound with the formula C_3H_6. The two formulae in the question both have the same structure.

(e) False. Hydrophilic ('water-loving') groups dissolve readily in water. Hydrophobic ('water-hating') groups are insoluble in water.

(f) True.

2. (a) G.F. of alkynes $= C_nH_{2n-2}$. When $n = 8$, the formula is C_8H_{14} (octyne).

(b) G.F. of alkenes $= C_nH_{2n}$. When $n = 8$, the formula is C_8H_{16} (octene).

(c) G.F. of carboxylic acids $= C_nH_{2n+1}CO_2H$; $n = 7$ when the carboxylic acid contains 8 carbon atoms (don't forget the carbon atom in the carboxyl group!). The formula is therefore $C_7H_{15}CO_2H$ and the compound is called octanoic acid.

(d) G.F. of alcohols $= C_nH_{2n+1}OH$. When $n = 8$, the alcohol has the formula $C_8H_{17}OH$ and is called octanol.

3. (a) Sodium methanoate, (b) methanamide, (c) ethanoic anhydride, (d) trichloroethanal, (e) propanone, (f) ethylamine, (g) propanonitrile, (h) hex-2-ene, (i) tri-iodomethane, (j) chloroethene.

4. (a)   (b)

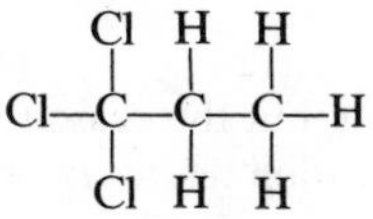

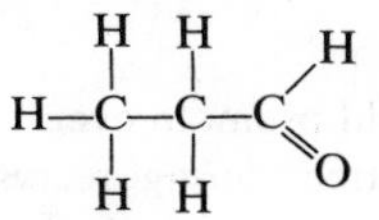

$C_nH_{2n+1}OH$.

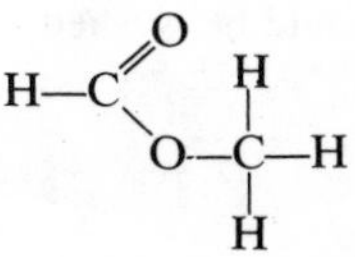

(c)   (d)

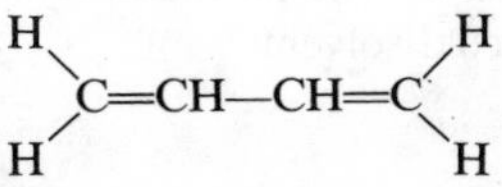

(e) 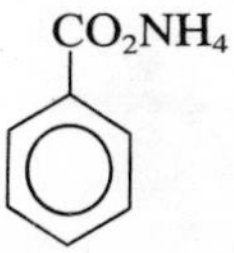   (f) 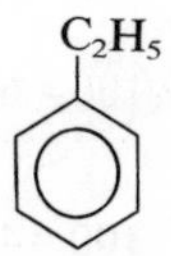   (g) 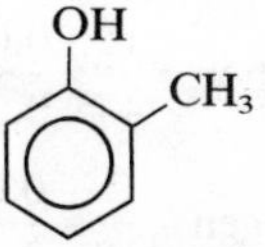   (h)

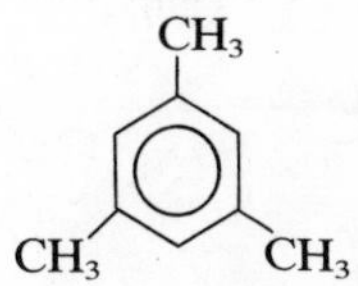

Unit Two

1. The material (m.p. 222°) was impure when it was prepared. The pure compound has a melting-point of 226° and was obtained after the second recrystallization. The material with m.p. 224° was purer than the original product but nevertheless still contained some impurity. The melting-points of pure S (226°) and the mixture $S + R$ are the same, indicating that S and R are identical.

2. False. Paper chromatography applies to both coloured and colourless compounds. Separation is more obvious with coloured components, but the location of colourless substances on the paper may be shown by ultra-violet light in some cases or by treatment with suitable chemicals to form coloured derivatives.

3. False. Separation is more efficient using three separate 25 cm^3 portions of ether.

4. False. Sublimation applies to substances which do not melt on heating but which pass directly into the vapour state.

5. True. A constant-boiling mixture of ethanol (approx. 96%) and water (4%) distils over first until all the ethanol is removed. The temperature then increases to 100° and pure water distils over.

6. False. The retention time of a component is constant only for a given set of experimental conditions (flow rate, column length, stationary phase, temperature etc.).

7. True.

8. False. The vapour pressure of a liquid increases with increasing temperature. As a liquid boils when its vapour pressure is equal to the external pressure, a reduction in pressure *lowers* the boiling-point of the liquid.

9. True. The rough surface provides nuclei for the formation of bubbles of vapour.

10. True.

11. False. Animal charcoal could promote even boiling, but the reason for adding it to the hot solution during recrystallization is to remove coloured impurities.

12. False. Washing the recrystallized solid with an excess of hot solvent would cause it to dissolve! The purified product should be washed with a limited amount of cold solvent.

Unit Three

4. Composition of aspirin:

$$\text{Carbon} = \frac{12}{44} \times \frac{0.057\,02}{0.025\,92} \times 100 = 60.0\%$$

$$\text{Hydrogen} = \frac{2}{18} \times \frac{0.010\,37}{0.025\,92} \times 100 = 4.45\%$$

$$\text{Oxygen} = 100 - (60.0 + 4.45) = 35.55\%$$

	C	:	H	:	O
Molar ratio:	60.0/12	:	4.45/1	:	35.55/16
	5	:	4.45	:	2.222
Divide by smallest:	2.25	:	2	:	1
Multiply by 4 to give whole numbers:	9	:	8	:	4

Empirical formula of aspirin $= (C_9H_8O_4)$

Its structural formula is

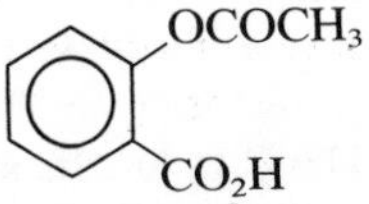

5. F contains C, 30.59%; H, 3.82%; Cl, 45.2%; O, 20.39%. Its empirical formula is C_2H_3ClO.

6. Volume of 0.100M HCl required to neutralize the ammonia from 0.304 4 g of the protein $= 50.0 - 22.2 = 27.8 \text{ cm}^3$.

$$NH_3 + HCl \rightarrow NH_4Cl$$

1 mol HCl $\equiv$ 1 mol $NH_3 \equiv$ 1 mol of nitrogen atoms $= 14$ g of nitrogen

$$27.8 \text{ cm}^3 \text{ of } 0.100M \text{ HCl} \equiv \frac{27.8}{1\,000} \times 0.1 \times 14 \text{ g of nitrogen}$$

$$\% \text{ nitrogen in the protein} = \frac{27.8}{1\,000} \times 0.1 \times \frac{14}{0.304\,4} \times 100$$

$$= 12.8\%$$

7. $\% \text{ iodine in } G = \frac{\text{RAM of I}}{\text{RMM of AgI}} \times \frac{\text{mass of AgI}}{\text{mass of compound}} \times 100$

$$= \frac{126.9}{234.8} \times \frac{0.288\,9}{0.161\,4} \times 100 = 96.7\%$$

G is CHI_3, tri-iodomethane (iodoform).

8. Composition of H:

$$\text{Carbon} = \frac{12}{44} \times \frac{0.052\,80}{0.024\,54} \times 100 = 58.68\%$$

$$\text{Hydrogen} = \frac{2}{18} \times \frac{0.016\,20}{0.024\,54} \times 100 = 7.33\%$$

1 mol (22 400 cm^3 at s.t.p.) of nitrogen (N_2) weighs 28 g.

$$8.85 \text{ cm}^3 N_2 \text{ at s.t.p. weighs } \frac{8.85}{22\,400} \times 28 = 0.011\,06 \text{ g}$$

$$\% \text{ nitrogen} = \frac{0.011\,06}{0.032\,39} \times 100 = 34.14$$

% oxygen $= 100 - (58.68 + 7.33 + 34.14) = -0.15\%$, i.e. zero, allowing for experimental error. H contains C, H and N only.

$$\text{Empirical formula} = \text{molecular formula} = C_2H_3N$$

Possible structural formulae are

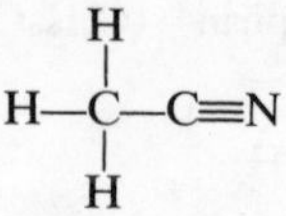

$$H-\underset{\underset{H}{|}}{\overset{\overset{H}{|}}{C}}-C{\equiv}N \quad \text{and} \quad H-\underset{\underset{H}{|}}{\overset{\overset{H}{|}}{C}}-N{\equiv}C$$

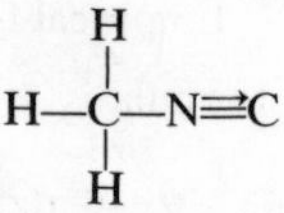

9. Molecular formula of acid $= C_3H_2O_2$. Its structural formula is

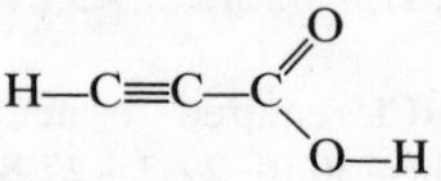

$$H-C{\equiv}C-\overset{\overset{\displaystyle O}{\|}}{C}{\diagdown}_{O-H}$$

10. E.F. of I = M.F. $= C_2H_5NO$. Three possible structural formulae are:

$$H-\underset{\underset{H}{|}}{\overset{\overset{H}{|}}{C}}-\underset{\underset{H}{|}}{\overset{\overset{H}{|}}{C}}-N{=}O \qquad H-\underset{\underset{H}{|}}{\overset{\overset{H}{|}}{C}}-\overset{\overset{\displaystyle O}{\|}}{C}\underset{\underset{\underset{H}{|}}{N}}{\diagup}^{H} \qquad H-\underset{\underset{H}{|}}{\overset{\overset{H}{|}}{C}}-\underset{\underset{H}{|}}{\overset{\overset{H}{|}}{C}}{=}N-\overset{\cdot\cdot}{O}-H$$

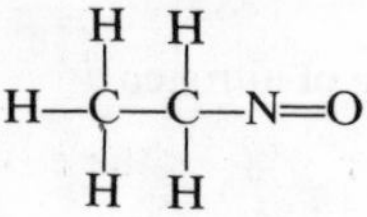

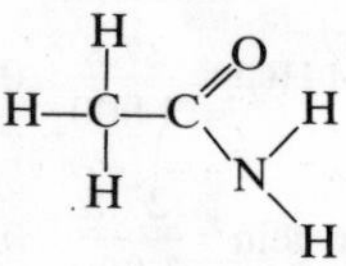

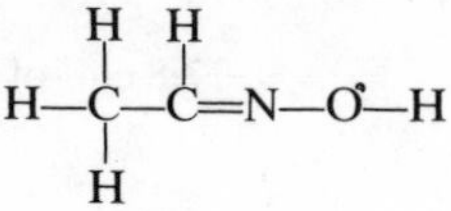

11. M.F. of $J = C_3H_9N$. Possible structural formulae of J are:

$CH_3CH_2CH_2NH_2$, $(CH_3)_2CHNH_2$, $CH_3NHCH_2CH_3$ and $(CH_3)_3N$.

12.

Equation	Volume of O_2 required (cm³)	Volume of CO_2 formed (cm³)
(a) $2C_2H_6 + 7O_2 \rightarrow 4CO_2 + 6H_2O$	42	24
(b) $CH_4 + 2O_2 \rightarrow CO_2 + 2H_2O$	24	12
(c) $2C_3H_6 + 9O_2 \rightarrow 6CO_2 + 6H_2O$	54	36
(d) $2C_2H_2 + 5O_2 \rightarrow 4CO_2 + 2H_2O$	30	24
(e) $C_3H_4 + 4O_2 \rightarrow 3CO_2 + 2H_2O$	48	36
(f) $2C_4H_{10} + 13O_2 \rightarrow 8CO_2 + 10H_2O$	78	48
(g) $C_2H_4 + 3O_2 \rightarrow 2CO_2 + 2H_2O$	36	24
(h) $C_4H_8 + 6O_2 \rightarrow 4CO_2 + 4H_2O$	72	48
(i) $C_3H_8 + 5O_2 \rightarrow 3CO_2 + 4H_2O$	60	36
(j) $2C_4H_6 + 11O_2 \rightarrow 8CO_2 + 6H_2O$	66	48

13. C_4H_{10}.

14. C_4H_8. Possible structural formulae of L:

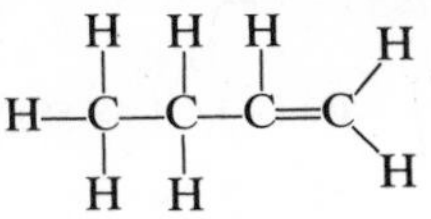

but-1-ene 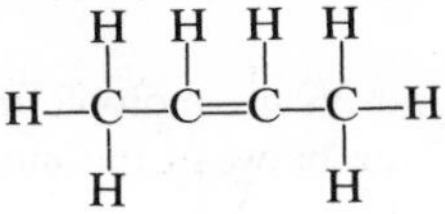   but-2-ene

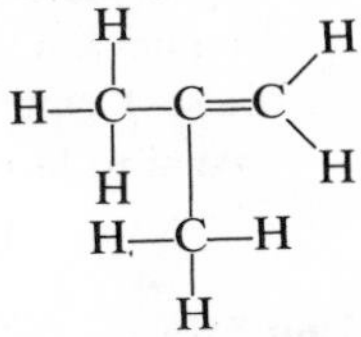

2-methylpropene

Other possibilities include cyclobutane and methylcyclopropane.

15. If the volumes of ethane and propane in the mixture are x and y cm^3 respectively,

$$x + y = 12 \text{ cm}^3 \qquad \text{(Equation 1)}$$

x cm^3 of C_2H_6 yields $2x$ cm^3 of CO_2 on combustion; similarly, y cm^3 of C_3H_8 yields $3y$ cm^3 of CO_2.

$$\text{Total volume of } CO_2 = 2x + 3y = 29.0 \text{ cm}^3 \quad \text{(Equation 2)}$$

Multiply Equation 1 by two and subtract it from Equation 2:

$$2x + 3y = 29$$
$$\underline{2x + 2y = 24}$$
$$y = 5 \text{ cm}^3 = \text{volume of propane in the mixture.}$$

From Equation 1:

$$\text{Volume of ethane} = x = 12 - 5 = 7 \text{ cm}^3.$$

16. The mixture contained 12 cm^3 of methane and 8 cm^3 of propene. Volume of oxygen required for the combustion $= 60$ cm^3.

Unit Four
1. (a) D; (b) (i) C, (ii) E; (c) E; (d) D; (e) (i) D, (ii) C; (f) (i) B, (ii) A, (iii) C.
2. B, C, A.
3. B, E, A, C, D.
4. $pK_b = -\log K_b = -\log(5.4 \times 10^{-4}) = -(\bar{4}.7324) = 3.27$.
5. (a) Addition; (b) substitution; (c) elimination; (d) condensation.
6. False (see Unit 4.4(c)).
7. True.
8. True.
9. True.
10. False. All the carbon–carbon bonds in cyclohexane are the same length but the molecule is not planar. The bond angle is about 105°, i.e. close to the angle between the unstrained bonds of an sp^3 hybridized carbon atom.
11. True.

12. True.

13. False. Heterolytic fission of a carbon–carbon σ-bond yields a carbonium ion.

14. False. Compounds possessing a dipole moment tend to be *less* volatile owing to the attraction between the molecules.

15. True.

Unit Five

1. (a) 3,3-Diethylpentane;
   (b) 2,2-dimethylpentane;
   (c) 2,3-dimethylbutane;
   (d) 1-chloro-3-methylpentane.

2. (a)

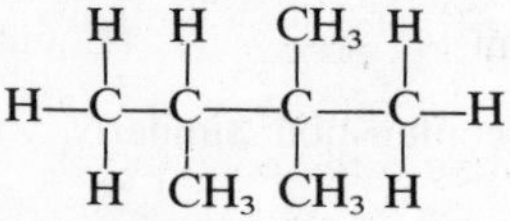

(b)

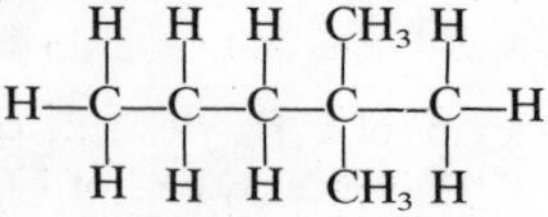

(c)

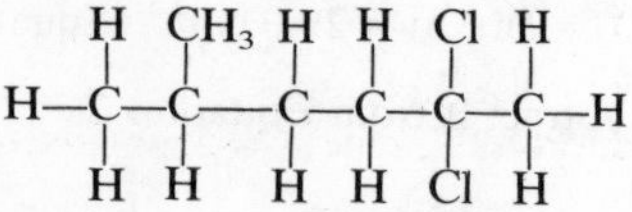

(d)

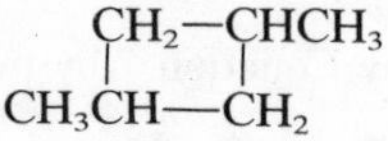

3. (i) and (c); (ii) and (f); (iii) and (e); (iv) and (a); (v) and (d); (vi) and (b); (vii) and (e).

4. (a) H_2/Raney nickel/heat/pressure; (b) Br_2/heat or Br_2+u.v. light; (c) reduction, e.g. with a zinc–copper couple + aqueous alcohol, or by catalytic hydrogenation (e.g. H_2/Pd–carbon); (d) CH_3Br + sodium (Wurtz reaction) – yields are low owing to the formation of C_2H_6 and C_4H_{10} as by-products, and a better yield is obtained from the following reaction sequence:

$$C_2H_5Br \xrightarrow{\text{Mg}} C_2H_5MgBr \xrightarrow{\text{CH}_3\text{Br}} C_3H_8 + MgBr_2$$

(e) sodium (Wurtz reaction); (f) zinc amalgam and concentrated hydrochloric acid (Clemmensen reduction); (g) heat with aluminium chloride (see Unit 4.9(d)).

Unit Seven

1. (a) 2-Methylbut-2-ene; (b) bromoethene; (c) penta-1,3-diene; (d) 4,4-dimethylpent-1-ene; (e) *trans*-hex-3-ene.

2. (a)

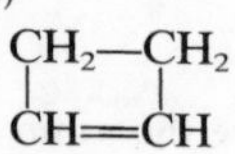

(b)

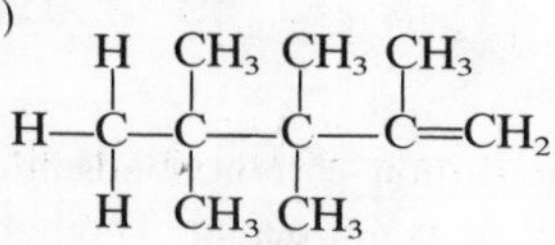

(c)

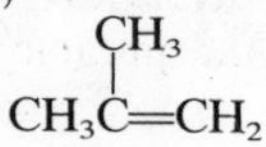

(d)

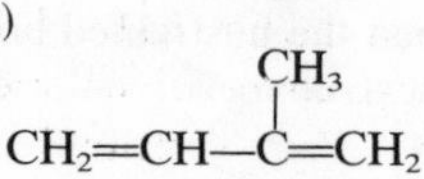

(e) $C_6H_5CH_2CH{=}CH_2$

6. True.

7. False.

8. True.

9. False. Hydration of propene yields propan-2-ol, $CH_3CHOHCH_3$, not propan-1-ol (Markownikoff's Rule, see Unit 7.6(f)).

10. True.

11. True.

12. False (see Unit 7.6(c)).

13. True.

14. False. Ethoxyethane, $(C_2H_5)_2O$, is the principal product. This general method does not apply to the halogenoethanes.

15. True. The carbon atoms forming the double bond are sp^2 hybridized in the alkene and sp^3 hybridized in the addition product.

16. True. The coefficient of friction of PTFE is extremely low (about the same as that between two blocks of melting ice), hence the use of this polymer for frictionless joints and 'non-stick' surfaces.

Unit Eight

1. (a) 5,5-Dimethylhex-2-yne; (b) 3-chlorobut-1-yne; (c) pent-3-en-1-yne; (d) hex-3-yne.

2. (a) $ClCH_2CH_2C{\equiv}CH$ (b)

$$H{-}\underset{\underset{H}{|}}{\overset{\overset{H}{|}}{C}}{-}\overset{\overset{H}{|}}{C}{=}\overset{\overset{CH_3}{|}}{C}{-}C{\equiv}CH$$

(c) $H_2C{=}CH{-}C{\equiv}C{-}CH{=}CH_2$

(d)

$$CH_3{-}\underset{\underset{CH_3}{|}}{\overset{\overset{CH_3}{|}}{C}}{-}CH_2{-}C{\equiv}C{-}CH_3$$

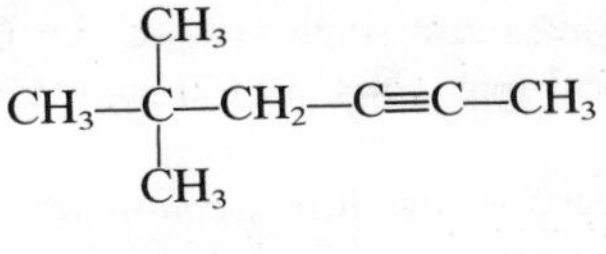

3. $CaO + 2C \text{ (coke)} \xrightarrow[\text{furnace}]{\text{electric}} CaC_2 \xrightarrow{H_2O} C_2H_2$

(a) $C_2H_2 \xrightarrow{Ni/H_2/\text{pressure}} C_2H_6$;

(b) $C_2H_2 \xrightarrow[\text{HgSO}_4 \text{ cat.}]{H_2O/H^+/60°} CH_3CHO$;

(c) $C_2H_2 + HCl \rightarrow CH_2{=}CHCl$;

(d) $C_2H_2 + 2HBr \xrightarrow{\text{peroxide}} CH_2BrCH_2Br$.

5. (a) Molecular formula of $A = C_4H_6$. (b) The formation of a red precipitate with ammoniacal copper(I) chloride indicates the presence of a $-C{\equiv}C-H$ group. The structural formula of A is therefore

$CH_3CH_2C{\equiv}CH$ (but-1-yne) and the reaction with boiling aqueous hydrogen bromide is:

$$CH_3CH_2C{\equiv}CH + 2HBr_{(aq)} \rightarrow CH_3CH_2CBr_2CH_3$$

(A) 2,2-dibromobutane (B)

Unit Nine

1. False. The chemistry of the aromatic hydrocarbons is characterized by electrophilic substitution reactions.

2. True.

3. True. Ethylbenzene, $C_6H_5C_2H_5$, and the 1,2-, 1,3- and 1,4-dimethylbenzenes, $C_6H_4(CH_3)_2$, all have the same molecular formula, C_8H_{10}.

4. True.

5. True. Benzene is a regular hexagon and both the C—C—C and C—C—H bond angles are all 120°.

6. False. *Ortho-*, *meta-* and *para-* refer to the 1,2-, 1,3- and 1,4-disubstituted benzenes respectively.

7. False. Benzene is not an equilibrium mixture of these two forms, the *actual* structure is somewhere between the two with all the carbon–carbon bonds identical.

8. False. The six orbitals concerned are all sp^2 hybridized (see Unit 9.5).

9. True.

10. False. The carbon–carbon bond lengths in benzene (0.140 nm) are intermediate between those of the pure single (C—C in $C_2H_6 = 0.154$ nm) and the pure double bond (e.g. C=C in $C_2H_4 = 0.133$ nm); the bond is *longer* than in ethene.

11. False. The symbol indicates that each of the forms *contributes* to the structure, but they are not in equilibrium.

12. True.

13. True.

14. True.

15. False. Benzenesulphonic acid, $C_6H_5SO_2OH$, has a carbon–sulphur bond, but in ethyl hydrogen sulphate, $C_2H_5OSO_2OH$, the bonding is carbon–oxygen–sulphur.

16. True (see Unit 9.6(a)(ii) and 9.7(c)(ii)).

17. False. The substituent chlorine atom is *ortho-/para*-directing; 3-chlorobenzenesulphonic acid is therefore prepared by the chlorination of benzenesulphonic acid (the —SO_3H group is *meta*-directing).

18. False. The nitro-group is *meta*-directing; *also* substitution by the Friedel–Crafts reaction does not take place in the highly deactivated nucleus of nitrobenzene and $C_6H_5NO_2$ is sometimes used as a solvent for this reaction. Methyl-4-nitrobenzene is prepared (mixed with the 2-isomer) by the nitration of methylbenzene.

Units Ten and Eleven

1. (*a*) 2-Bromopropane; (*b*) 2-chloro-2-methylpropane; (*c*) 1,1,4-trichloro-2,2,4-trimethylpentane; (*d*) 2,4-dichloro(chloromethyl)benzene.

2. (*a*) $CH_2=CHCH_2Br$;   (*b*) 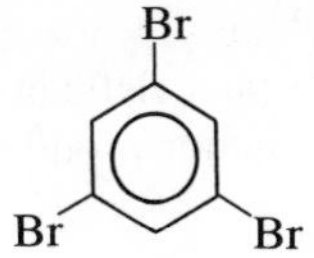   (*c*) $CH_3CH_2CCl_3$;

(*d*) 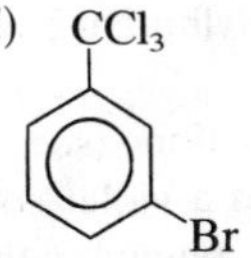   (*e*)

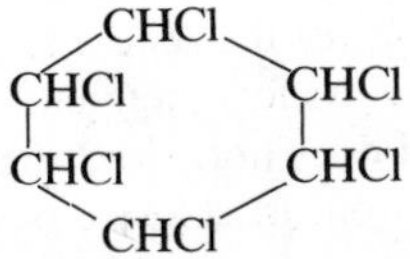

4. (*a*) $C_2H_5Br \xrightarrow{\text{aq. NaOH}} C_2H_5OH \xrightarrow[\substack{\text{or excess of}\\\text{conc. } H_2SO_4>170°}]{Al_2O_3/350°} C_2H_4$

(*b*) action of dry silver(I) oxide;

(*c*) $CH_3I \xrightarrow{KCN} CH_3CN \xrightarrow[\text{reflux aq. HCl}]{\text{hydrolysis}} CH_3CO_2H$

(*d*) $C_2H_5I \xrightarrow[\text{anhyd. }(C_2H_5)_2O]{\text{Mg turnings in}} C_2H_5MgI \xrightarrow[\text{(ii) } H^+/H_2O]{\text{(i) }(CH_2)_2O} C_2H_5CH_2CH_2OH$

(*e*) $C_2H_5Br \xrightarrow[\text{anhyd. }(C_2H_5)_2O]{\text{Mg in}} C_2H_5MgBr \xrightarrow[\text{(ii) } H^+/H_2O]{\text{(i) } CH_3CHO} CH_3CHOHC_2H_5$

(*f*)

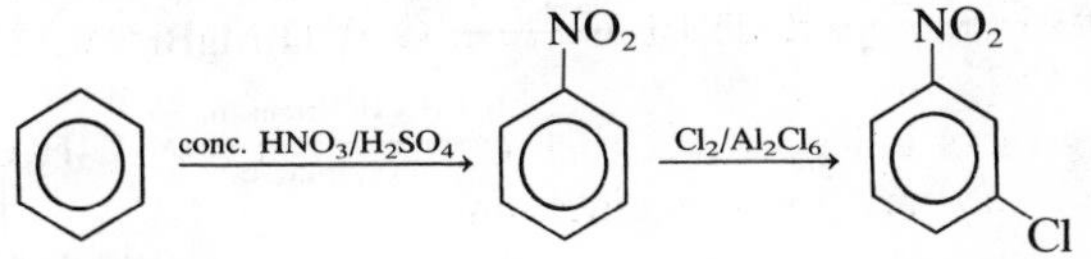

(*g*) $C_2H_6 \xrightarrow{Br_2/\text{heat}} C_2H_5Br \xrightarrow{NH_3} C_2H_5NH_3{}^+Br^- \xrightarrow{\text{aq. NaOH}} C_2H_5NH_2$

(*h*)

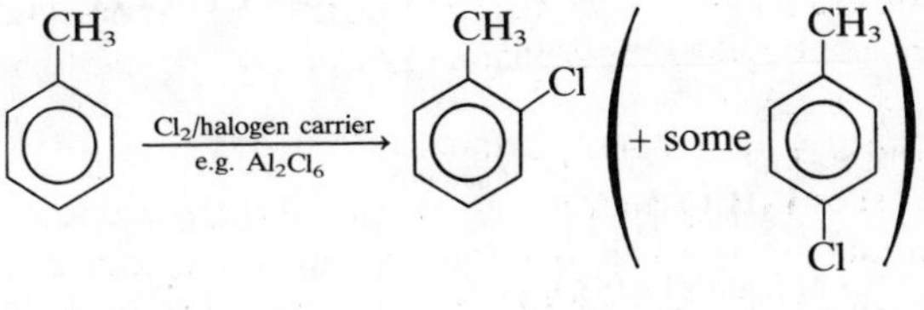

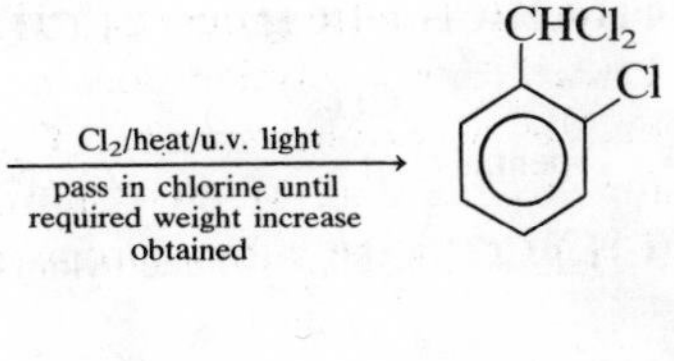

5. See Unit 10.6(a)(i)

6. (a) Under normal reaction conditions bromobenzene does not react with aqueous sodium hydroxide; at 300° under pressure sodium phenoxide is obtained (see Unit 11.6(a)); (b) ethylmagnesium(II) iodide, C_2H_5MgI; (c) none; (d) phenylethanonitrile, $C_6H_5CH_2CN$; (e) ethoxyethane, $(C_2H_5)_2O$, is the major product; virtually no ethene is obtained.

Units Twelve and Thirteen

1. (a) 1-Phenylethanol; (b) propane-1,3-diol; (c) 3-methylbutan-2-ol, (d) 2-methylbutan-2-ol; (e) benzene-1,2-diol.

2. (a) Ethanol gives tri-iodomethane (iodoform) reaction (see Unit 12.6(h)), methanol does not; (b) 2-methylphenol gives a violet coloration with aqueous iron(III) chloride (see Unit 13.6(b)), phenylmethanol will not; (c) 2-methylpropan-2-ol is a 3° alcohol and is difficult to oxidize (see Unit 12.6(e)). It also reacts with cold conc. hydrochloric acid to form oily drops of $(CH_3)_3CCl$; (d) phenol gives a violet colour with $FeCl_{3(aq)}$ (see Unit 13.6(b)); ethanoic acid liberates carbon dioxide from aqueous sodium carbonate, but phenol will not; (e) ethanol effervesces on adding sodium and hydrogen is evolved, but anhydrous ethoxyethane does not react. Ethanol also gives the tri-iodomethane reaction (see Unit 12.6(h)).

3. (a) See Unit 13.7(b)(ii); (b) see Unit 13.6(a); (c) see Unit 9.9 and 13.7(b)(i): (d) see Unit 13.5.

4. (a) $C_2H_5OH \xrightarrow{K_2Cr_2O_7/H_2SO_4} CH_3CHO$ (distil off as it forms to prevent further oxidation)

(b) $C_2H_5OH \xrightarrow{NaBr/H_2SO_4} C_2H_5Br \xrightarrow{\text{Mg in } (C_2H_5)_2O} C_2H_5MgBr$

$$\xrightarrow[\text{(ii) hydrolysis}]{\text{(i) } CH_3CHO \text{ (from 4(}a\text{))}} \underset{\underset{CH_3}{|}}{C_2H_5CHOH}$$

(c) $C_2H_5OH \xrightarrow[\text{heat under reflux}]{K_2Cr_2O_7/H_2SO_4} CH_3CO_2H$; $\quad CH_3CO_2H + C_2H_5OH$

$$\xrightleftharpoons{H^+} CH_3CO_2C_2H_5 + H_2O$$

(d) $C_2H_5OH \xrightarrow[<140°]{\text{excess of alcohol/conc. } H_2SO_4} (C_2H_5)_2O$

$$\xrightarrow{Na} \quad C_2H_5O^-Na^+ \xrightarrow[\text{(from 4(}b\text{))}]{C_2H_5Br}$$

5. See Units 7.6(c)–(f) and 12.6(g).

6. $CH_3CH_2CH_2\underset{\underset{CH_3}{|}}{CH}CH_3 \qquad CH_3CH_2CHOHCH_2CH_3 \qquad (CH_3)_2CH\underset{\underset{OH}{|}}{CH}CH_3$

pentan-2-ol $\qquad\qquad$ pentan-3-ol $\qquad\qquad$ 3-methylbutan-2-ol

$(CH_3)_2COHC_2H_5 \quad$ 2-methylbutan-2-ol

7. See Table 12.2 (Unit 12.6).

8. (a) Br_2/CCl_4 (see Unit 13.7(b)(i)); (b) fuming H_2SO_4/reflux (ii) fuse NaOH (iii) HCl; (c) anaerobic fermentation with yeast (see Unit 12.4(b)(i); (d) oxidation with $Cr_2O_7^{2-}/H_2SO_4$ (see Unit 12.6(e)); (e) chlorine water (see Unit 13.7(b)(i)).

10. See Units 12.4 and 13.3.

11. (a) See Unit 12.6(g)—note formation of either ether or alkene; (b) see Unit 13.7(b)(iii); (c) formation of toxic $(CH_3)_2SO_4$ (see Unit 12.6(g)).

12. A is a 3° alcohol, $(CH_3)_3COH$; B is a 1° alcohol and is either $CH_3CH_2CH_2CH_2OH$ or $(CH_3)_2CHCH_2OH$; C is an aldehyde $(CH_3CH_2CH_2CHO$ or $(CH_3)_2CHCHO)$, and D is the corresponding carboxylic acid, $CH_3CH_2CH_2CO_2H$ or $(CH_3)_2CHCO_2H$; E is $(CH_3)_3CCl$ and F is the ester of B with E, i.e. either $CH_3CH_2CH_2CO_2CH_2CH_2CH_2CH_3$ or $(CH_3)_2CHCO_2CH_2CH(CH_3)_2$. A is dehydrated by the action of sulphuric acid to form $(CH_3)_2C{=}CH_2$ which with bromine yields G, $(CH_3)_2CBrCH_2Br$.

Unit Fourteen

1.

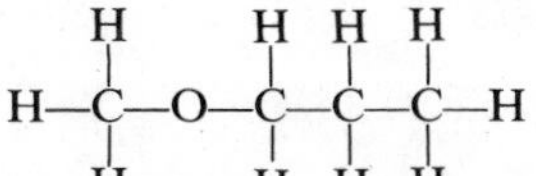

   1-methoxypropane (methyl n-propyl ether)

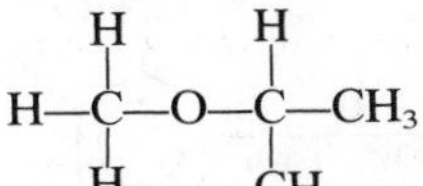

   2-methoxypropane (methyl isopropyl ether)

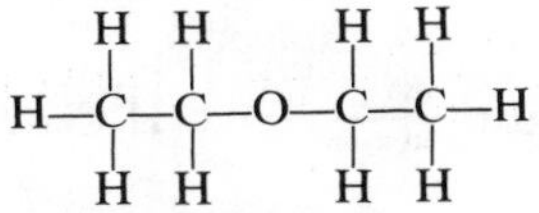

   ethoxyethane (diethyl ether)

2. See Units 14.2 and 14.5(c).

3. 3-Methylphenol (a) gives a violet-blue colour with $FeCl_{3(aq)}$, (b) reacts with and dissolves in $NaOH_{(aq)}$, (c) gives hydrogen with metallic sodium. Methoxybenzene does not react with any of these reagents.

4. (a) See Unit 14.2; (b) see Units 12.2(a) and 14.2; (c) see Unit 14.2.

5. Empirical formula of $Q = C_5H_{12}O$. Q does not contain an —OH group, since it does not react with sodium or yield hydrogen chloride with phosphorus pentachloride; it is therefore an ether.

$$(CH_3)_2CHO^-Na^+ + R = Q, C_5H_{12}O$$

R is thus C_2H_5I and Q is therefore $(CH_3)_2CHOC_2H_5$ (2-ethoxypropane, or ethyl isopropyl ether).

7. See Unit 14.8.

Unit Fifteen

1. (a) 2,2-Dimethylpropanal; (b) pentane-2,4-dione; (c) phenyl-propanone; (d) 2,4-dimethylhexanal; (e) 4,4-dimethylpentan-3-one.

2. The fact that A gives a yellow precipitate with 2,4-DNPH indicates that it is an aldehyde or a ketone. The use of either Tollen's reagent or Fehling's solution will distinguish between the two classes. The tri-iodomethane (iodoform) reaction will indicate the presence or absence of a CH_3CHO group. Finally the compound can be identified by its boiling-point and the melting-point of its 2,4-DNPH derivative. Confirmation may be obtained by carrying out a mixed melting-point of the 2,4-DNPH derivative with the 2,4-DNPH derivative of an authentic sample of the suspected aldehyde or ketone.

3. See Unit 15.5.

5. B is C_3H_6O, i.e. either CH_3CH_2CHO or CH_3COCH_3. These isomers may be distinguished by the action of ammoniacal silver nitrate or by the tri-iodomethane reaction.

6. (a)

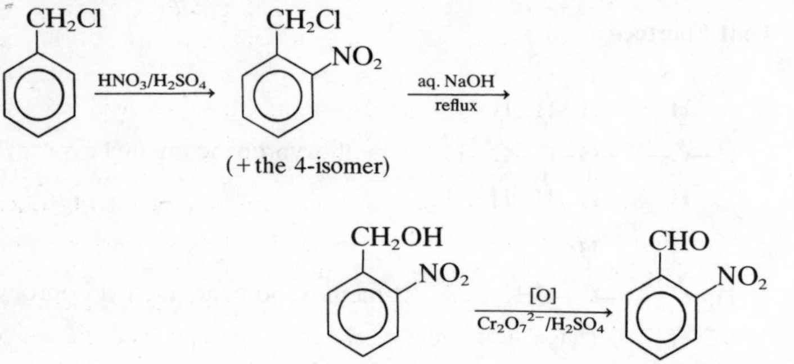

(+ the 4-isomer)

(b) $C_6H_6 \xrightarrow[Al_2Br_6]{Br_2+} C_6H_5Br \xrightarrow[\text{in THF}]{Mg} C_6H_5MgBr \xrightarrow[\text{(ii) hydrolysis}]{\text{(i) } CH_3CHO} C_6H_5CHOHCH$

(c) $(CH_3)_2CO \xrightarrow{HCN} (CH_3)_2C{\overset{OH}{\underset{CN}{\Big\langle}}} \xrightarrow[\text{hydrolysis}]{H^+/H_2O} CH_3CH{\overset{OH}{\underset{CO_2H}{\Big\langle}}}$

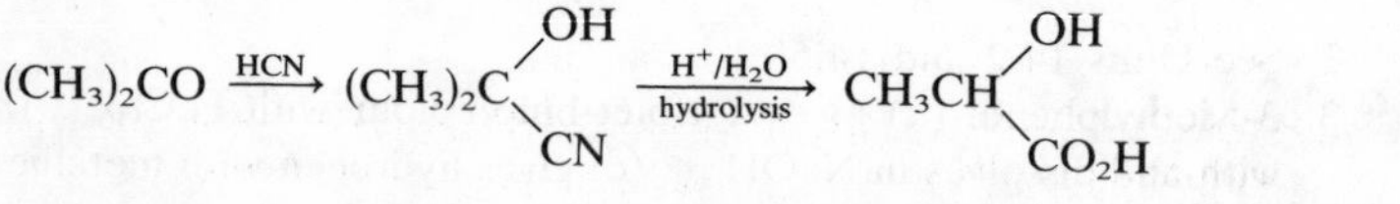

(d)

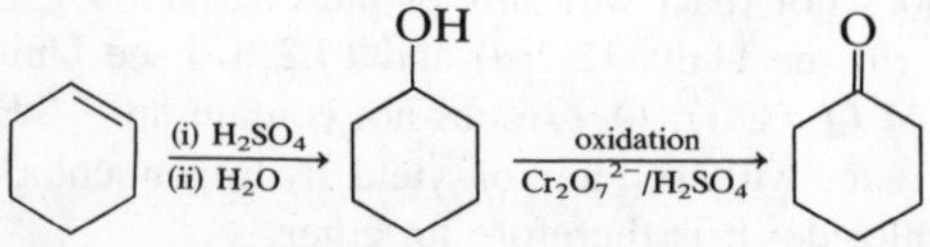

10. D. X must be the aldehyde, CH_3CHO, because of (a) its reaction with Fehling's solution and (b):

$$CH_3CHO \rightarrow CH_3CHOHCN \rightarrow CH_3CHOHCO_2H$$

Y must be a ketone as it does not react with Fehling's solution. Only the ozonide of D yields this combination of compounds on hydrolysis (see Unit 7.6(i)).

11. A is either a 1° or a 2° alcohol: 1° and 2° alcohols yield aldehydes (or carboxylic acids) and ketones respectively without loss of carbon atoms. 3° alcohols break up on oxidation to yield fragments each containing fewer carbon atoms than the original alcohol. The most probable formulae for A and C are as in (ii). E must be a 3° alcohol as it yields a mixture of products on oxidation; E is therefore $(CH_3)_3COH$. A must be $(CH_3)_2CHCH_2OH$ and C is $(CH_3)_2C=CH_2$.

12. A, $CH_3CH_2CHCl_2$; B, CH_3CH_2CHO; C, $CH_3C\equiv CH$; D, $CH_3CCl_2CH_3$; E, CH_3COCH_3.

Unit Sixteen

1. (a) 2,2-Dichloropropanoic acid; (b) 2,2-dimethylpropanoic acid; (c) pentane-1,5-dioic acid; (d) phenylethanoic acid.

2. (a) (i) Sodium carbonate effervesces with dilute hydrochloric acid, sodium ethanoate does not; (ii) sodium ethanoate will form an ester, ethyl ethanoate (which has, a distinctive, pleasant odour), on warming with ethanol and a few drops of concentrated sulphuric acid; (b) (i) methanoic acid yields carbon monoxide on treatment with concentrated sulphuric acid, (ii) methanoic acid (but not ethanoic acid) will reduce ammoniacal silver nitrate and mercury(II) chloride to silver and mercury + mercury(I) chloride respectively; (c) methanoic acid gives a silver mirror on treatment with ammoniacal silver nitrate and will reduce $HgCl_{2(aq)}$ to Hg and Hg_2Cl_2, ethanedioic acid does not; (d) benzoic acid effervesces with sodium carbonate solution, phenol does not; phenol gives a violet colour with $FeCl_{3(aq)}$, benzoic acid does not.

3. (a) $CH_2O \xrightarrow{\text{oxidation}} HCO_2H \xrightarrow{\text{NaOH}} HCO_2Na \xrightarrow{\text{heat}} (CO_2Na)_2 + H_2$

(b) $C_6H_6 \xrightarrow[\text{Al}_2\text{Br}_6]{\text{Br}_2+} C_6H_5Br \xrightarrow[\text{THF}]{\text{Mg in}} C_6H_5MgBr \xrightarrow[\text{(ii) hydrolysis}]{\text{(i) CO}_2} C_6H_5CO_2H$

(c) Oxidize part of the ethanol:

$$C_2H_5OH \xrightarrow{\text{Cr}_2\text{O}_7{}^{2-}/\text{H}_2\text{SO}_4} CH_3CO_2H$$

and then treat the product with the remaining ethanol to form the ester:

$$CH_3CO_2H + C_2H_5OH \xrightleftharpoons{\text{H}^+/\text{H}_2\text{O}} CH_3CO_2C_2H_5 + H_2O$$

(d) $C_2H_5Br \xrightarrow{KCN} C_2H_5CN \xrightarrow[\text{hydrolysis}]{H^+/H_2O} C_2H_5CO_2H$;

(e) $CH_3CHO \xrightarrow{Cr_2O_7^{2-}/H_2SO_4} CH_3CO_2H \xrightarrow[SOCl_2]{PCl_5 \text{ or}} CH_3COCl$

4. (a) Phenol, carbonic acid, ethanoic acid, methanoic acid; (b) ethanoic acid, iodoethanoic acid, bromoethanoic acid, fluoroethanoic acid; (c) 4-methylbenzoic acid, benzoic acid, 2-nitrobenzoic acid.

5. There is only one acid: $CH_3CH_2CO_2H$ (propanoic acid). This may be distinguished from the esters by its immediate effervescence with sodium carbonate. The two esters may be distinguished by the reactions of their hydrolysis products:

$$CH_3CO_2CH_3 \xrightarrow{\text{hydrolysis}} CH_3CO_2H + CH_3OH$$
methyl ethanoate

$$HCO_2C_2H_5 \xrightarrow{\text{hydrolysis}} HCO_2H + C_2H_5OH$$
ethyl methanoate

e.g. by the tri-iodomethane reaction of ethanol (but not methanol) and the reaction of methanoic acid (but not ethanoic acid) with conc. H_2SO_4 or aqueous $KMnO_4$ or ammoniacal silver nitrate or $HgCl_{2(aq)}$.

6. See Unit 16.7(c)(i).

9. E. 2, 3, 4 and 5 are correct. The products of these reactions are usually in the form of the acyl chloride.

10. E. 1 and 5 are correct.

11. E. 1, 2 and 3 are correct.

12. E. 1 and 2 are correct.

13. A. 1, 3 and 4 are correct.

14. A. 1, 3 and 4 are correct.

15. E. 1, 3 and 5 are correct.

16. A. The gas obtained at the anode contains 2 carbon atoms, since:

$$\frac{\text{Volume of } CO_2 \text{ obtained on combustion}}{\text{Volume of gaseous hydrocarbon}} = \frac{13.6}{6.8} = 2$$

On electrolysis, 1 yields C_2H_6, 2 does not yield a hydrocarbon, 3 yields C_2H_4, 4 yields C_2H_2 and 5 yields C_4H_{10}. Thus 1, 3 and 4 are possible formulae for P.

Unit Seventeen

1. (a) N,N-Dimethylmethanamide; (b) methylethyl methanoate (isopropyl methanoate); (c) phenylethanoyl chloride; (d) ethanoic propanoic anhydride; (e) 2,2-dimethylpropanonitrile.

2. See Unit 17.5(b)(i) and Unit 17.5(d).

3. (a) CH_3COCl gives an immediate precipitate with aqueous $AgNO_3$,

CH_2ClCO_2H does not; *or* CH_3COCl vapour forms white fumes with ammonia in moist air; (*b*) $CH_3CO_2^-NH_4^+$ yields ammonia immediately with aqueous NaOH, CH_3CN has to be boiled with $NaOH_{(aq)}$ to yield ammonia; (*c*) HCO_2CH_3 gives a silver mirror on warming with ammoniacal silver nitrate.

4. See Unit 16.2(*e*).

(*a*) $HCO_2H \xrightarrow{\text{NaOH}} HCO_2^-Na^+ \xrightarrow{\text{heat}} (CO_2^-Na^+)_2 + H_2$

(*b*) $HCO_2H \xrightarrow{\text{CH}_3\text{OH}} HCO_2CH_3$

(*c*) $HCO_2H \xrightarrow{\text{NH}_4\text{OH}} HCO_2^-NH_4^+ \xrightarrow{\text{heat}} HCONH_2$

5. *B*. The explanation is that methanoic acid contains an aldehyde group, ethanoic acid does not.
6. *A*.
7. *C*. The reason is that ethanol forms a constant-boiling mixture with water.
8. *E*. Ethanoic acid is dimerized in benzene and thus gives *half* the expected freezing-point depression.
9. *B*. The concentrated acid is added as a catalyst to speed up the reaction.
10. *D*.
11. *A*.
12. *D*. The acid would contain the ^{18}O isotope after acyl–oxygen fission in $H_2{}^{18}O$.
13. *A*.
14. (*a*) *E*; (*b*) *A*. The reaction sequence is:

$$C_2H_5CO_2C_2H_5 \xrightarrow{\text{hydrolysis}} C_2H_5CO_2H + C_2H_5OH$$
$$(P) \qquad\qquad (Q) \qquad\qquad (R)$$

$$C_2H_5Br \xrightarrow{\text{silver cyanide}} C_2H_5CN + C_2H_5NC$$
$$(S) \qquad (T)$$

$$\downarrow \text{hydrolysis} \qquad \searrow$$

$$C_2H_5CO_2H \qquad C_2H_5NH_2 + HCO_2H$$
$$(Q)$$

Unit Eighteen

1. 1° amines: $CH_3CH_2CH_2NH_2$ (1-aminopropane), $(CH_3)_2CHNH_2$ (2-aminopropane); 2° amine: $C_2H_5NHCH_3$ (ethylmethylamine); 3° amine: $(CH_3)_3N$ (trimethylamine).

2. $E < B < D < C < F < A < G$. (See Unit 18.5(a).)

3. (a) $C_6H_5NO_2$ $\xrightarrow[\text{(ii) NaOH}]{\text{(i) Sn/HCl}}$ $C_6H_5NH_2$ $\xrightarrow[\text{warm}]{\text{CHCl}_3/\text{ethanolic KOH}}$ C_6H_5NC

(b) CH_3NH_2 $\xrightarrow{\text{'HNO}_2\text{'}}$ $(CH_3)_2O$ (See Unit 18.5(g).)

(c) $C_2H_5NH_2$ $\xrightarrow{\text{'HNO}_2\text{'}}$ C_2H_5OH $\xrightarrow{\text{Al}_2O_3/350°}$ C_2H_4

(d) C_2H_5Br $\xrightarrow{\text{NH}_3}$ $C_2H_5NH_3{}^+Br^-$ $\xrightarrow[\text{C}_2\text{H}_5\text{Br}]{\text{excess of}}$ $(C_2H_5)_4N^+Br^-$

$\xrightarrow{\text{Ag}_2\text{O/H}_2\text{O}}$ $(C_2H_5)_4N^+OH^-$

(e) C_2H_5Br $\xrightarrow{\text{KCN}}$ C_2H_5CN $\xrightarrow{\text{reduction}}$ $C_2H_5CH_2NH_2$

8. A is

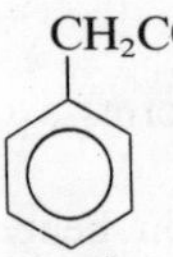

phenylethanoic acid

(The isomeric 2-, 3- and 4-methylbenzoic acids would yield the corresponding benzenedicarboxylic acid on oxidation, e.g.,

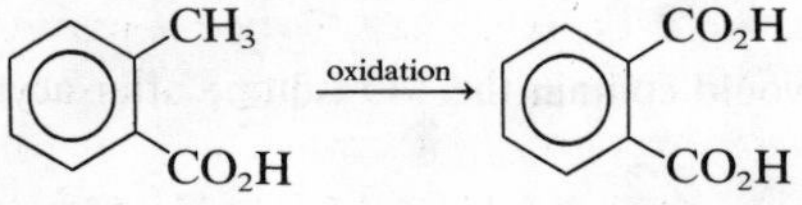

and not benzoic acid, E.)
B is one of the isomeric methylphenylamines, and may be written

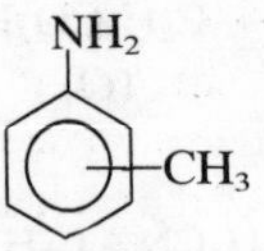

B undergoes diazotization and is therefore a primary aromatic amine. There is no chemical evidence to show the position of the methyl group in the ring, although the fact that the substance is an oily liquid indicates that it is not 4-methylphenylamine (m.p. 43.5°).

C is   D: 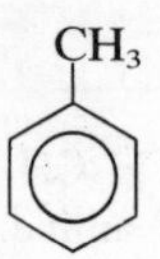   E:

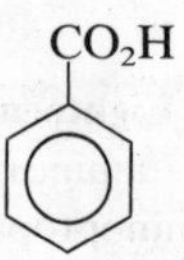

Unit Nineteen
1. (a)

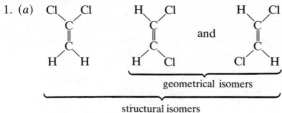

and

geometrical isomers

structural isomers

(b) There are three isomeric ethers of formula $C_4H_{10}O$: $CH_3OCH(CH_3)_2$, $CH_3OCH_2CH_2CH_3$ and $(C_2H_5)_2O$, and four isomeric alcohols: $CH_3CH_2CH_2CH_2OH$, $CH_3CH_2CHOHCH_3$, $(CH_3)_2CHCH_2OH$ and $(CH_3)_3COH$. One of these alcohols, $CH_3CH_2CHOHCH_3$, contains an asymmetric carbon atom and can therefore exist in two different optically active forms ($+$ and $-$). (c) The following isomers are possible: $CH_3CH{=}CCl_2$, $CH_3CCl{=}CHCl$ (cis and trans), $CH_2ClCH{=}CHCl$ (cis and trans) and $CHCl_2CH{=}CH_2$.

Unit Twenty
1. (a) Glucose decolorizes bromine water, fructose does not (see Unit 20.6(b)); (b) glucose reduces both Fehling's solution and ammoniacal silver nitrate, sucrose reduces neither; (c) starch gives a blue colour with iodine solution; (d) Molisch's test for carbohydrates and biuret test or xanthoproteic test for proteins (see Experiments 20.1.1, 20.3.2 and 20.3.3); (e) maltose reduces both Fehling's solution and ammoniacal silver nitrate, sucrose reduces neither.
2. (a) None, since sucrose is not a reducing sugar (see Unit 20.7(a)(ii)); (b) sucrose is dehydrated to carbon by warm, conc. H_2SO_4 (see Unit 20.7(a)(ii)), dilute H_2SO_4 acts as a catalyst in sucrose hydrolysis to yield an equimolecular mixture of glucose and fructose (see Unit 20.7(a)(i)); (c) ethanedioic acid (oxalic acid) and a mixture of other oxidation products are obtained by the action of conc. HNO_3 on sucrose (see Unit 16.7), the reaction being catalysed by vanadium(v) oxide.
3. (a) This reaction is the xanthoproteic test (see Experiment 20.3.2) and the yellow colour confirms that skin contains proteins (see Unit 20.1); (b) the very high m.p. of aminoethanoic acid is due to the strong intermolecular electrostatic attraction between the oppositely charged parts of the zwitterions (see Unit 20.12(c)(i)); (c) enzymes (like other proteins) are denatured at temperatures above about 70–80° (see Unit 20.9(b)) and therefore lose their catalytic activity; (d) sucrose is not a reducing sugar (see Unit 20.7(a)(ii)); (e) this change is due to mutarotation of the aqueous solution of α-D($+$)-glucose to yield an equilibrium mixture of the α- and β-forms (see Unit 20.4).

Index

In this index, substituted organic compounds are listed under the name of the parent compound, and esters and salts under the name of the acid constituent

Substituted organic compounds are indexed under the name of the parent compound.

Substituted organic compounds are indexed
under the name of the parent compound.

Substituted organic compounds are indexed
under the name of the parent compound.